*The Gods,
the Little Guys
and the Police*

HUMBERTO COSTANTINI

 The Gods, the Little Guys and the Police

TRANSLATED FROM THE SPANISH
BY TOBY TALBOT

HARPER & ROW, PUBLISHERS, New York

Cambridge, Philadelphia, San Francisco, London
Mexico City, São Paulo, Sydney

1817

THE GODS, THE LITTLE GUYS AND THE POLICE. English translation copyright © 1984 by Harper & Row, Publishers, Inc. All rights reserved. Printed in the United States of America. No part of this book may be used or reproduced in any manner whatsoever without written permission except in the case of brief quotations embodied in critical articles and reviews. For information address Harper & Row, Publishers, Inc., 10 East 53rd Street, New York, N.Y. 10022. Published simultaneously in Canada by Fitzhenry & Whiteside Limited, Toronto.

FIRST EDITION

Designer: Sidney Feinberg

Library of Congress Cataloging in Publication Data

Costantini, Humberto.
   The gods, the little guys, and the police.

   Translation of : De dioses, hombrecitos y policías.
   I. Title.
PQ7798.13.075D413 1984   863   83-48339
ISBN 0-06-015252-4

84 85 86 87 88 10 9 8 7 6 5 4 3 2 1

Acknowledgments

To dedicate this little book to a score of people, to say that without their joint and courageous support it would never have been written, might seem simply to be one of those formula courtesies, or at best, an exaggeration. Nevertheless, I feel obliged to state that this is absolutely true: without the providential help of those people, the book, and perhaps the author, would in fact not exist.

The book was written at a particularly difficult time for both the country and myself, a time when the mere possession of a table, a chair, some light and a bit of peace were virtually impossible, and thus I must acknowledge never having been in want of someone to provide these luxuries.

I'm unable, for example, to forget a certain carpenter's horse, converted in a wink, thanks to the love of the people in whose house I was staying, into a wonderful, spacious, unforgettable desk which, for better or worse, was responsible for Chapters XXXIV and XXXV.

I'm unable to forget a certain little room shared by a young couple, their month-old baby, a dog and myself; and I imagine that they, too, won't forget that annoying tapping which started coming from the kitchen at six in the morning (I swear, in my defense, that I neglected only a few times to close the door carefully, and to place a folded blanket under my typewriter).

I'm unable to forget the person who zealously hid a copy of the original manuscript, chapter by chapter (all of us remembering vividly the tragic fate of the disappeared writer Harold Conti), nor the one who devoted hours of work in helping me along with the novel, nor the one who supplied me with paper, nor the one who devised a strange device (as yet unpatented) so that I could write while my arm was in a cast, nor those who read portions of the original manuscript and had much more faith in the book than the author himself, nor those close and dear individuals who decided that I was to leave the country (not to say dragged me out kicking), nor the one who, with a gesture of friendship, made my trip to Mexico possible.

Nor can I forget the person in Mexico who typed the final draft of the entire novel, nor the one who gave me (and continues giving me) strength to go on writing.

There were obviously many. I said that there were a score of individuals, but there must have been more. This book therefore is dedicated to them all. A story of love, humor and poetry beneath the ominous threat of death. Life, in short. Except that no story as brief as this one could ever so justifiably be attributed to so many authors.

*The Gods,
the Little Guys
and the Police*

I

Mrs. Viviana Mastrocarbone de Giannello was entertaining us most delightfully with a beautiful poem that she herself had penned. Just a few moments before, Mr. Chávez, our president, had introduced her with his customary charm. I can remember distinctly some of his wonderful lines: "a blossoming torrent of luminous song," he remarked, and went on, rather surprisingly perhaps, to allude to "the feminine power of her amorous call." These comments linger in my mind for, as everyone knows, those brilliant prologues of Mr. Chávez, who, let me add, is a Spaniard and a sales manager at a prominent real estate firm, are generally as fascinating and memorable as the very poems which he, as president of our institution, finds himself most happily called upon to introduce. But I remember them for another reason as well, a seemingly trivial detail: As Mr. Chávez was enunciating his introductory remarks, and more precisely, when he made that comment in a deep, suggestive voice about "her amorous call," Mr. Frugoni, standing up for some reason behind the last row of chairs, cleared his throat twice, I won't say loudly but indeed rudely and in a downright conspicuous way. I attributed this ill-timed hemming of his to surprise or perhaps to the rush of feeling stirred up in him by Mr. Chávez's words, though I was later to realize, much to my astonishment, that the cause of his uneasiness, as we shall soon see, was something else altogether.

Well, to continue: Though the poetic inspiration of our recording secretary does not, we must acknowledge, vie with the delicacy and loftiness attained by Irene (who, incidentally, had been unanimously appointed financial secretary at our meeting of Wednesday, November 26), the truth is that her inspired, tender and at times doleful stanzas touched all of us deeply. And so I was sorrowfully dismayed to notice Mr. Frugoni, usually so responsive and sensitive to our associates' poems, particularly those of the fair sex, leave the meeting abruptly and, with ill-disguised anxiety, stride across the wide courtyard, with its wisterias, and head toward the small room in the rear where the telephone is.

Out of the corner of my eye, I glanced to my right. Irene, hanging on Mrs. Giannello's suggestive images and rhythmical intonations, seemed unaware of anything out of the ordinary. Quite the contrary. Her delicate profile, outlined like an antique cameo against the blue wallpaper of our meeting room, was the picture of concentration and of that "magical communion in poetry" set forth in our statutes. Her slender, tense neck was leaning forward and her eyes were half shut. Her delicate facial muscles were contracting slightly and strands of her soft blond tresses shadowed her temples, beneath whose transparent pallor you could faintly detect a rhythmic throbbing. As I was watching her, rather furtively, she seemed, I remember, to experience a kind of cold shudder. How strange. Though her elegant sky-blue dress was lightweight and sleeveless, the afternoon was quite warm and not a soul—obviously so as not to distract Mrs. Giannello—had cared to turn on the fan. Maybe she has a slight chill, I thought. Her gaze hadn't strayed from the rostrum, but it was clear that she felt either chilled or feverish, and she reached for a woolen cardigan that lay folded next to her purse and placed it over her shoulders. Luckily, it was nothing serious. Her chill soon subsided and her face resumed its habitual serenity. How I longed, at that moment, to seize her hand. I longed to kiss her and to declare the totality of my feelings of yearning for her.

I remember being on the verge of doing just that on Wednesday the twenty-sixth, after the meeting when she was appointed, at my motion, financial secretary, but the very sad truth is that I didn't dare. That night, I accompanied her through the darkness of Marcos Sastre Street as far as Nazca, where she takes the No. 110 bus. We strolled along, contemplating the trees, the hedges and the gardens. The night was balmy and beautiful. Suddenly we spied something above a privet hedge, something nearly impossible to find these days in Buenos Aires: a firefly. We paused for quite a while to gaze at it. We watched the wondrous creature take flight into the hedge, and from the darkness, flicker its little light on and off as if it were greeting us. We watched it soar to the top of an arborvitae, and then, still flickering on and off, fly toward the rear of the garden until it disappeared behind a lush bougainvillea.

Irene seemed in no hurry to go home. From time to time she cast a tender, questioning gaze in my direction, as if she were actually expecting something or other from me. A more propitious moment had never, I believe, presented itself. And yet, during our entire stroll, there seemed to be some mysterious force preventing me from giving natural vent to my true feelings, and I confined myself to discussing the excellence of her creations, and the worthiness of the distinction bestowed upon her by the Executive Committee in full session. Foolishness on my part, I don't deny, yet it was impossible for me to do otherwise.

I left Irene at her bus, and walked a few blocks along Nazca Street, ashamed of myself, and cursing my almost incredible timidity, my stupid, unpardonable indecisiveness. I remember hearing, as I crossed the tracks, the clear screech of an owl. I had the sense of being mocked by heaven itself.

Anyhow, here we were now, at our organization's headquarters, and this was not the moment—I was well aware of that—to attempt what my timidity, or, to put it more bluntly, my sudden cowardliness, had prevented me from accomplishing at a more appropriate time and place. And so I restrained my untimely impulses and continued listening to Mrs. Giannello with the attention and respect customary to our organization.

In her poem, our recording secretary was referring to twilights and downpours of rain. I can still remember one of her lines: "Like a caryatid numb in its grief," which, despite my anxiety (prompted as much by Irene's agitating presence as by Mr. Frugoni's sudden departure), I found painfully moving. Mrs. Giannello was reading in a warm, measured voice, although the page from her classroom looseleaf, inscribed in her impassioned, slightly aggressive angular handwriting, was trembling slightly in her hand. The fluttering of the page grew more visible, I noticed, when Mr. Frugoni left, and it was this small detail which suddenly clarified a situation I'd initially found confusing and inexplicable. The fervent words of the poem contributed, I won't deny, to that clarification. Mrs. Giannello spoke of the unbearable loneliness of waiting—a loneliness, she said, that was "unmitigated by your craven bosom / imprisoned like Laocoön wounded by the serpents / in futile, horrendous bondage."

I then recalled that Mr. Frugoni—an excellent poet in the gauchoesque vein and proprietor of the Flor de Lis variety store—had a few weeks earlier confided in me about the serious difficulties he and his wife were having. They were so serious, he claimed, that they had prevented him that week from completing the extensive poem, "Phantom of the Wagon," which he'd committed himself to reading to the group this Wednesday.

———

The quarrels, as he led me to believe, stemmed from an unexpected "tormented and impossible love." I also recalled that Mrs. Giannello had been signing her poems lately with her unmarried name. And that Mr. Giannello, who normally waited in his van for her after meetings, hadn't shown up for some time at 2562 Teodoro Vilardebó, the site of our headquarters.

At that point I realized what a trying situation both of our dear members were undergoing. My heart went out to them and I actually was worried that something serious might come to pass that Wednesday, December 3, on the occasion of the 356th poetry meeting of Polimnia's tenth year.

II

FROM: Officer Pascuali
TO: Adjutant Covas

On Tuesday, November 18, 1975, at 1430 hours, I posted myself at the corner of Marcos Sastre and Teodoro Vilardebó, in which vicinity I remained until 2043 hours, at which time Corporal Nicodemo Ramírez did appear, with the express mission of relieving me.

Observing upon arrival at scene no suspicious movements of persons or vehicles, I proceeded to walk along Teodoro Vilardebó, on the even side of the street where the numbers run in the 2500s, in order to perform an on-the-spot eye check. The foregoing did confirm the existence at the domicile located at 2562 Teodoro Vilardebó of a group, social club or committee operating under the name of POLIMNIA, as announced by a bronze plaque, approximately 15 × 30 centimeters in size, situated at the upper-right-hand corner of the entrance.

Said domicile remained totally closed up during my entire watch, that is, no person was seen entering or leaving said premises between the hours of 1430 and 2043 on Tuesday the 18th.

Information from neighbors and merchants to whom I posed as a health inspector confirms the data disclosed in the denunciation received on day 15 of the past month. Namely: Every Wednesday, at approximately 1700 hours, between 15 and 20 individuals of both sexes assemble at said domicile and remain until approximately 2130 hours, whereupon they disperse in small groups with the evident object of not attracting attention.

It has been corroborated through the aforementioned channel of information that the individual who figures as president of said organization is in fact Romualdo Chávez, whose record is now on file at this office.

Jesús Meijide, proprietor of the Golden Thorn Bakery, located at 2199 Baigorria, discloses that on Monday, Wednesday and Friday mornings, a female known in the area as Zulema arrives at said domicile in order to perform certain housecleaning duties. The aforementioned Zulema, who likewise performed these duties at Meijide's home, resides or appears to reside at 4045 Helguera Street, in rear.

Meijide likewise reports that prior to a few years ago, the Teodoro Vilardebó property belonged to an old woman, now deceased, by the name of Lobos. It was acquired through Delos Real Estate, where the aforementioned Romualdo Chávez is apparently employed, and was, through his intervention, rented to Polimnia.

In view of the aforesaid, I do suggest reinforcement of surveillance on Wednesdays. The camera crew of which I was verbally informed can be stationed opposite 2541 Teodoro Vilardebó if it is installed inside a vehicle registered as a taxi and properly disguised in Sergeant Longo's own inimitable fashion.

From the top of a solitary high peak of Olympus, Aphrodite, who loves smiles, cast her divine gaze, now veiled by displeasure, toward an old house on Teodoro Vilardebó Street, bordered with chinaberry trees, where a group of prudent, well-groomed mortals were hanging reverently on Mrs. Giannello's words.

Alongside the goddess stood swift-footed Hermes, filled with ominous dread at Aphrodite's displeasure, and farther away was Athena, Zeus's indomitable daughter, leaning solemnly on her stout and solid spear, her clear eyes flashing with pride and with joy at a recent victory.

And Hermes was saddened and worried by the violent Discord that had erupted between the two goddesses and feared the evil that this Discord might wreak upon his protégé Mr. Frugoni, a man of great commercial skill. And so handsome Hermes, he of the golden sandals, spoke up, addressing Aphrodite with these winged words:

"O incomparable daughter of Uranus, slender-waisted, golden Aphrodite, you whose perfect bosom arouses desire, whose tender gaze incites multitudinous flowers to burst into bloom, excites the lust of beasts, and flings men and women into the sweet transports of love: tell me, I beseech you, what it is that prompts that grimace of displeasure which, like a black cloud rising from a stormy summer sea and rapidly covering a vast expanse of earth, now covers your divine countenance, so beloved of gods and mortals alike?"

And fair Aphrodite, born of the foam of the sea, replied:

"Why do you question me, O divine Messenger whom once I did ardently love? Better to question that one standing before you, armed with a mighty spear as if she were the very deity of gory war, her owlish eyes gleaming triumphantly and rejoicingly at the infamy wrought upon my protégé on a tree-lined street in Villa del Parque.

"Question her so that she herself may provide a reply and inform you of the ruse, so unworthy of an Immortal, which she employed in summoning Timidity and Indecision to paralyze my dearly beloved Pulicicchio with Cowardliness, preventing him from declaring his love to the irreproachable, golden-haired Irene, whose bosom I myself, in the guise of a firefly, had ignited with gentle passion, flashing and shining my little light as I kept diligent watch from a dark garden on Marcos Sastre Street."

Without waiting for Aphrodite to conclude her anguished discourse, Athena, the gray-eyed daughter of Zeus, shook her mane of hair from its gleaming helmet and rose up in great fury as she spoke.

"Quiet once and for all, you charlatan, procuress, harlot, impenitent adulteress, caught by your lawful husband, Hephaestus, that most excellent of blacksmiths, in the arms of your lover, warlike Ares, thus exposing you for an entire day to the mockery of the Immortals.

"What you say is true. I did indeed, with all haste, dispatch Timidity and Indecision to hover over Marcos Sastre Street while I, transformed into a chattering owl, witnessed their faithful compliance with my precise commands.

"My object was to stifle any impetuous language on the part of your protégé José María Pulicicchio, a bank installment loan manager, so as to preserve chaste Irene Bengoechea (pleasing to my eyes as a virgin, an expert crocheter and a woman totally dedicated to intellectual pursuits) from the upheavals, madness and bitter disappointments of fickle love, which only leads mortals astray from virtue and the righteous path.

"And that is not all I did, loose and licentious Aphrodite. I also instilled a stern sense of conjugal duty into the faltering heart of Hermes' favorite, Mr. Frugoni, whom Mrs. Mastrocarbone de Giannello, under your incitement, O indefatigable, insidious, ensnaring contriver, strove passionately to separate from his lawful spouse and lead into sharing her contemptible adulterous bed.

"You must surely know, procuress and destroyer of men, that I shall never accede to your wiles, for Teodoro Giannello, that brawny, magnificent truckdriver, has long been under my protection, and owing to his own meager inclination for the pleasures of the bed, has remained faithful despite the extensive journeys he undertakes in his enormous truck. And so I'll not allow his lawful wife, seconded by you, to cover him with dishonor."

So spoke indomitable Athena, and gentle Aphrodite was obliged to contain her wrath, inasmuch as the goddess's gleaming shield and heavy infallible spear were quivering dangerously beneath the force of her divine wrath.

——————

And divine Hermes trembled with fear from the tip of his staff to the little wings on the crown of his hat and upon his sandals, for Athena's anger was like an omen of a terrible impending storm, and the handsome, youthful Messenger dared not defend with eloquent words his former lover, the fair-cheeked Aphrodite, or even less attempt to dispel with his staff the violent discord between the two goddesses.

Anxiously the god turned his gaze toward the corner of Marcos Sastre and Teodoro Vilardebó in the shaded quarter of Villa del Parque, fearing the misfortune that this divine anger might incur upon the mortals, particularly upon Mr. Aníbal Frugoni, whom the swift Messenger had provided with good fortune in business, and abundant, profitable sales in his variety store, the Flor de Lis.

And behold, like a huge, voracious, carrion-eating bird flitting inexorably in ever-diminishing circles around a dying cow, a black shadow hovered menacingly overhead, circling slowly around the house at 2562 Teodoro Vilardebó, in the Villa del Parque quarter.

And winged Hermes, filled with fear and dire presentiments by that dark shadow, addressed both goddesses with prudent words.

"Beloved goddesses, I beseech you to contain your terrible wrath at least for a few moments, and to turn your gaze toward Teodoro Vilardebó Street, where you'll see that slow, ominous shadow circling implacably around the house where our protégés, totally unaware, are listening blissfully to the impassioned Mrs. Giannello.

"I implore you to await my return before pursuing your dispute, for I shall arrive with the swiftness of thought at

Teodoro Vilardebó, between Baigorria and Marcos Sastre, and shall promptly and diligently ascertain the identity of that shadow, who it was that dispatched it, and what it is that it seeks or awaits in that delightful spot. And then I will return to provide you with truthful tidings."

The goddesses assented with a slight nod, whereupon Hermes the Messenger, like a bow stretched to its utmost by a stout arm, departed in the direction of the house at 2562 Teodoro Vilardebó, where the wisterias were in bloom.

IV

Little guys, brothers, amusing fellow members of the species, comrades in this wacky, transient adventure we call life, fleeting passengers on this ephemeral ball that keeps spinning stupidly in space.

Little guys, barely a nothing, an invisible tickle in the cosmos, barely a crystal goblet, skeletons, acrylic smidgens amidst the dried-up dust of an extinct planet that will keep spinning on and on tomorrow, spinning stupidly in space.

Little guys, dammit, flea-ridden, scared stiff, parading little monkeys, conceived by some fucked-up fluke of the genes from a poor, wise-guy monkey (a jewel of a stud, if the truth be told).

Little guys, poor relatives, half-degenerate cousins of such beautiful beasts, calm, without crazy fits, perfect (I mean the lemur, the splendid monkey, richer than anyone in food, the bison of noble brow, the sly wolf that preys in packs, the panther, the dolphin, the zebra, the self-assured elephant, the swift, evasive deer, the prodigious cat, the whale, the lion . . . all so right in their presence, so worthy, so in earnest).

Oh, shit! My little guys, ill-made, anxious, scared stiff, suffering, eternal stargazers, curious, snooping around with their useless questions, dancers of loony rituals, nervous, restless, charlatans, dream-tellers, tellers of strange nightmares in which gods intervene (in metered hexameters, most likely), unflagging botchers of wood, clay, bronze, wool, leather, of absurd little drawings that symbolize dreams, outcries or words.

Little guys, fire-worshipers, flute-blowers, drum-beaters, players of strings stretched on bows, howlers, declaimers of nutty speeches that arouse ecstasy, or terror, or desire, or laughter.

Little guys, dammit, knowing about death, yet desperate inventors of parodies of life, desperate inventors of useless toys: the colored outline of a hand on stone, a mask, a dolmen, the Bible, the Taj Mahal, a garden dwarf, Mrs. Giannello's verses, everything the same, voices bleating in the desert, brothers, craving not to die completely, and that's it.

Little guys, dearly beloved, lovable little guys: underwear, curlers, boils, pottery, nighties, rheumatism, fainting spells, hemorrhoids, fears, colds, indigestion.

Little guys, yes, but suddenly there's generosity, courage, sparks of splendid looniness, love, wonder, wonderful beauty and heroism. Little parading monkeys, yes, but suddenly men, resembling gods, and suddenly gods.

Little guys, my little guys, little dots swarming like ants on Earth, still at it, playacting in strange ways, hovering on the brink of death, singing, questioning, cursing . . . quite amusing if you look at them carefully.

V

The Polimnia Group Villa del Parque Association of Poets
(as our invitation cards clearly read) is a nonprofit institution dedicated totally to the fostering and greater dissemi-
nation of its members' poetic efforts. It was founded on
September 21, 1965, by an elite group of outstanding poets
in the area, and was the inspiration of two stalwart figures
in Villa del Parque's cultural activity: the imponderable
aforementioned Mr. Romualdo Chávez, and Mrs. Brígida
Ramírez de Urdampilleta, our defunct first president. A
portrait of her noble, austere countenance presently hangs
alongside a watercolor portrait of our national patriarch,
Domingo Faustino Sarmiento, painted by herself and
donated to Polimnia on the occasion of its first anniversary,
and it presides to this day in the way of everlasting homage
over our little meeting room. In further homage and
memoriam, our ex-president's poems are frequently read
by Mr. Chávez, Mrs. Zimmerman or young Romilio Sosa.
These are short, diaphanous compositions of a patriotic
bent, dedicated generally to our heroes, various scholars
and educators, and institutions (such as the Armed Forces,
the National Highway Commission or the Savings Bank), as
well as to various national symbols. They were in fact compositions which Mrs. Ramírez de Urdampilleta, a native of
Tucumán and a retired headmistress, used to read on com-

memorative occasions at her school, and which many of her ex-pupils, Irene amongst them, recall with great affection and profound admiration. Young Romilio Sosa, a particularly extraordinary reader, of telluric resonances, imbues these poems, which are lyrical in nature but didactic and moralistic in content, with a sweeping, evocative impact that leaves all of us absolutely quivering.

Polimnia thus constitutes a beautiful arena in which all of us are able to practice and display our calling, and in addition—why not say so?—a friendly refuge for many solitudes. I personally am especially indebted to Polimnia for much more than can at first glance be imagined. In truth, my unblemished poetic calling goes back many years, but it is equally true that never—with the exception of two sonnets of mine published in *La Razón* in Villa Devoto, and another which the *Journal of Associated Banks* was kind enough to include—never, I repeat, never did I have the opportunity to acquaint anyone assiduously with this, my inveterate calling, and most of all, to enjoy that sensitive, cordial and intelligent reception which our organization prides itself on.

My specialty—I mention this with a certain diffidence— is the sonnet. This hermetic, intimate, perfect poetic form, carved like a gem, its chiseled geometry capable of expressing the subtlest and most complex of sentiments, is and will assuredly remain my natural lifelong form of expression. As some individuals must know, it is by no means an easy form, and there are few among our members (with the exception of Mr. Mastandrea, whose sonnets I prefer for the time being not to comment upon) who attempt it even occasionally. This has awarded me a certain modest prestige within the group, and ever since my first public readings, has endowed me with a certain status, as they say, making my name one that people remember and, if I may venture to say so, one that is respected amongst Polimnia's members.

At this very moment I happen to be working on a triptych of sonnets secretly addressed to none other than Irene. My burning desire is to have them ready for one of the upcoming meetings. And I'm wondering whether, strategically, it might not be better for me to wait and see the effect these sonnets will undoubtedly produce upon my colleagues, and especially of course on Irene, whose poetic sensibility, I can say without exaggeration, is exquisite, before I formally proceed to declare my feelings to her.

At the beginning, Polimnia's weekly meetings were held on the premises of the folklore club El Ombú, or in an unoccupied office made available to us by the merchants organization on Cuenca Street. But for approximately the last five years, owing to Mr. Chávez's generous and intelligent negotiation, we've been able to rent the beautiful house on Teodoro Vilardebó Street where we currently meet and which, within a short time, we may be able to acquire as our very own property.

Polimnia's members—it's best perhaps to make this clear—belong to extremely diverse social strata. It is sheer slander when people insinuate that we form a tight, hermetic, impenetrable circle. There are no special requirements for being admitted as an active member, other than the elementary requisites of public and private morality which any group or club normally establishes. The thing that unites us is our love of poetry, and any discussion relating to religion or politics is specifically prohibited by our statutes. Our ranks include schoolteachers, jobholders, businessmen, an occasional member of the neighborhood Rotary Club, music teachers and professionals. But also— and I wish to stress this—there are manual laborers, housekeepers, and even a random student who occasionally finds his way to the group.

Polimnia's capacity to provide honorable solace and warm spiritual refuge has frequently drawn to its headquarters retired people who get no satisfaction from your typical random encounters in cafés and squares (this doesn't apply in my case, though in a few years I may find myself suddenly faced with retirement), solitary women, unmarried women (as in Irene's case), widows, or women with grown children and ample time therefore to resume old interests. It isn't uncommon, for the same reason, to find amongst us people with some physical impairment that makes it difficult for them to participate in other types of social activity. One example is Miss Kisternmacher, a terribly cultivated private teacher of various subjects, the German language being among them, and likewise an outstanding poetess (with two published books, and some poems included in the literary section of *La Prensa*), who is brought to our meetings in a wheelchair by her mother, and sometimes by a servant. Or the previously mentioned Carlos Mastandrea, like myself a cultivator of the sonnet (with numerous shortcomings, I must confess), who gets around on crutches. And I'm almost forgetting Mr. Pasco, author of some lovely lyrics for folkloric songs, who is blind.

Polimnia is clearly what unites us. In the midst of the violent chaos and sinister appetites encircling Buenos Aires in this summer of 1975, our group serves as an island for us, an oasis of peace, a place where the cult of the spirit rules over coarse matter and beneath whose roof, and near whose garden abloom with wisteria, we're able at long last to find what life has so stubbornly denied us for all too many years: the potential for growth within the bosom of poetic fraternity (these words come directly from our statutes), for establishing contact with all those beautiful spirits beneath the spell of that selfless, sincere unwavering calling—that great equalizer: Poetry.

VI

FROM: Adjutant Covas
TO: Chief Officer Farías

On Wednesday, December 19, at 1548 hours, the division taxi vehicle was posted at the spot designated by Officer Pascuali, but at Sergeant Longo's suggestion was later transferred down to Baigorria Street due to the presence of a private automobile, a green Peugeot, license plate No. 456-764, Federal Capital, from which suspect Romualdo Chávez descended and which partially obstructed our line of vision.

We lifted the hood of our vehicle to simulate a motor problem or overheating, and our crew divided up in accordance with the following plan: The undersigned stationed himself in front of the steering wheel and from time to time got out to check the motor, using the opportunity to glance inside the domicile under surveillance whenever the front door of the latter opened up. Corporal Ramírez was positioned alongside—in other words, in the same front street—holding his tommy gun, but concealing it properly under a jacket, in the event of a surprise attack. Sergeant Longo, equipped with all the camera gear, occupied the back seat.

From the time of our arrival until 1624, there was nothing to report at the aforementioned domicile at 2562 Teodoro Vilardebó. At said hour, the first of those to attend the meeting rang the bell: a heavyset male, with graying hair, between the ages of 50 and 60, who was, or appeared to be, lame inasmuch as he came down the street with the aid of 2 (two) crutches, though with startling speed, according to Sergeant Longo's observation. Concerning this individual, it is my obligation to report that Corporal Ramírez believes that he recalls the suspect's face and other identifying features, dating back to his inspection duty with the 37th Precinct, but states that he prefers to withhold his opinion and wait for the transcript identification data prior to confirmation. The aforementioned suspect was admitted by another individual, a young, dark-skinned man with a clipped mustache, who, according to our informant, was in possession of the keys and had entered in the morning. Several photographs were taken of both persons.

After 1640 hours, the remaining individuals began to arrive. They appeared singly, or in groups of two or three. They did not ring the bell since the front door was unlocked, allowing them to open it by themselves and to enter without ringing. They were carefully photographed by Sergeant Longo, whose camera shutter was kept busily in motion, and twice he was forced to change his roll of film.

Subject Romualdo Chávez did arrive at 1654 hours. He alighted from the previously described green Peugeot (which he parked in front of the house) in the company of a female, not his usual mistress, according to information we have on him.

At 1658 hours, subject Aníbal Frugoni appeared at the corner of Marcos Sastre and shortly thereafter entered said premises at Teodoro Vilardebó, thereby corroborating fully the accusation received on day 15 of the past month with reference to his attendance at meetings at said domicile.

At precisely 1700 hours, a female of approximately 30 years of age did appear in a wheelchair pushed by an elderly woman dressed with certain elegance.

At 1708 hours, a short, dark-skinned individual of approximately 40 years of age did turn the corner, appearing to be blind inasmuch as he kept hitting the ground with a thin white cane. He likewise entered said premises, being the last to arrive, with no one appearing after him.

Exactly 18 individuals did enter the domicile at 2562 Teodoro Vilardebó, in addition to the one who was already inside, bringing the number to a total of 19 persons in attendance at the meeting.

Careful surveillance did continue until 2200 hours, with the exception of two brief departures which Sergeant Longo did make to a bar located on Cuenca Street with the object of performing certain urgent needs, inasmuch as the latter was suffering from upset stomach.

During our stay in the vicinity of said domicile, we were able on repeated occasions to hear loud applause, prompted apparently by speeches or proclamations delivered by various speakers.

At 2135 hours, the lights of the building were extinguished and the suspects began departing in small groups. The camera, due to insufficient light, was not utilized.

The last to leave was the aforementioned Romualdo Chávez, who did lock the door and thereupon proceeded toward the Peugeot in the company of two females who were invited by him to enter said vehicle, with said offer being accepted.

The enclosed envelope contains a total of 52 (fifty-two) photographs.

Awaiting identifying data to proceed with broadening of investigation.

Suggest immediate dispatch of a trailing agent and/or house surveillance with respect to suspects Romualdo Chávez and Aníbal Frugoni.

P.S. With reference to the identity of the suspect whom Corporal Ramírez believes he recalls, it would appear, according to latest reports just transmitted to me, that the aforementioned is an ex-numbers man and a police informant with whom Corporal Ramírez had some dealings in 1962, and who could prove to be of utmost usefulness to us in this instance.

VII

With the swiftness of thought, or a blink of an eyelid as it scans distant seas, mountains, vast meadows, forests populated by satyrs, and cities where humans speak strange tongues, so did the divine Messenger Hermes in his swift sandals reach the well-established Villa del Parque quarter and come to a halt.

And there, a black shadow, like a huge vulture, was hovering ceaselessly, slowly, ominously over the old house at 2562 Teodoro Vilardebó, between Baigorria and Marcos Sastre streets.

And every now and then in its interminable revolutions it would cross above the house, assuming the guise then of a huge splotch, crawling like an icy, loathsome creature along the corrugated tin roof, trailing along the solid whitewashed walls, descending to the tiled courtyard where wellwatered plants grew, and soaring upward again toward the wisteria with its dense foliage.

The Shadow was invisible, however, to mortal eyes, and none of those inside the house, seated in parallel rows of chairs within the blue-wallpapered room, listening to the words Mrs. Mastrocarbone de Giannello was reading from a two-holed classroom looseleaf notebook, could see it or have any suspicion of it.

Only Irene Bengoechea, who was favored by the gods and endowed with sibylic qualities, experienced a slight shudder at the very moment that the Shadow crossed above the roof. Unaware of the true cause of her chill, and thinking it was due simply to the cold, she reached for a woolen cardigan and threw it over her shoulders, much to the consternation of Mr. José María Pulicicchio.

But Hermes the Messenger, beloved by Aphrodite, was indeed able, with his divine eyes, to discern the Shadow with utmost clarity and, filled with foreboding, his body poised for shameful flight, he addressed it.

"O unknown Shadow, I am an emissary of the Olympian gods, and Hermes the Messenger is my name. I am the son of Maia and of thundering Zeus. In the name of the Immortals, I entreat you to reveal your name, and tell me who it is that has sent you to Villa del Parque, with its thriving chinaberry trees. What is it that you await or seek from the humans occupying this tranquil site?"

And the Shadow, pausing on top of a huge chinaberry tree, which suddenly turned dark as though struck by the blackness of night, spoke in a hoarse, grim voice and uttered these terrible words:

"I recognize who you are, prudent Messenger, and know that the gods entrust you with important messages. Listen carefully, therefore, and transmit what I'm about to tell you so that none of the Immortals dares to disrupt the mission that I've been dispatched to perform by another mighty Immortal.

"I am, if you must know, the Herald of Death, and have been sent by Hades, he of the black steeds, to spend the entire day today, the third of December, 1975, circling around the house at 2562 Teodoro Vilardebó, waiting for the right moment to transport the souls of various mortals who are presently beneath that roof, and whose names are guarded in my infallible memory, to that dark realm yonder whence I come."

Indefatigable Hermes trembled and posed another question: "Tell me, I beseech you, O ominous Herald of Death, how many among those mortals now comfortably seated and listening to Mrs. Giannello's fervent words has implacable Hades destined to descend to his ominous realm? What are their first and last names, and what reason has the deity for proceeding in such a ruthless manner?"

Fiercely shaking the branches of the chinaberry tree, the Herald of Death replied: "Listen carefully, divine Messenger. The mortals I've come for are exactly twelve in number, but I'm not permitted to reveal their names, nor what has prompted Hades' actions. If I were to do so, you would undoubtedly rush off to inform certain Immortals, and they might attempt (in vain, I can assure you) to obstruct the deed which the ruler of the underworld has so deliberately planned, arousing thereby his dreadful displeasure."

And swift-footed Hermes, overcoming his fear, put yet a third question: "Be not impatient with my questions, O divine herald of Hades' underworld, for this is the last that I shall ask. How will you proceed? What human or divine means will that grim deity employ in order to reap twelve lives from amongst those innocently and trustingly ensconced in the respectful silence of that blue-wallpapered room?"

But the shadowy Herald of Death would not answer Hermes' diligent question; instead, with an unpleasant rustling, he abandoned the boughs of the chinaberry tree, causing them to shake as though an icy wind had blown over them, and then continued on in his slow, forbidding flight around the house at 2562 Teodoro Vilardebó.

Once again, Hermes was seized with fear, and he shrank away, imagining that the Shadow might attack him, and then swiftly flew toward Olympus to transmit these doleful tidings to the goddesses.

VIII

Mrs. Giannello's reading of her beautiful poem was drawing to a close. She fixed her gaze, serene and dignified, on the spot Mr. Frugoni had occupied, then shifted it upward, toward some heavenly listener, dropped her arms in an unexpected gesture of resignation and humility, and completed her reading with a line that will remain embedded forever in my memory: "If 'tis my fate to wait, then so be it," whereupon she lowered her head like someone who's just made a painful confession.

There was a burst of loud, uninterrupted applause. Seldom, I believe, has a composition in our hall been accorded such an ardent, unrestrained response. It clearly bespoke the deep reverberations that the poem aroused among our members. Irene applauded nervously, her eyelids fluttering and the tip of her chin quivering in a stirring response to Mrs. Giannello's words and gestures, while the poetess herself, still clutching the pages of her classroom looseleaf, expressed her gratitude with a tight smile. I, too, clapped enthusiastically, though I must say that my concern over Mr. Frugoni's recent behavior was mounting. I simply had to know where he'd gone and if I could possibly help him. I delayed no longer; some applause was still resounding when I rose to my feet and told Irene to wait for me a moment.

Passing down the row and disturbing, as I did so, the occupants of the nearby seats—Mr. Pasco, an unknown young woman whose entrance, surprisingly, I hadn't noticed, and Miss Kisternmacher's mother—I left our meeting room and went out into the courtyard.

I headed for the little room in the rear where I assumed I'd find Mr. Frugoni, but on crossing the courtyard, now in near darkness, my eyes were accosted by the most blessed sight—the, for me, ever wondrous spectacle of wisteria. The ancient shrub, supported by equally ancient, and rusty, stakes, covers nearly the entire courtyard of our headquarters. I couldn't refrain from pausing a moment to behold it. Though it was the beginning of December, there were still some blossoms lingering amid the dense foliage. I gazed in delight at the intertwining of old stems and new. Some vigorous young shoots that had sprung up this past spring were curled with thrusting sensuality around the old knobby stalks. Thus shall they remain forever, I thought to myself: united in an ever firmer and tighter embrace. And suddenly it struck me that this reflection concerning vigor, sensuality, and especially the tight embrace were fitting images to include in my third sonnet to Irene. So as not to forget, I took out my notebook and quickly jotted down the gist of this thought. I was delayed no more than a few seconds, and then continued on in search of Mr. Frugoni.

I found him in fact in the little back room. He was seated in front of the phone, with his head in his hands. Young Romilio Sosa—whom I guess I hadn't noticed when he passed, absorbed as I was in the notes I was taking—had arrived ahead of me. He, too, must have sensed something disquieting in Mr. Frugoni's behavior, and had followed close behind him, but without my hesitation or delay, and was now standing beside him, warmly patting his shoulders as if trying to calm or console him.

I was truly moved by Romilio's gesture. That swarthy provincial lad, a worker in a textile factory, who had appeared one day in our midst through sheer coincidence (he was the boyfriend of Miss Kisternmacher's maid) and who hadn't missed a single one of our meetings ever since, was now demonstrating by his simple show of solidarity a quality of humanity, a sharp awareness of his fellow being's problems, that was clearly lacking, at least in this instance, amongst many of us. It reminded me of his varied activity on behalf of our group: the way he'd taken it upon himself to paint the front of the building, to straighten up the garden, to stop up some of the leaks, and to repair the lintel over the door. All on his own initiative, nobody having suggested the need to do so. His great desire to learn showed itself in other ways, including his ease in retaining long poems, which he'd recite in his rhythmical Tucumán accent. He was doing some writing of his own, but as yet had for some reason refused to share his compositions with us. He was always smiling and congenial toward everyone, felt comfortable, obviously, in our company, and enjoyed our Wednesday meetings.

I found myself, I repeat, moved by young Sosa's warm gesture. I felt that at that moment his friendly, communicative, tender yet manly gesture (which, owing to a certain rigidity of character, I found myself incapable of offering) was the only appropriate and undoubtedly the only beneficial one. Romilio's simplicity and confidence were truly enviable: He didn't ask any questions or utter any superfluous words; he simply patted Mr. Frugoni's shoulder in sympathetic silence, as if actually consoling a brother, a lad his own age. Realizing the need to respect that silence, I remained leaning against the doorframe, gazing at them both, without uttering a word myself.

But luckily, or unluckily—I don't dare to say which—I was followed almost immediately by Mrs. Zimmerman, like myself a registered member of the group. Not that I doubt Mrs. Zimmerman's intelligence or good judgment, though an attitude and a temperament more dissimilar to young

Romilio's would I think have been hard at that moment to find in that little room.

I'll try to explain. Mrs. Zimmerman, in the forties, was an actress in the Jewish amateur theater. Though she retains a slight Yiddish accent, she is, like Romilio, an extraordinary reciter. Her remarkable range allows her to express with utmost richness of nuance the impassioned, the dramatic, the tender or the childlike tone required of the poems, written often by others, which she is fond of reciting. She herself has authored countless compositions, most of them for children, some of which have been published in literary magazines. Aside from working feverishly at Polimnia (and invariably calling attention to this fact at each of the Executive Committee meetings), Mrs. Zimmerman is active in the Union of Argentine Women, is a member of the cultural subcommittee of a Jewish organization, gives lectures on child education and publishes journalistic articles in women's magazines. She must have been an extremely beautiful woman at one time. Now she's a rather short, plump lady, a bit on the authoritarian side.

In any event, she, too, had noticed—much better, naturally, than any of us, according to the modest opinion she was almost certainly expressing to herself—the obscure private drama that lay hidden behind Mrs. Giannello's poem and Mr. Frugoni's flight. She hesitated not one second. Sitting down next to Mr. Frugoni, and indicating with a gentle, indisputable motion to Romilio and myself that we leave, she addressed him in her best, most maternal Yiddish tone: "You and I, we have a lot to talk about, don't we, darling?"

IX

FROM: Chief Officer Farías
TO: Inspector Bevilacqua
November 21, 1975

The following notification is to fully confirm to the above commanding office Corporal Ramos's suspicions with respect to the alleged suspect in the report of November 20, which did appear under the heading: SURVEILLANCE OF 2562 TEODORO VILARDEBÓ. To wit, we are currently in possession of said suspect's file.

The fact that said suspicion arose prior to our obtaining possession of the pertinent documentation attests clearly to the zeal and devotion to service displayed as always by Corporal Nicodemo Ramírez in complying with his patriotic duty.

In view of these considerations, I suggest that Corporal Ramírez be most particularly kept in mind when applications for promotion arise at headquarters.

Having attended to this fundamental act of justice toward personnel under my jurisdiction, I shall proceed with the principal subject of this report.

The suspect under observation was in actuality Carlos Argentino Mastandrea (alias The Gimp), Argentine, 59 years old, widower, ID No. 1,453,806, Federal Capital, residing at 934 Charlone in said capital, who, having completed a 30-day jail sentence in the year 1962 for infraction of the Gambling Law, agreed voluntarily to collaborate, without benefit of payment, as a police informant in Section 37.

In order to emphasize the high level of intelligence and dedication displayed by my subordinate, I must clarify further that in order to achieve his difficult objective, Corporal Ramírez did appear (though off duty) on Thursday the 20th, at 2100 hours, at the bar located at the corner of Federico Lacroze and Álvarez Thomas, remembering that the aforementioned Mastandrea had frequented it in the past. He found the said suspect there, as anticipated, participating in a card game with three other persons. Without making his presence known, Corporal Ramírez waited at a separate table. The remarks he overheard (at least the loud ones) referred exclusively to the contingencies of the game and bore no reference to political topics or related matters, hence a search was deemed inadvisable.

At 2337 hours, Mastandrea paid for the drinks, said good-bye to his buddies and left the bar, with Corporal Ramírez, *ipso facto,* proceeding on his trail.

In addition to the data mentioned *ut supra,* Corporal Ramírez utilized his neighborhood connections to obtain additional information which will be of utmost importance in the eventuality that Mastandrea insists on withholding his collaboration, to wit:

1. His co-dwellers in the aforementioned domicile at 934 Charlone Street are his daughter, Clara; his son-in-law, surname Rosales, occupation bus driver on No. 63 line; two sons of said marriage, ages 9 and 7, given names Tito and Pucho, respectively.

2. The subject's principal means of support appears to be that of moneylender, which he alternates or conceals by selling watches and jewelry on installment among the personnel of the various bus lines.

At precisely 0009 hours on the above date, Corporal Ramírez arrived at said domicile at 934 Charlone, whereupon his presence was promptly made known inasmuch as Mastandrea himself answered the door.

The subject at first pretended not to remember him, but upon being presented with various pieces of documentation (his date of arrest, his participation in clearing up the Forest Avenue furniture store assault by squealing on the plumber who was manufacturing spiked jacks for blowing out police tires, etc.), he wound up admitting he did.

When questioned as to whether he still maintained ties with the police precinct, he answered in the negative, and claimed to have performed these functions only briefly and because he had no choice.

When questioned as to what he meant by "having no choice," his reply was that the late Commissioner Ducasse had threatened to jail him again and beat him to a pulp if he refused to collaborate.

When questioned as to when he had severed his ties with district headquarters, and what had led him to do so, he replied that he had done so as of December 1964, as a result of Commissioner Ducasse's death at that precise time.

When informed of our knowledge of his close ties with Polimnia suspects and questioned as to his interest in collaborating voluntarily so that we could ascertain certain minor details, he expressed his regret and indicated that he preferred, due to his age and precarious state of health, not to reinstate his contacts with headquarters.

When questioned with respect to the manner in which his involvement with Polimnia had commenced, he replied that it had been through a certain Aurelia Kisternmacher, whom he'd met accidentally at the Institute for the Rehabilitation of the Crippled.

When questioned about the true motive for said involvement, he replied that his fondness for poetry had led him to accept the invitation extended by said Kisternmacher, and to attend subsequently, with no commitment on his part, some of the meetings of the aforementioned group.

When questioned on the nature of the subject matter of the poems he composed, his reply was that they were usually of a sad nature.

When warned not to play dumb and to confess once and for all what was going on at those damned meetings, he replied that the only thing they did, at least at those he attended, was recite poetry and/or lines of verse, and that as far as he knew they didn't play the numbers or cards or any other games of chance, nor did they practice any illicit commerce.

When questioned while off guard regarding his knowledge of Marxist elements who frequented the group, his reply was that as far as he knew, there was no Marxist element in the group.

On the basis of this insolent, disrespectful reply, Corporal Ramírez informed him that he was under arrest and ordered him to appear immediately before the chief officer. The subject complied with the order without offering any resistance.

When the aforementioned was brought before me, we proceeded with a slight softening up in order to have him desist in his obstinate, rebellious attitude. He was reminded, as if casually, of some of the dirty deals he'd been involved in. And had it proved to him that we possessed complete knowledge of his daughter's and son-in-law's place of employment, as well as the address of the schools his grandchildren attended. Following this, and a few relatively easy minutes of interrogation, Mastandrea decided in a nice way and on his own to lend us his unselfish collaboration. He was informed that all he'd be asked for, essentially, would be a complete list of Polimnia's members, with their full names and respective residences.

When questioned as to whether he was in a position to obtain this information by the following day, his reply was that he could count on having it only by Wednesday the 26th, that is, at the next meeting, and that once it was in his possession, he'd personally turn it over to whomsoever was indicated.

When informed that Corporal Ramírez, in order to save him any trouble, would come to his domicile in person on November 27 at 8:00 A.M., he raised no further objections.

Surveillance continues on 2562 Teodoro Vilardebó, with four daily shifts at present. No further information as of now.

X

And as the Shadow kept tracing its slow, menacing circles around the house on Teodoro Vilardebó, the ultimate aim being to inflict icy death that very night on twelve of its magnanimous occupants, the Messenger flew swiftly toward the summits of Olympus and arrived there in the briefest of time.

And indomitable Athena and incomparable Aphrodite were seated on the same summit, their backs to one another, smitten by their ancient rancor, loath to speak to one another or even to exchange a single glance of their flashing eyes.

And so Hermes, in his golden sandals, his bosom still heaving from his recent sinister encounter, addressed the two goddesses with bitter and reproachful words.

"The beleaguered mortals would indeed do well to forget once and for all their petty, indifferent goddesses who, owing perhaps to the weight of years or to their everlasting, debilitating grudges, or merely to their contemptible vanity, have permitted their eyes to grow dim, their ears to become muffled and their hearts, once valiant and generous, to shrink and wither.

"O goddesses, I will have you know that while both of you are planted here, engaged in your endless, futile wrangles, odious Hades, unlike yourselves, is not squandering his time in futile disputes, but is plotting indefatigably and diligently the destruction of the mortals you so unjustifiably claim to have under your protection.

"O frivolous, squabbling Olympians, yonder shadow that we see is none other than the Herald of Death, sent by underworld Hades in order to consummate on this very night the ineluctable death of twelve human beings who at this very moment are happily and innocently listening to Mrs. Giannello's stirring words.

"I know neither the first nor the last names of any of the twelve whom Hades has condemned, nor the reason behind the unnamable deity's act, nor the cruel and surely bloody method he will employ to execute his carefully conceived scheme on this very night. All that I do know is that Hades' schemes are inescapable, and that the other gods, even if all were to unite, would be powerless to prevent it."

So spoke the divine Messenger, and Athena's intrepid heart went out on behalf of the irreproachable Irene Bengoechea. And Aphrodite shed hot tears for the fate that awaited José María Pulicicchio and the incomparable Mrs. Giannello. And Hermes grieved for his own charges, Mr. Aníbal Frugoni and Mr. Romualdo Chávez, both of whom were skilled and eloquent salesmen.

And then Athena, Zeus' valiant, indomitable daughter, pronounced these winged words: "Wisely have you spoken, O prudent Hermes, though your words have been hardened by cruel reproach.

"Clearly can I see from here the ominous, implacable circles that are being drawn around our beloved mortals by the cold Herald of Death, sent by Hades from his abode in the shades of the lower world.

"And though I know as well as you do that no one can sway Hades, he of the noble steeds, from his schemes, allow me, I pray, to ponder briefly, and I invite you, fair Aphrodite, to do the same.

"For we must decide on the measures, within our powers, that need be taken in the forthcoming hours. Though unable to save our charges from the black Ker of death, at least let us make their last moments on earth both fertile and pleasurable.

"As for you, O prudent Messenger, go forth with all the speed of your winged sandals, and slip secretly into Hades' dark abode.

"Though the Shadow has refused to tell you the reason for Hades' implacable behavior, or the ruthless means he will employ before the day is out to transport twelve souls to his abode, perhaps there is a servant, one of the many roaming about amidst the shades, who, unaware of our schemes, will agree to tell you the truth.

"Go forth then, without delay, and by the time you return to Olympus, shaking the wings of your hat and your sandals, both Aphrodite and I will have settled our differences sufficiently, and, in accordance with the news you bring, will then decide on the course of action to be taken in the brief time remaining to us."

And Hermes diligently obeyed, and flew as swift as the wind toward the dark abode, with its iron gates, over which grim Hades did rule, while the goddesses, from atop Olympus, gazed with furrowed brow toward the house at 2562 Teodoro Vilardebó and pondered in deep silence.

XI

Both young Romilio Sosa and myself felt rather snubbed at first, and even, why not confess, slightly humiliated by Mrs. Zimmerman's rather authoritarian behavior. Not that we dared to dispute her status as psychologist and lecturer in child-rearing, but we found the manner in which she treated us as pesky creatures to be a bit excessive. We exchanged meaningful, eloquent glances and left Mrs. Zimmerman alone with Mr. Frugoni in the small back room.

As we crossed the courtyard on our way back to the meeting room, Romilio remarked: "Well, I guess it's for the best, after all." I understood him perfectly, and couldn't help feeling glad and agreeing with him. Both of us—as if suddenly illumined by a simultaneous clarity—realized, in fact, that we ought not in any way feel slighted by what had happened a few minutes before, for if anyone was capable of appeasing Mr. Frugoni's tormented mind, that someone was none other than Mrs. Zimmerman. A beautiful spirit—this thought I'm sure occurred to both of us simultaneously—despite her forgivably tyrannical attitude, and one who possessed an infinite capacity for understanding.

With hearts totally free of any resentment, we thus placed all our trust in Mrs. Zimmerman, whom God most assuredly was enlightening, and entered the meeting room, where the first half of the session was still in progress.

The night, as I mentioned earlier, was quite warm. I don't know who finally had the idea to turn on the fan, but that beautiful, newly acquired and highly utilitarian standing appliance of ours, with its pleasant pale-green enamel paint, its wide blades and nearly silent movement, was benignly shedding its cool, invigorating breeze upon everyone.

Irene had left her seat and was standing next to our recording secretary. I couldn't help observing Mrs. Giannello's hands: they nervously kept folding and unfolding the three manuscript pages of her classroom looseleaf. Just then I heard Irene's voice, and I must confess that upon hearing it, I experienced once again that same flood of gentle emotion as always. The tone of her voice is slightly deep, having at the same time crystal reverberations. Her voice, in fact, is precisely the theme of my second sonnet (now virtually completed), in which I compare it to a glass bell submerged in the waters of a serene lake of great depth.

Irene, with utmost intelligence, praised the structure of the beautiful poem we had just heard. She congratulated Mrs. Giannello with that wonderful openness of hers, despite its hint of appealing shyness—for me, one of her principal charms. She commented on the dramatic sense of the poem, the correct distribution of the hendecasyllables into stanzas, the emotion mounting in each of the lovely strophes. Mrs. Giannello, with simplicity and forced composure, smiled and thanked her for the praise, but kept casting rapid, anxious glances toward the now totally dark courtyard. She tried impatiently to light a cigarette, but twice in a row the air blown by the fan extinguished her match. At that point, something occurred which I feel obliged to mention. Mr. Chávez, who was standing at the other end of the room, chatting most animatedly with Miss Kisternmacher and Mr. Mastandrea, rushed across the room and, with a broad, courtly gesture, offered her a flame from his lighter. I can't say I was surprised by that gracious gesture, which was quite typical of Mr. Chávez, but in this instance I found it somewhat overly solicitous and maybe even purposeful. Irene, too, was startled by the speed of our president's reaction, and communicated this to me with a barely perceptible motion of her eyebrows. Maybe, I thought, this was my opportunity, in the light of our blatant complicity, to initiate a more intimate, confidential relationship with her. And so, conveying that I'd caught and understood her gesture, but that under the circumstances felt it necessary to be circumspect, I turned to Mrs. Giannello, kissed her hand, and expressed my own sincere praise for her poem.

Just at that moment, Mr. Mastandrea, who had been moving forward quietly on his crutches, followed apparently by Mr. Chávez, approached us quite inopportunely. His forehead was beaded with perspiration and his expression was uneasy and evasive. He stammered some awkward (and ignorant) remark in attempted praise of Mrs. Giannello, and then clumsily stood near us in a manner I can unhesitatingly call embarrassing. He had nothing to say, and in my opinion barely understood the conversation we were holding.

As a result, the rest of us (Irene, Mrs. Giannello, Mr. Chávez and myself) gradually fell silent, affected, I suppose, in some incomprehensible way, by Mastandrea's annoying, uncivil silence. I had the feeling that his thoughts were very much elsewhere. Maybe on his awful sonnets, I remember myself thinking, just as Mastandrea, with his utter lack of tact or good breeding, took my arm and drew me aside. For the second time that evening, I exchanged a conspiratorial glance with Irene and a comical "What can we do?" gesture, which she received smilingly, as I resigned myself to hearing him out.

Mr. Mastandrea, dear fellow, still sweating buckets,

hesitated and stammered. He began babbling to me
vaguely about the group's meetings, which he labeled as
imprudent, "especially with everything going on," as he
put it. And then, surprisingly, he went on to say that we
ought to be more discreet, more cautious, "more on the sly,
you know what I mean?" he said, bringing the back of his
hand to his mouth, as if transmitting some sort of important secret to me. Quite annoyed by now, I asked him
directly what it was that he wanted to tell me.

XII

FROM: Inspector Bevilacqua
TO: Chief Inspector Guso, Security Headquarters
November 28, 1975

Dear Blackie:

I had every intention of dropping by your office last night, but things got all screwed up here at the last minute. Anyhow, seeing that Adjutant Grossi is on his way over, I'm sending along with him all the paperwork I intended to give to you personally (a pretext, actually, to have a little chat with you, which I hope will be possible at some other time).

Listen, Blackie, most of the crap in that report is baloney, but there are two or three things in it that I really wanted to discuss with you. One is the business about that guy I had to hand over to The Goat's men. I just found out that that jerk Assistant Inspector Dileo treated him like a nobody. And then, to top it off, he even committed the blooper of notifying the guy's relatives. Poor bastard, never misses a detail, does he? And now some newspaper has gone ahead and printed petitions and other crap like that. And my own name appears. Let's see what we can do to straighten this out, pal. I'm close to retirement, and must confess that I've had a bellyful of it.

Another matter that in a way has to do with the first, and

that's a circular from the First Army Commander which I received yesterday morning. In view of the numerous assassination attempts, etc., etc., he's ordering reinforcement of house guards on twenty-six brass hats in my zone, with at least 3 (three) of them to be posted at each residence.

Will you tell me where the hell I'm supposed to dig up 52 plainclothesmen, without leaving half of our upper ranks in shreds or having to remove at least a dozen from important factories? You're more up on this stuff than I am, so tell me, please, what I'm to do.

And the third matter I wanted to raise concerns the property on Teodoro Vilardebó. I didn't attach much importance to it at the beginning, as I told you, because of the origin of the denunciation. You know, of course, what I mean: the street table at the corner of Cuenca and Nogoyá streets. Coincidentally, where Frugoni's wife is planted—what a nut. Anyhow, the whole business looks to be more serious than we thought. You'll find out what I mean when you take a look at these papers. The reports are from Officer Pascuali, Adjutant Covas and Chief Officer Farías. Also enclosed is an envelope containing the 52 photographs that were shot. You'll notice, inside the same envelope, a list with complete names, domiciles and ID numbers of all the members of Polimnia, and those who attended meetings. It's an exact duplicate of the one Mastandrea gave Corporal Ramírez when Ramírez showed up at his house on Thursday the 27th, at 8:00 A.M., to pick up the pictures, as had been arranged.

In order to get this valuable list, the guy told the president that he needed it because he wanted to send New Year's greetings to all the members. So there are no problems about him having aroused any suspicion.

One more thing. According to Corporal Ramírez, Mastandrea was pretty scared and contradicted himself several times when spoken to. This means that the suspect's commitment to the group is greater than he led us to believe in his previous statements. Bear this in mind.

Anyhow (I'm saying this for your peace of mind), Corporal Ramírez didn't try to pressure him too much. On the contrary. He acted real friendly, and told him that since he was collaborating so nicely with us (and if he promised not to mention a word about this to anyone), he had no reason to be afraid for himself or his family. I did it right, don't you think?

Out of gratitude, Mastandrea presented us—Corporal Ramírez, Farías and myself—with three of the watches he sells on credit. Just to cover ourselves, I sent Ramírez straight back to that son of a bitch to get a sweet, paid-in-cash receipt.

Personally, I feel that with one more interrogation, we'll have that guy singing the tango "La Cumparsita," with variations and all. But for the time being, it's better to sit tight, give him plenty of rope, and not let those birds out of the bush.

Incidentally, Blackie, their domiciles have all been verified. Also, at any minute now, Mr. Mastandrea will be sending you a lady's watch to help you score with some chick. Or maybe you prefer a man's watch?

Anyhow, let me hear from you about that business concerning guard reinforcement, and try to come up with some quick solution to that mess with the petition. Now that you've got all the documents, try to move fast on getting the personal files, which we're all waiting for here.

Come and have dinner with the missus and kiddies on Saturday. How about it?

Love,
Bevilacqua

XIII

As the hawk swoops down in a straight line upon a tiny mouse scurrying defenselessly across a field, so did divine Hermes hasten toward the nether realm of Hades in order to fulfill the wishes of gray-eyed Athena.

He arrived with dizzying speed, crossed the bronze threshold and iron gates, passing so swiftly that he could not be detained by the forbidding boatman or bloodthirsty three-headed dog guarding the gate.

And Hades' realm was like a vast cavern furrowed with deep black rivers. The awesome darkness and cold oozed ceaselessly from its damp walls. And an oppressive silence, interrupted only by distant, mysterious echoes, weighed heavily upon valiant Hermes' heart.

And a horde of spirits of the dead silently roamed amidst the infinite labyrinths, while the Keres, the Fates and the servants of the unnamable deity occupied privileged positions along the banks of the rivers or in protected valleys and plains.

And Hermes spied a favored group occupying choice positions apart from the other ghosts, on a broad and spacious promontory. And divine Hermes thought that perhaps one of Hades' favorites or manservants, unaware of the Olympian messenger's identity, might provide him with the prompt reply that the Shadow had malevolently denied him.

The group was composed of the most illustrious ghosts, those who had been soldiers or guardians of order while alive. And all had died in the hands of subversive elements. And all had earned the love of grim Hades, for having procured during their sojourn on earth countless souls for his underworld realm.

And so, assuming the guise of a superior military officer, Hermes of the winged sandals spoke to them:

"O illustrious dead and loyal servants of mighty Hades, since I'm a newcomer in this dark abode and unfamiliar with the laws and customs of the land, I would like, if you're willing, to ask you certain questions."

The ghost of Ramón Falcón, who has been the first to arrive in that realm, on May 3, 1909, stepped forth as spokesman.

"Speak up, illustrious newcomer, and we'll be glad to satisfy your request, for it's plain to us all, from your showy uniform, your numerous medals and your erect stance while speaking that you are a military officer of high rank."

And so Hermes, in the tone and stance of a superior military officer, did speak, and he asked his questions:

"I know nothing about this vast realm, O guardians, and hence would like you to inform me as to Hades' motive in transporting on this very night unto this very place the souls of twelve mortals now peacefully seated in a beautiful house on Teodoro Vilardebó Street, and also what human or divine devices the mighty god intends to employ in order to reap so swiftly twelve mortal lives?"

Twisting the end of his black mustache, Ramón Falcón's illustrious ghost replied: "This is what I know, O distinguished spirit. Three weeks ago, on November 15 to be exact, mighty Hades was forewarned by infallible soothsayers that on December 3, 1975, subversive elements (undoubtedly anarchists with Polish names, using, I'd predict, homemade bombs) would be dispatching to this black realm a mortal beloved on numerous counts by insatiable Hades, the most excellent General Cáceres Monié.

"This heinous crime has prompted Hades to prepare his vengeance meticulously. On that particular prophetic day, the day of doom for his illustrious protégé, Hades instilled the spirit of Denunciation in Aníbal Frugoni's lawful wife, whereupon she, in her capacity as secretary at a street-corner table, transmitted her information to the 45th Precinct.

"Then, on November 21, the deity whose commands governed us all while alive imbued Corporal Nicodemo Ramírez's heart with Diligence, Professional Suspicion and the Call to Duty, thereby prompting him on his own to make all the necessary inquiries concerning Carlos Argentino Mastandrea, an ex-cardsharp and a member of Polimnia.

"As a further measure, and to avoid leaving anything to fickle chance, on November 22 he imbued Mastandrea with the spirit of Cowardliness and Terror in order to make him accept all of Corporal Ramírez's proposals and to dutifully provide the membership list.

"Only once, we must admit, did Mastandrea falter and verge unwittingly on upsetting Hades' meticulous plans. That, if you care to know, occurred this very evening, when Mastandrea, undoubtedly encouraged by scheming Aphrodite, tried to confide his misfortunes to Mr. José María Pulicicchio by taking his arm and drawing him aside.

"But the moment implacable Hades detected this imminent unforeseen confession, which undoubtedly would have jeopardized the orderly course of his plans (Mastandrea's revelation would have resulted in the flight of many of those assembled at 2562 Teodoro Vilardebó), the god took immediate precautions.

"Borne by his swift black chariot, with its noble steeds, Hades arrived at the foundation of the structure on Teodoro Vilardebó, halted beneath the floor of the blue-wallpapered room, and with the tip of his whip, struck the wooden parquet floor three consecutive times.

"This signal from mighty Hades produced an abrupt interruption in Mastandrea's barely begun confession, and he switched in fright to some idiotic babbling having to do with sonnets, much to the astonishment of patient José María Pulicicchio.

"And so, to spare you useless details, O gallant soldier, let me inform you that the records pertaining to the individuals attending Polimnia are now all in the hands of security agencies. And in view of the grave nature of these records—for each of Polimnia's members is in some way or other linked to stateless, subversive delinquency—you, O illustrious newcomer, can draw your own intelligent conclusions."

And again diligent Hermes spoke up, in the gruff voice of a superior army officer: "Colonel Ramón L. Falcón, magnanimous protégé of Hades, I've listened most attentively to all your words, but still have not been informed of the means that the relentless god intends to employ in order to execute his task."

And in a booming, military voice, Colonel Ramón Falcón's ghost replied, while smoothing once again the tips of his black handlebar mustache: "O illustrious officer, I don't know which South American country was the recipient of your distinguished service, but judging from your great naiveté, I don't imagine that it was Argentina, Uruguay, Brazil or Chile.

"For your information, a terrorist group of the extreme right, totally unconnected, of course, with our own glorious institutions, will be thoroughly informed, via channels unknown to us, of the serious records on the Polimnians." While the colonel (who had died in 1909) was speaking, Hermes seemed to detect a nearly imperceptible smile on his austere countenance.

And then, sighing as if in resignation, Colonel Ramón Falcón's ghost continued talking, addressing Hermes with his grim words.

"For your information, it is this group of unknown individuals—commanded by a mysterious chief nicknamed 'The Goat'—and not our own pure comrades in arms, who will be executing Hades' command with professional efficiency.

"These unknown individuals, on this very night, in four shiny Ford Falcon cars, will pull up in front of the house on

Teodoro Vilardebó. They will descend, each provided with powerful weapons, and, pretending to be policemen, will carry off the twelve mortals whom Hades has condemned.

"Hours later, if you're interested in knowing the details, O gallant soldier, the twelve persons in attendance at Polimnia, some of them women, will be found dead amidst the pasturelands of Ezeiza. Their hands will be tied behind their backs, strips of adhesive tape will gag their mouths, and several high-caliber bullets will have pierced their beaten bodies. Is there something else, O illustrious newcomer, that you wish to inquire of me?"

But diligent Hermes wasted no time in further questions. Transformed once more into the swift Olympian Messenger, he shook the wings on his sandals and hat, and flew off to relay all the terrible news to Athena and Aphrodite, who were awaiting him impatiently.

XIV

Mastandrea hesitated at my rather brusque, impatient question. He lowered his eyes as if searching for something on the parquet floor and, avoiding a direct reply, sank once again into his annoying silence. I guess it was his crutches that hit the floor two or three times. He was obviously extremely anxious or nervous. It was as if something or somebody were threatening him to hold his tongue. In order to calm him, I repeated my question in a more inviting, cordial tone. "Mr. Mastandrea, why don't you explain more clearly to me what you mean? I really don't understand."

And then, abruptly, as if suddenly forgetting everything he'd started to tell me, he reached into the inner pocket of his jacket, with the rapid, decisive motion of someone reaching for a gun, and took out some papers, which he thrust against my chest. "I want you to read this," he blurted out. "I'm going to be sending it to all the members." Then, in a roundabout manner, he labored to explain what he had in mind.

He wanted, at the end of the current year, to send each of Polimnia's members a sort of commemorative brochure —"a little token," he called it—containing some of his most recent sonnets. In order to do this, he'd asked Mr. Chávez the previous week to provide him with a complete membership list, including the respective domiciles of each of the members. I told him that it sounded like an excellent idea, and congratulated him. Despite the low, or even nonexistent, caliber of his awful sonnets, I found it touching nonetheless that a fellow like Mastandrea, whom I'd once regarded as uncivil, was capable of extending such an original, refined gesture toward each of us.

In other words, what Mastandrea had in mind when he took my arm and practically dragged me from where I was standing was really quite simple. He wanted to show me his sonnets. To seek my approval, maybe, or my criticism. And all the rest, that business about "prudence," "discretion," etc., which I failed to understand, was simply a way, a rather absurd way, and quite typical of good old Mastandrea, of broaching the subject.

I must confess that the privilege he bestowed upon me in making me his sole critic didn't please me one iota. As the organization's acknowledged cultivator of the sonnet, I'd always forbidden myself from expressing any criticism of his efforts. Quite the contrary. Though his sonnets, as I believe I've indicated, leave much to be desired, and his readings are quite painful, I've gone out of my way when the occasion has presented itself, and congratulated and encouraged him in the most sincere and cordial manner. Under the present circumstances, however, the demand was for a reading, no less, of the material he himself had selected for inclusion in the famous brochure before it was "sent to press."

I informed him that I indeed felt most honored to have the distinction bestowed upon me. I'd gladly read his sonnets, at that very moment and with my utmost attention. In fact, I was merely carrying out our recommended statutory guidelines—namely, "reading with utmost attention the material presented by each of the members, whenever said request is tendered."

So I slipped on my glasses and began reading. The

series of sonnets was entitled "Confessions and Lamentations of a Recluse," and all of them apparently dealt with the same theme, the author's suffering and woes.

They were, as usual, unequivocally bad. Bad, without any redeeming feature. Limping along and plagued with clichés, pitiful rhymes, stylistic incongruities, lacking the most minimal clarity.

I can recall the first disheartening quatrain. If I'm not mistaken, it went like this:

> What utter captivity doth suffer my soul
> My sadness no longer knows whither to go
> Like a phantom pursuing me unto its goal
> Evil from the past plunges me in woe!

I finished reading, put away my eyeglasses, and told him that I found the poems exceedingly beautiful, liked them enormously, and felt certain that they'd elicit a great emotional impact from each of the members when received imprinted upon the brochure.

"Miss Kisternmacher had exactly the same opinion," remarked the lame (in several senses) Mr. Mastandrea. This, in other words, meant that I hadn't been the sole individual entrusted as first reader of the sonnets. Oh, well.

The fellow wanted to keep talking—that is, to hear me say more about his plaintive poems—but I had little more to say.

Luckily, at that moment, Mr. Frugoni entered, along with Mrs. Zimmerman. He was very pale and walking stiffly, as though his body were refusing to obey the impulses of a firm inner decision. He headed toward the group standing around Mrs. Giannello (that friendly, animated group which included Irene, and which I'd reluctantly been compelled to abandon due to Mr. Mastandrea's inconvenient and tiresome summons). I tried to avail myself of the arrival of both friends to get back to the group, but things that evening weren't destined to work out so easily for me. I'd barely left Mastandrea when Mrs. Zimmerman this time, bless her soul, took me by the arm in a friendly and urgent manner, dragged me to one side of the room and, without giving me the slightest opportunity to resist, forced me to sit down beside her. Naturally, I obeyed, and prepared to hear her out.

"I'll fix everything," she told me in a confidential tone, her right hand simultaneously tracing a quick semicircle in the air, starting at the top and moving to the bottom, as if this simple gesture of shooing mosquitoes could instantly, in one fell swoop, dissipate not only Mr. Frugoni's serious and tormenting problems but, magically, all the problems of the world.

I told her I was happy to hear that, but, lamentably, didn't quite understand what was going on, due to the inexorable order she'd issued in the little back room. Mrs. Zimmerman sighed and attempted, condescendingly, with maternal resignation, as if talking to a totally inexperienced creature, a baby perhaps, to sum up everything, as though making it accessible to my presumed meager capacity to understand.

I managed rather hazily, since she spoke quickly and in a low voice and with a heavier Yiddish accent than usual, to piece together something that had to do with Mrs. Frugoni's behavior, which Mrs. Zimmerman several times labeled as "irrational." The reason for this, it seemed, was that Mrs. Frugoni refused, "for anything in the world," to grant her husband a divorce. And in addition to that, her primitive and "totally irrational" tantrums had terrified poor Mr. Frugoni. "Do you want to know how she does it, darling? With threats, truly dreadful threats." At which point, she proceeded to enumerate each of the dreadful threats, her right-hand index finger ticking off the fingers of her left hand as follows: killing herself (thumb), doing away with the children or having them disappear (index finger), reporting him to some security organization whose name I didn't quite catch (middle finger), getting him killed by hit men (ring finger), taking his store away from him (pinkie), blackmailing him (again the thumb), etc.

"And what's behind all those threats—shall we see?" Mrs. Zimmerman asked, stretching out her palms, tilting her head, and squinting as if getting ready to test a somewhat feeble-minded student. I made a humble, apologetic gesture for not knowing the answer. And then, with pedagogical tenderness, she informed me of the wise conclusion she'd reached thanks to her vast psychological knowledge. Her indisputable conclusion was that Mrs. Frugoni would do absolutely nothing and would soon willingly grant her husband a divorce. "When?" Naturally, once she, Mrs. Zimmerman, had spoken to her and made her understand a whole bunch of things. "What sort of things, darling?" Oh, things, important things that she personally knew a lot about, having to do with love, couples, fate, pursuits that bind people together spiritually, money—naturally, no problem after her divorce from Mr. Frugoni—which reminded her of an identical situation experienced by her own sister-in-law, who had then subsequently remarried, this time a manager of the Israeli Bank, and was now in sheer bliss. "Do you understand me, darling?"

I replied that I understood perfectly, despite my hopeless imbecility, and kept glancing meanwhile toward the group that included Irene, attempting, I confess, to overhear some of the things that were being said. Even from where we sat, at the opposite end of the room, I could clearly make out the annoyed expression on Mr. Frugoni's face as a result of Mr. Chávez's rather old-fashioned gallantries toward Mrs. Giannello. At one point, I noticed Mr. Frugoni taking a step forward, with a grim expression of suppressed violence, and positioning himself next to Mrs. Giannello in such a way that their shoulders nearly touched, and from there he glared at Mr. Chávez with combined resentment and defiance. Mr. Chávez, of course, detected all this (an outright scene of jealousy despite the subject matter of the conversation), but once more he demonstrated his savoir faire and the magnanimity of his worldly, chivalrous spirit. He smiled in a friendly way at both of them and addressed one of his typical gallantries to Irene, as if thereby proving to them what little significance these gallantries played to a Don Juan, who customarily yielded to a suitor of serious intentions, thereby leaving a clear path for the unintended rival. I couldn't determine whether Mr. Frugoni, consumed as he was by unjustified jealousy, was aware of our president's worthy, fraternal and, in a way, exemplary behavior. All I know is that Mr. Frugoni's contact with Mrs. Giannello became closer and closer, until her head was practically resting on his shoulder. Just then Irene sought my gaze, threw me a smile, and even waved in a childlike gesture of greeting. I hope she doesn't imagine—I remember thinking with some alarm—that Mrs. Zimmerman and I . . . Without even completing the thought, I believe I involuntarily moved a few inches away from my didactic lady friend. In any event, I'd already heard everything she wanted to tell me and was eager to return to Irene's group.

Mr. Chávez was now saying something, and with his Castilian accent it must have been particularly funny, for everyone laughed at it. Frankly, I was at a loss as to what to say to Mrs. Zimmerman to have us rejoin the group. While trying to come up with something that wouldn't appear rude, I heard the word "threats" clearly voiced by Mr. Chávez. Mrs. Zimmerman heard it too, for she looked at me, her forehead wrinkling. I thought, as did Mrs. Zimmerman, I'm sure, that the secret matter relating to Mrs. Frugoni had unexpectedly assumed a public dimension. And so, delaying no further, I suggested that we join the group, since the matter was probably of interest to her: without so much as asking her permission, they were infringing upon her psychological domain.

Mr. Chávez reiterated the word "threats," but clearly in a context quite different from the one we attributed to it. "... threats," he said, "to which we, as upright, law-abiding men and women dedicated to the sublime priesthood of poetry, ought not to concede the slightest importance." The term, in other words, was being used in reference to some other matter. I questioned Mr. Chávez, who smiled and, taking things somewhat jokingly, enlightened me. There had apparently been some coarse phone calls to group headquarters in the past few days, and at Mr. Chávez's residence as well. Rather concerned, I inquired further as to the nature of these threats. "Sheer poppycock," Mr. Chávez replied, twisting elegantly on his heels and addressing everyone. "Threats of a, shall we say, political nature. Certainly some ludicrous error. We've undoubtedly been confused with a committee or something of that sort. Let us not be at all alarmed. I shall take it upon myself to see that matters are clarified with the appropriate individual." And then, with the most worldly and enticing of gestures, he added: "And now, what do you think, my friends: shall we, after this interlude, proceed to listen to the voices of our dear and admired poets?"

XV

FROM: Chief Officer Farías
TO: Inspector Bevilacqua
November 29, 1975

This is to report that on the above date, at approximately 1400 hours, Corporal Ramírez did perform an additional eye inspection upon the domicile of Carlos Argentino Mastandrea, availing himself of the circumstances of having been dispatched to said premises by the undersigned to effectuate an exchange of a recently acquired watch since said watch was defective in operation.

The suspect received Corporal Ramírez in a small room serving both as storage space for odds and ends and as study. He happened to be engaged at the moment in drawing up with his ballpoint pen and carbon paper a final copy of a sort of circular addressed to Polimnia's members.

When questioned about what he was writing, his reply was that since he'd asked the group president for the membership list in order to send out New Year's greetings, he was obliged to do so to avoid arousing suspicion.

When questioned as to whether he intended to send these greetings on carbon copies, he replied in the negative, and said that what he was now doing was making a clean copy for the printer.

When questioned as to whether he didn't think that what he'd written was too extensive for a greeting card, his reply was that he was going to utilize said salutation for including some of his own poetry on a sheet of orange oak tag which he referred to as a brochure.

When questioned as to whether he had any objections to providing us with a copy of what he was preparing, he was negative and hesitant at first, but then wound up handing it over, with extreme reluctance and nervousness.

Though the circular reveals no material which can interfere with the progress of our investigation, I herewith enclose the carbon copy requisitioned by Corporal Ramírez in order to add it to our corresponding file and in the further eventuality that the aforementioned may contain some coded messages.

Dear Member:

On the occasion of the year about to conclude, the undersigned takes great pleasure in sending you and your family the most effusive auguries for happiness, the sole object being to hope that the forthcoming year of 1976 provide for you and your dear ones a pristine fountain of felicity, money and good fortune, free from any sort of illness, compulsion or evil thoughts, but, on the contrary, dedicated totally to the spiritual task of sublime, redemptive Poetry, and united forever beneath the altar of Mrs. Brígida Ramírez de Urdampilleta in pursuit of the society's lofty goals.

I avail myself of this timely missive to transmit to you by way of a token or souvenir some poems (sonnets) composed by the undersigned author, which though not attaining perhaps the elevated and profound levels achieved by other celebrated poets, such as Ruben Darïio, Amado Nervo, Santo Chocano, Margarita Abella Caprile, etc., have nonetheless the merit at least of the author's untainted sincerity, which stems from the grave adversities he has undergone in the course of a doleful existence strewn with adversities.

In the wake of these adversities, which, like hungry wolves howling upon a vast steppe, have ceaselessly and fiercely pursued him for years and years, these heartfelt poems were born, and now are being offered to you as proof of my abiding regard and affection, without the expectation of any recompense whatsoever.

And so, without further ado, and with the hope of enlightened understanding on your part, which is to say, that your eyes have the capacity to fathom (as one is able to discern a shiny gold coin amidst the murky waters of a filthy ditch) all that the author's lips normally repress, owing to numerous circumstances pointless to enumerate here, but of whose great effect our Lord Who art in Heaven is well aware, my most respectful salutations to you and yours,

C. A. Mastandrea

CONFESSIONS AND LAMENTATIONS
OF A RECLUSE

by Carlos Argentino Mastandrea

I
Oh, but I am sorely pressed
And my sadness knows no bounds

Apparitions from the past
Pursue me like evil hounds.

I dwelt in peace and did good deeds
My shield and motto: God, Country and Home.
Many a heart did my money console
In collecting debts, I was not hard as stone.

But then came accusations: contumacy, usury!
And ipso facto into service they indentured me,
To do their bidding, and to do it silently.

And here am I in woeful straits,
Enslaved to false and wicked baalim,
Knaves with hearts of stone, and blood
    black as vermin.

II
He who falls into criminal ways
Is marked for life, poor soul.
Compassion and clemency are not his lot,
His past forever wreaks its heavy toll.

They'll seek him out and seal his fate,
Ignoble creatures, godless foes,
Luring their Judas Iscariot not with shiny
    coins
But with sinister threats and mighty blows.

Lament ye not, for the strong will prevail,
Keep faith in the Lord who seeth all
And will come to the rescue, without fail.

And those abusive nefarious Foes
Will suffer their befitting lot,

For they will perish, Heaven knows, while the
    tormented assuredly will not.

III
And now, here's the unhappy story
Of an upright man beset by woes.
Pray that God take him unto His glory.
His name: C. A. Mastandrea, from Colegiales.

Believe not the slander imputed to him,
Hearken instead to his anguished secrets,
Of untold suffering and unflagging
  perseverance
To forge, despite all, these enclosed sonnets.

Yea, he walked in the valley of the shadow of
    death
With Lucifer ever his guide, whispering into
    his ear:
"Go thee to the baals," and in sheer ignorance,
    the wretch complied.

Insatiable and cruel were those false gods
Who allowed him no time in his quest for God,
But hounded him ceaselessly merely to prod any
    information that could be construed as odd.

IV
Nineteen hundred seventy-two: a year
Misfortune did strike at my door.
And a cruel and heartless brute appeared
Bursting with power, contumacy, and more.

In a moment of weakness, I succumbed to evil
And the wicked exploited my innocent fall.

As darkness doth ever follow twilight,
So was my wretched life consumed by night.

I went and whispered into evil ears,
Beheld sinister things no one else ever saw,
Whereupon with wooden crutches I pounded
    and pounded at earth's infamous core.

And at last when I thought 'twas over forever
Those evil times, that repulsive aura—
Evil strikes again in all its fury: is there
    to be peace never?

XVI

Once again Hermes flashed across the vast Ether, flying swiftly toward the heights of Olympus, where he was being anxiously awaited by gray-eyed Athena and peerless Aphrodite, each buried in deep thought, since both were patronesses of several mortals who at that very moment were fervently applauding Mrs. Giannello as she finished reading her poem.

No sooner did Hermes set winged foot upon golden Olympian soil, his divine heart pounding strenuously from his dizzying journey, than he addressed both goddesses hastily and at the same time.

"O goddesses, in compliance with divine Athena's wishes, I've learned all that was needed to know.

"The reason vindictive Hades has been enraged at our twelve protégés is, as always, capricious and hence irrefutable. He has been forewarned by his infallible soothsayers that on this day, December 3, 1975, subversive elements would be dispatching to his black abode the illustrious General Jorge Estéban Cáceres Monié, who is beloved on many accounts by insatiable Hades.

"And so, in deadly vengeance, Hades is determined to extinguish in a most painful and bloody manner twelve of his mortal foes, and to transport them on this very night to his iron-gated abode.

"His fearsome eyes are fixed upon those assembled at the house on Teodoro Vilardebó, merely because they, as you well know, happen to be conveniently congregated tonight in one small room, which will greatly facilitate the task of Hades' fierce emissaries. And besides, this indiscriminate slaughter will rapidly disseminate Terror amidst the numerous mortals whom this barren divinity has justifiably designated as his enemies.

"O goddesses, Hades has already taken his preliminary measures. On November 15, after having heard the auguries of his soothsayers, he proceeded in a manner so cunning and efficient that at this very moment the implacable security agencies regard each of the peaceful, well-groomed Polimnians as anarchistic, subversive delinquents with international Marxist links, and already have their records on file in the exhaustive archives of the Office of Federal Security.

"As for the odious means that Hades intends to employ in order to execute his bloody deed, they are as follows: Some unidentifiable men belonging to a terrorist group of the extreme right, and driving four shiny Ford Falcon automobiles, will on this very night come to a stop in front of the house on Teodoro Vilardebó. They will descend, each armed with powerful weapons, and, pretending to be policemen, will force the twelve mortals condemned by Hades into their swift vehicles.

"Hours later, twelve of the people who customarily attend Polimnia, some of them women, will be found dead amidst the pasturelands of Ezeiza. Their hands will be tied behind them, bands of adhesive tape will gag their mouths, and their bodies will reveal the impact of numerous high-caliber bullets and show signs of having been brutally beaten and tortured."

So spoke dauntless Hermes, and indomitable Athena was the first to reply, with these winged words:

"We have listened most attentively to what you've told us, O prudent Messenger. I realize now that it is quite impossible to forestall mighty Hades from seizing the spoils he has so meticulously prepared. It is equally impossible, due to his gruff, frigid, intractable temperament, to persuade him to renounce it. And thus I firmly believe, unless fair Aphrodite be of another mind, that we must accept the certain death of our charges as a consummated act."

Hearing this, fair-cheeked Aphrodite turned to Athena, the patroness of war, and spoke:

"Everything you say, valiant maiden, is true. But I should like to think that the grave musing proposed by yourself has not been in vain. I, too, at your behest, have mused and, if you care to hear me out, I'll tell you the conclusion I have reached.

"Indeed, there is nothing now that we Olympians can do to contest implacable Hades, whom Zeus himself, his mighty brother, is loath to engage in harsh combat. And yet, in some measure, slight though it be, we can be of benefit to our beloved mortals.

"Let us have Happiness and Love, both blindly obedient to my commands, as well as the Pleasures born of intelligence—which is your private domain—stream forth tonight in great abundance, O Athena, upon the magnanimous beings assembled at 2562 Teodoro Vilardebó, in order to make their so very brief remaining moments of life sweet and pleasurable."

And Zeus' indomitable daughter replied in this manner:

"Joyfully I confirm, peerless Aphrodite, that you have anticipated my thoughts. My own pondering, following, to be sure, very different paths from yours, has led me to the same conclusion. And I was in fact waiting for your fair lips to give eloquent expression to it, so as to propose an indestructible pact which the two of us must steadfastly honor.

"Let us, if you are willing, take an oath to cast aside our rivalry and desist from our ancient, merciless struggle until that moment when Hades' bloodlusting scheme against the assembled group at 2562 Teodoro Vilardebó has reached its conclusion.

"And as proof of this pact's having gone into effect, I shall promptly free Aníbal Frugoni's unblemished spirit from strict Conjugal Duty, so that he be well-disposed to submit to Mrs. Giannello's amorous overtures. And then also I'll compel Timidity and Indecision to take flight like hares pursued by swift hounds in order to enable well-tailored José María Pulicicchio to approach his beloved Irene without fear.

"And you, fair Aphrodite, on your part will pledge to have Acceptance and Gentle Tenderness overwhelm the invincible heart of faultless Irene Bengoechea, a thirty-nine-year-old virgin, and thus pleasing to my eyes, though I'll do nothing to prevent her from accepting the amorous proposals of your charge, the estimable Mr. Pulicicchio.

"But in addition, O seductive goddess, you are to enable diligent Mrs. Zimmerman to yield readily to the spirit of Enlightened Reconciliation that I shall dispatch, in order that she be amenable to resolving her difficult situation intelligently, and spare Mrs. Frugoni, a mortal under my protection, from being excessively hurt.

"Once these token acts have been performed, indicating mutual acceptance of our pact, then, Aphrodite, we can indeed apply our powers, yours and mine combined, and free from reciprocal rivalry, in order to accomplish what you in your wisdom have proposed: We shall allow the Pleasures of Love and of the Intellect to stream forth copiously upon those humans who are presently applauding Mrs. Giannello in that old house on Teodoro Vilardebó Street, in order to render their so very brief remaining moments of life sweet and pleasurable.

"But I wish you to be fully aware, O cunning Aphrodite, that as soon as Hades' bloody scheme has drawn to an end, our ancient enmity will be renewed, for my heart is repelled by your wily ruses, just as yours rejects my virtuous conduct. Tell me then whether you accept the pact with the conditions I've just stipulated."

And, impatiently, divine Aphrodite replied: "I accept all the terms of the pact that you've proposed, O virginal Aphrodite, and if you turn your gaze toward the house on Teodoro Vilardebó, you will see prompt indications to that effect.

———

"But I implore you, O goddess, in the name of Zeus, your wrathful father, not to waste any more precious time. Let us fly swiftly toward the tree-lined quarter of Villa del Parque and remain beside our dearly beloved mortals until that sorrowful moment when the four shiny Ford Falcons make their stealthy approach and implacable Hades' scheme is fulfilled.

"I shall lodge myself amidst the fast-revolving blades of the newly acquired floor fan, and from there shall disperse upon all the occupants of that lovely little blue-wallpapered room a pleasant breeze which will produce delightful tingling on their skin and arouse the sweet swoon of love amongst even the most disdainful and fainthearted.

"And you, transformed into an unknown young woman, will sit in the unoccupied chair between Mr. Pasco, who is blind in both eyes, and Miss Kisternmacher's mother, in the same row as Irene and Mr. Pulicicchio, and will keep watch from your spot and exert a benign influence when your heart bids you so to do.

"As for you, divine and dauntless Hermes, I ask you to remain outside the room and cover the courtyard with its well-watered plants, the dense wisteria, the corrugated zinc roof and back wall, the front entrance which has been diligently repaired by the skillful hands of young Romilio Sosa, and the nocturnal street of Teodoro Vilardebó with its chinaberry trees. The moment you see the bumper of the first Ford Falcon appearing from around the corner, or hear the distant sinister hum of a motor, you are to warn us."

So spoke golden Aphrodite. And then the three gods, wasting no further time in futile wrangling, flew swiftly from lofty Olympus, quickly reached the shady quarter of Villa del Parque, hovered overhead a few moments like messenger pigeons hastily seeking their dovecote, and promptly occupied the posts Aphrodite had so wisely appointed to each.

And Athena, transformed into an unknown young woman, fervently applauded Mrs. Giannello's impassioned words. And the only one to show any surprise at seeing her was Mr. Pulicicchio when he excused himself in passing between the rows in order to go out into the courtyard in search of tormented Mr. Frugoni.

And Hermes, in the guise of a nocturnal butterfly, flitted about the courtyard, perched on one of the well-watered plants, and went as far as the front gate that led out into the street, where he kept a sharp lookout on both sides of Teodoro Vilardebó. And whenever the Shadow flew overhead, Hermes would assume the background color of wherever he happened to be, in order that the Shadow might not see him.

And Aphrodite lodged herself amidst the fast blades of the newly acquired floor fan and, converted into a pleasant breeze, produced delightful tinglings on all those who were exposed to it, dispelling thereby the mute fear that had been invoked in their hearts by the word "threat."

And Athena, placed strategically between Mr. Pasco and Miss Kisternmacher's mother, summoned the spirit of strict Conjugal Duty and promptly issued a command: "Abandon tormented Mr. Frugoni at once." And she summoned Timidity and Indecisiveness, both ensconced in Mr. Pulicicchio's heart, and shouted angrily: "Away with you!"

Then she summoned the spirit of Intelligent Reconciliation and commanded: "Install yourself instantly within Mrs. Zimmerman." Whereupon Mrs. Zimmerman wanted to settle the difficult situation in an enlightened manner, and resolutely marched off toward the little back room in order to engage Mr. Frugoni in enlightened conversation.

And Aphrodite directed the pleasant, balmy breeze toward the tense, chaste thirty-nine-year-old body of Irene Bengoechea, who suddenly blushed, lowered her gaze, and began flipping the fifty pages of her spiral notebook, which were all penciled in with poems.

Then, wafting over seductive Mr. Chávez, Aphrodite imbued him with an overpowering spirit of Gallantry in order that his courtly gestures toward Mrs. Giannello might provoke violent Fits of Jealousy within Mr. Frugoni's aching heart. And as Mr. Chávez, impelled by Aphrodite's wafting breeze, hurried across the room with a flaming cigarette lighter in his hand, uncontrollable jealousy found easy prey in Mr. Frugoni, and enabled him to act decisively toward the love that was being offered him by impassioned Mrs. Giannello.

But Aphrodite sensed that the timid heart of José María Pulicicchio, the installment loan manager, had not been totally dispelled of fear, for he'd been somewhat more affected by news of telephone threats than the others, and thus she went and issued a command.

"Come forth at once, spirits of Memory and of Distracting Revision, and penetrate Mr. Pulicicchio's spirit, a mortal under my protection, so that during intermission he engages in a leisurely scrutiny of the political background of each of Polimnia's members, and comes to the realization that the crude threats could not possibly be directed toward any one of them, and thus his fear will vanish."

And so the three deities solicitously devoted themselves to tending the magnanimous humans assembled at the house on Teodoro Vilardebó, and not one of the three grew impatient at the prolonged reading, or betrayed the slightest displeasure at the awful poems that they heard, for in their eyes, as we know, Homer, Whitman and Mrs. Mastrocarbone had all been and all were mere fragile little people, exposed to certain doom, trembling for but the briefest fraction of a moment upon the surface of a planet equally small, fragile and ephemeral.

XVII

The motion so engagingly proposed by dear Mr. Chávez was warmly seconded by each of us in his or her own inimitable fashion. "Yes, sir," cried out Mrs. Zimmerman, clapping her hands as if to indicate that recreation period was over and that we were to form a straight line, at arms' distance, calling out our numbers from left to right, and occupying our seats in perfect order. Mrs. Giannello responded with a funny, obedient schoolroom gesture. And since she happened to be standing quite close to the fan while doing so, a few strands of her lovely, intensely black hair began fluttering and playfully brushed Mr. Frugoni's cheek. Then, with a delightful smile and utter naturalness, she took the arm of the author of "Phantom of the Wagon," who was gazing at her, enthralled. Mr. Frugoni, as a result of Mrs. Zimmerman's intelligent words, or the stroke of those playful tresses, appeared much more contained and almost happy. The two of them began slowly wending their way toward the rear of the room and sat down very close to one another in the last row. Mr. Mastandrea, out of his element as always, mumbled something that sounded like, "I vote in the affirmative," and then in an undertone added some coarse remark, addressed I think to the mother of the perpetrator of the threats. He leaned his two crutches against the wall and sank into a chair by the door. He was sweating buckets, and to avoid staining his shirt, I suppose, with the streams of sweat gushing from his double chin, had placed a huge brown striped kerchief around his neck like a napkin or bib.

The remaining members—showing no sign of either haste, fear or nervousness—gradually began moving up and reoccupying the vacant seats.

This unanimous decision to return to our recitation, despite all obstacles, was a sort of tacit agreement. I'd venture to summarize it as follows: Nothing—neither the recent tensions created by Mr. Frugoni's behavior, nor the existence of a couple of bothersome, ridiculous phone calls —nothing, absolutely nothing could deter us, even temporarily, from the profound raison d'être of our group: Fraternity in Poetry, attained through listening attentively and sensitively to our members' compositions.

Mrs. Zimmerman went out to the courtyard, clapped her hands again, and called those who had taken advantage of the break to get a breath of fresh air under the wisterias or to smoke a cigarette. "Let's go, everybody, let's go. The second part is about to begin," she cried out.

The threats, it seemed, had been largely dismissed from everyone's mind and already—all too readily, in my opinion—they were being interpreted variously as the result of: a joke (Miss Kisternmacher), or envy (Mrs. Giannello), or an error (Mr. Pasco and Mrs. Zimmerman), or, as young Romilio Sosa whispered in my ear, a simple vindictive act on the part of Mr. Frugoni's spiteful wife.

I, too, forced myself to minimize their significance. Yet, as I made my way between the third and fourth rows of chairs in order to occupy my seat (finding myself obliged once again to disturb that unknown young woman, whom I wasn't able to locate during intermission), I couldn't help but mull, with some concern, I must confess, upon those ridiculous threats and their presumed political overtones. Political? I recall asking myself, and at once answered myself, reiterating once again that our group was statutorily and definitively apolitical. And so I tended to lean toward the error theory (as propounded by the infallible Mrs. Zimmerman), and suddenly recalled that at one time there had existed on this very block, on Teodoro Vilardebó Street, a small, makeshift branch of Peronist Youth. That must be the source of the matter, I told myself with a laugh, straightening the chair next to mine which Irene was to occupy. Still and all, I thought it was funny to have Polimnia confused with that other group—Basic Union, as it was called —and Mr. Chávez and myself, with the aggressive leaders of those rebellious, incomprehensible young people of our times.

Automatically, I looked around for Mr. Chávez, who was standing in the back of the room next to Miss Kisternmacher, scrutinizing the list of those who were scheduled to read in the second portion of the recitation, and going over in his mind, no doubt, his flowery introductory remarks.

This slight delay gave me time to recover from the recent unpleasantness, and at the same time to do a sort of rundown, more for my own distraction than for anything else, of the presumed political affiliation of each of our members. It was, I confess, a rather distracting, innocent pastime, and for some reason, managed totally to dispel all my fears and worries that had arisen from the threats. My rundown, I believe, warrants telling.

I began, naturally, with our president. Mr. Chávez, I said to myself, is a Spaniard and a sales manager in a prestigious real estate firm, and a member of Villa del Parque's Rotary Club. Aside from his vague republican ideals, and a casual reference to Masonic lodges, which, according to him, had played an active role in our independence, he had never betrayed any ideology other than one that was strictly and wholesomely democratic. Furthermore, the reference to lodges had been made on May 25, in the course of an emotional and patriotic joint Poetry/Music session held in conjunction with the Society for the Improvement of Villa del Parque and the Merchants Union of Cuenca Street. It was ridiculous to imagine Mr. Chávez being the object of any threats.

And Mr. Frugoni? Of him, one knew only that he was an old-style Peronist, though not militant. The truly militant one was his wife (an unknown figure for most of us, but mentioned at various times in these pages), who, we were soon to learn, belonged to one of those so-called street-corner work tables—to be precise, the one at the corner of Cuenca and Nogoyá. She was, therefore, an advocate of the most official orthodoxy and obviously free of the slightest taint of political suspicion. As for Mr. Frugoni himself, one thing was utterly self-evident: between the multiple tasks of the Flor de Lis variety store, the grave family and romantic problems that afflicted him, his punctual attendance at all group meetings, the responsibilities connected with his position as treasurer—which he never neglected—and his meticulous execution of those extensive gauchoesque poems (which he generally wrote with India ink on paper of stippled imitation animal skin and accompanied by a profusion of allusive drawings), it seemed unlikely that the man had much free time left over to devote to his party. I'd like to mention in passing that those poems of his, so beautifully executed in elegant left-handed calligraphy (since Mr. Frugoni is left-handed), are the pride of our organization. They've been presented at various folkloric clubs and societies, and one of them, entitled "The Skeleton," and framed in carob wood, presently adorns one of the walls of our meeting room.

During all this, Mr. Chávez, with the list of participants in his pocket, was being delayed in conversation with Miss Kisternmacher. I overheard the words "astral body" and "karma," as well as reverent mention of the names of Annie Besant and Blavatsky. This meant they were discussing a subject dear to Miss Kisternmacher's heart, and clearly Mr. Chávez wouldn't find it at all easy to interrupt the conversation brusquely and mount the platform to begin the second part of the recitation. Thus, I still had a little more time at my disposal. Irene hadn't come as yet to occupy her seat next to mine, and so, while waiting, truly to kill time now, I allowed myself to resume the distracting rundown on the members.

I refused even to skip over myself, thinking that, though people might believe me to be a radical inasmuch as my entire family had always been so, I, aside from registering my vote and at one point, at the request of some relatives, having served as poll official, have never engaged in any political activity whatsoever. That is, unless one could regard as political, I remember thinking ironically, my thorough reading of *La Prensa*, a newspaper openly opposed to the regime, or certain disparaging remarks made in jest (though, at times, frankly indignant, I won't deny) regarding some government and military measures, the sort one is apt to make when running into a couple of neighbors on the street in my quarter, Villa Devoto.

Just then, young Romilio Sosa entered the room and quietly took his seat in the next to last row, prompting me to focus my attention upon him. There was no doubt in anyone's mind about Romilio's Peronist affiliation. What was amusing, however, was his assumption that all of us, whom he regarded as nice people, shared it. Once I remember having been warmly invited by him to attend one of those gay, tumultuous demonstrations that used to be held, which he regarded as genuine patriotic celebrations.

Seated next to him, fanning herself with a magazine, continually asking the time, and explaining to Romilio the profound meaning of the poems she'd be reciting that evening, was Mrs. Zimmerman. With regard to her political affiliation, there was also not the slightest doubt. Still, I remember her generous and correct comportment in our group, and realized that, aside from that time when she may have drawn some attention to herself here at our headquarters by trying to sell bonds on behalf of the Communist Party's financial campaign, she'd never attempted any sort of political or ideological proselytizing. At the time, as I recall, Mrs. Zimmerman, in begrudging though befitting self-criticism, had confessed her error, and though we subsequently might, from time to time, see her name in the newspapers, linked generally to some action or message on behalf of the Union of Argentine Women, never again, it's only fair to admit, did she violate our statutes.

This brought me now to Mr. Pasco, our blind member, and no matter how hard I reflected, I was unable to recall the slightest detail to orient me regarding his political convictions. In all likelihood, therefore, he simply had none.

Mr. Mastandrea had extracted a second handkerchief and was now mopping his forehead. Mastandrea, simply on the basis of the many sonnets of his with which I was familiar, I would describe as being an odd mixture of conservative, Seventh-Day Adventist and erstwhile tango enthusiast, with nationalistic leanings and, I'd even venture to state, a penchant for the nineteenth-century dictator Rosas, though he'd never personally have mentioned any of this, especially the latter. The reason perhaps being, I imagined, that our ex-president, Mrs. Urdampilleta, as was universally known, had been a fervent admirer of the schoolmaster president, Sarmiento, whose watercolor portrait which she had painted and donated to Polimnia on the occasion of its first anniversary, now hung alongside the large photograph of the artist on the front wall of our room.

Mr. Chávez, with his typical tact and refinement, apologized to Miss Kisternmacher for having to interrupt her impassioned conversation, tenderly took both her hands in his, and headed finally toward the platform. A smile of gratification and rapture issued forth from Miss Kisternmacher. I watched her maneuvering her wheelchair, and moving down the aisle to position herself, as always, in the first row. There still remained a few seconds to devote to her in my rundown. And I recalled a sort of poetic homage she had once read to us in celebration of a Goethe anniversary, on which occasion she revealed in passing her opposition to Nazism, though it was overly clear that her interests veered much more toward theosophy and the occult sciences than toward politics.

Our president once again was holding in his hand this Wednesday's list of scheduled poets (a list drawn up, according to organizational policy, by our recording secretary in conjunction with two other members at the start of each meeting) and he was preparing to announce the first poet in the second half of the recitation. At this juncture, though with utmost brevity, I'd like to clarify one thing: the poems that we read must, according to our statutes, be recorded in their entirety into our minutes. Lamentably, however, our recording secretary, Mrs. Giannello, owing to circumstances disclosed only as of today, is quite remiss in this function. In fact, I happened to be thinking of how to broach this delicate matter at the next Executive Committee meeting, when Irene, who'd been a trifle delayed, entered the room nervously, tiptoed over and sat down next to me.

I thereupon considered my rundown of the members as completed. I'd reached the felicitous conclusion that none of us could possibly be the object of those presumed (and now virtually forgotten) threats. And the group itself even less so, since its Executive Committee had consistently safeguarded faithful compliance with the fifth article of our statutes, which refers to the prohibition of "political and /or religious topics in discussions raised among the members."

Totally freed, therefore, of any further concern, I settled down to listen. Blind Mr. Pasco was the first to recite. Mr. Chávez referred to him in his introductory words as "our beloved bard endowed with telluric feelings." Then he took him fraternally by the arm and escorted him to the platform.

XVIII

FROM: Chief Inspector Guso, Security Headquarters
TO: Inspector Bevilacqua, 45th Precinct
November 29, 1975

Dear Bevilacqua:

I request you in the future to avoid any sort of correspondence of a personal tone. It does not befit my rank. Moreover, if you'll forgive me, I don't trust either your intelligence or your discretion. What else is there to say?

This letter, a reply to yours of the 28th (which I've just burned), is an exception, and I hope it's the last time I find myself obliged to reprimand you. You've held the position of inspector for too many years, and your experience, it seems to me, ought to have taught you differently.

Not to beat around the bush, Bevilacqua, I'm not at all pleased by the manner in which you've been handling things in your section. I'll give you one example of what I mean. That shitty little aide you sent over had the nerve (the cheek, as my old man would say) to tell the officer on guard to ask me whether my "reply to [your] letter was ready because it was getting kind of late" for him. It was only out of consideration for you that I didn't have that creep kicked into the clink, but he sure did get one hell of a wait for that letter remark of his. He was stuck here till four in the morning.

I guess your answer to this will be that that was merely an underling's goof and you had nothing to do with it. That may well be, dear Bevilacqua, but it's that sort of attitude that clearly explains Assistant Inspector Dileo's grave misconduct—what you glibly call a "blooper." I want you to understand once and for all, Fatty, it was not just a blooper. It revealed the gravest lack of discipline, which you must penalize severely, and which you yourself are now paying the consequences for. If it weren't for all the years we've known each other, I'd tell you to go fuck yourself, Inspector.

And so, Bevilacqua, let's see if we can come to an agreement: "Errors" such as Dileo committed *cannot under any circumstances happen again.*

And another thing that can in no way happen again is for you to let loose so liberally in your letters with all those details and confidential stuff which, as you must certainly realize, compromise the balls off you.

Bevilacqua, we're living in extremely difficult times. I'm well aware that you're close to retirement. And also well aware that you never showed any real interest in the training and improvement courses given in the United States, which I proposed to you many times. But you'd better understand that nowadays in Buenos Aires you can't behave as you did twenty years ago, when I was a petty clerk and reviewed your orders in the 45th.

If my career, as you told me that day at the banquet, has been "meteoric and brilliant," it's simply because I understood from the start the fucking times we live in and that these days we must above all confront a new form of delinquency: subversive delinquency. And also because I understood that in order for us to confront it successfully, educational trips abroad were indispensable. That's it in a nutshell, Bevilacqua, the whole secret of my "meteoric and brilliant" career.

Now let me explain something to you. The fact that your aide asked if my reply was ready was no coincidence, but has a lot in common with the "blooper" committed by Assistant Inspector Dileo.

I tell you, in all frankness, Bevilacqua, the blame is exclusively yours.

I don't care, for obvious reasons, to go into details (I'm not interested, I want to make it clear, in knowing details), but I guess you know by now that that guy whom Dileo searched and who got lost in your shuffle of papers was the nephew of a congressman. That in itself wouldn't be so serious if the congressman weren't chummy with several active generals.

I deeply regret that business about your application, Bevilacqua, but I can't do a thing for you. Everything depends on the decision of the three branches of the Armed Forces in the next few weeks regarding various matters which they apparently have a certain interest in uncovering. And if things go ahead, Fatty, I'm afraid you'll be forced to request retirement. Chances are that no heads will fall, but there's not much you can do, anyhow. So keep calm and trust in God. That's all I can tell you on this.

One more matter: the business about house guards on senior staff members of the Armed Forces. (I ask you never again to put the term "brass hats" in your letters, even if they're personal letters.) Tell me, Bevilacqua, what period do you think we're living in? Where do you get off questioning whether to provide guards here or there when it's the Commander of the First Army himself who's put in the request? Fuck the factories, honey. Let your own higher-ups stick themselves in a strongbox, if that's the only solution they've got. Don't be surprised, Bevilacqua, but it's this kind of attitude that explains why you sometimes feel neglected or left out or whatever. Do you understand?

With respect to the third point that you raise, probably the most important of them all: the subversive cell at 2562

Teodoro Vilardebó. Luckily, Chief Officer Farías has I think handled things correctly. By the way, I found out, through Farías, about some errors on your part which we must talk about someday. I've read all the reports carefully, especially Farías's. Corporal Nicodemo Ramírez is to be commended for his excellent work. I'm extremely interested in that boy. Tell him to come to my office on Monday morning at ten. His direct collaboration with this department may be of interest to me.

At your request, I'm having copies of the personal files sent over to you. Actually, as you'll see, they're the usual sort of summaries we make around here to speed up proceedings. There are some people whose personal files are puffed up with lots of details. I don't know if you get what I mean.

You'll see soon enough what kind of fish are floating around in your precinct. But watch out, Bevilacqua, when it comes to this matter: From now on, everything pertaining to 2562 Teodoro Vilardebó goes directly to Security Headquarters. Is that clear?

Subversive delinquency, as you must know, has been virtually wiped out in rural areas, but will now be concentrating its efforts on densely populated zones. This was clearly proven to us in Mr. Thomas's courses. The Teodoro Vilardebó matter is therefore of utmost gravity. The joint forces will be in charge of all future measures.

Make special note of this last statement, and this time try to be intelligent and don't interfere, no matter what happens. Agreed? If your collaboration becomes necessary, we'll let you know in advance.

The policy that was followed with Mastandrea was, I recognize, useful up until now and hasn't, according to the assurance you've given me, aroused any suspicion. That may be. In any event, said subject has already provided everything that he could, and I think it's risky to keep using him. What's at stake here is not investigation of the assault on the Forest Avenue furniture store, but something of much greater importance, having to do with the country's sacred interests. And when it comes to guys like Mastandrea, you can't trust them. Forget about him, and leave the matter in my hands. If it's of any interest to you, your name will not appear on any petition.

According to the data in our possession, the cell activity is quite intense. And, once we've decided to act, a whole series of terrorist acts perpetrated in the area will undoubtedly be cleared up. Suspects Romualdo Chávez and Sara Zimmerman seem to be especially significant elements within the delinquent organization. Also, José María Pulicicchio, a suspect known to be highly dangerous. Though the cell functions outwardly under the cover-up organization Polimnia, we're not ruling out the existence of an arsenal inside the premises of Teodoro Vilardebó. If such is the case, the delinquents might attempt desperate resistance. Therefore, we're the ones who will be acting, exclusively. Do not risk your men uselessly.

I don't want to conclude this letter, which is already becoming too long, without making a couple of details perfectly clear:

1. I don't understand, nor do I wish to understand, anything on the subject of those watches. I forbid you to mention it to me again.

2. I don't know who you're referring to when you mention an individual nicknamed "The Goat." I don't know who he is and I'm not interested in knowing. The congressman's nephew was never detained in the 45th Precinct. Therefore, no one came to get him out of there. Let's see whether you can correct the newspapers when they start talking about parapolice groups, etc.

Anyhow, I'm enclosing a copy of the summary of the aforementioned personal files; all the names, in alphabetical order, appear on a separate sheet next to their ID numbers and current place of residence. You can look through this, but don't butt in. Starting tomorrow at 0 hour, we're in exclusive charge of surveillance. Bear this in mind, and once more I repeat: don't interfere for anything in the world. I'm giving you this piece of advice for your own good, and hope you understand what I mean.

Thank you for the invitation, but I can't come to your house on Saturday, and I don't think I can come for quite a long time.

Yours,
Guso

XIX

CHÁVEZ, ROMUALDO *(alias Golden Beak, The Galician)*

Spaniard, 59 years old, single, employed

Born in Villapando (Zamora), Spain, in 1917. Activities in country of origin unknown, but arrived in Argentina in 1934, with name already appearing several times between February and July 1937 on contributors lists of the International Red Cross.

In 1938, an active participant in the tumultuous anti-Franco demonstration on Avenida de Mayo, where he was detained along with forty-two other Spaniards, ostensibly reds. On that occasion, though it could not be proved, he was in fact believed to have participated in the transport along aforesaid artery of a Republican flag of great dimensions. He remains at liberty for "lack of evidence."

In 1958, he figures as an alternate member on the executive committee of a social and sports club called Oriente Argentino, the propaganda organ of the Oriente lodge, which is closely linked to Synarchy through the International Freemasons.

His bachelor apartment on Argerich Street, which has been placed under round-the-clock surveillance, is frequented by loose women, young men and women carrying books and/or packages of a suspicious nature, and by fellow countrymen with avowed Marxist affiliations. At least three of the female members of the Polimnia group have come to this apartment during the current period of surveillance. In all three instances, the concierge reports being able to hear through the door old bolero records, and sometimes the clink of glasses. A familiar practice which, in addition to preventing conversations from being heard, attempts to disguise such meetings of a presumably high organizational level as mere romantic rendezvous.

Important: As sales manager of Delos Real Estate, his name was twice implicated in connection with the sale of properties that later were used as hideouts for subversive delinquents. One of these was the residence on Condarco Street where, during a raid, Sergeant Retamar gloriously lost his life. On both occasions, owing to the skillful defense of various lawyers, the subject succeeded in proving his innocence before the presiding judge. It is significant to note that, coincidentally, one of these lawyers was Dr. Francisco Sotomayor (alias Frankie), murdered recently by unknown persons, and accused of abetting subversion by attempting to blemish the good name of the police force with denunciations of presumed tortures.

The subject is skilled in legal subterfuge. He seems to be a key figure within the delinquent organization. Though Zimmerman's lieutenant, he serves as Polimnia's president.

BENGOECHEA, IRENE DE LA INMACULADA CONCEPCIÓN

Argentine, 39 years old, single, teacher in parochial schools

Grandniece, apparently, of the noted anarchist Prudencio Bengoechea, a Buenos Aires stevedore and head of FORA, who was killed accidentally in 1932 at Second Police Headquarters.

In 1957, a chorus member in the Basque Euskadi Society. In that same year, the chorus participated in a crypto-Communist festival held in Luna Park. According to Interpol reports, some members of the Euskadi are presently linked to the Basque terrorist organization ETA.

Since 1961, subject is a Spanish language and literature teacher at the Sacred Heart School. Our informant at the school classifies her as a third world revolutionary.

Aside from the meetings at Polimnia, where she occupies an important position in charge of finances, she periodically participates in meetings with former pupils of the School of our Lady of the Grove, a den of third world priests and a meeting place for subversive Peronist elements.

She attends Mass every Sunday and takes confession with Father Correa. Father Correa traveled to Cuba in 1971, and as a result of this has had several attempts made on his life.

XX

And as indomitable Athena and fair Aphrodite, bound by their irrevocable pact that forbade them any dispute, engaged, along with Hermes in his golden sandals, in keeping solicitous watch over their human charges, whose doomed fates were soon to be sealed at the hands of the ruthless parapolice in four Ford Falcons, Hades, grim, unfathomable Hades, observed them sullenly from a jagged peak of his icy abode.

And just as Mr. Romualdo Chávez was magnanimously extending his arm in a gracious fraternal gesture to escort irreproachable blind Mr. Pasco to the platform, a horrible jeering grimace blackened still more Hades' dark countenance, and enveloping himself in the folds of his great black cape, he summoned his vast legion of brutal servants.

"Cast away your fear, O faithful servants, you who share the rigors of my damp abode. And while protecting you from the bitter cold with this great, heavy woolen cape woven for me by the indefatigable Moirai, I ask you to cast a solemn gaze toward that old house on Teodoro Vilardebó Street, in the well-established residential quarter of Villa del Parque.

"Behold the interior of that blue-wallpapered room, and also how fickle Aphrodite and vain Athena have, for the sake of their charges, temporarily abandoned their ancient rivalry. Like growling bitches deluded into thinking that their vigilance can save their playful pups from being over-powered by beasts of prey, so are the goddesses keeping solicitous watch over that wretched cluster of mortals, twelve of whom are to be transported here on this very night.

"And behold, too, the unflagging Olympian messenger, that cunning, thieving, deceitful Hermes, transformed into a harmless nocturnal butterfly with dusty gray wings, flitting vigilantly over the courtyard with its borders of well-watered plants and dense, overgrown wisteria, and over the corrugated tin roof, and the chinaberry trees along Teodoro Vilardebó Street, so that he can alert his allies, the two Olympian goddesses, the moment he spies my relentless emissaries, the parapolice in the four Ford Falcons.

"And behold irate Athena: how she has hypocritically divested herself of her shiny helmet, her awesome lance and glorious aegis, and is sitting there, her hands primly crossed on her lap, in the serene guise of a beautiful young woman, her divine brows absurdly arched, all set to listen attentively to the telluric poems of blind, dark-skinned Mr. Pasco.

"And behold, if you will, intriguing Aphrodite, cunningly lodged between the translucent plastic blades of a brand-new floor fan, generously scattering delicious tinglings and gentle swoons of love upon those heedless mortals seated in parallel rows, listening to Mr. Chávez's eloquent introductory words.

"Behold, behold, my countless legions, proud holders of privileged positions in this vast underworld of Erebus: violent Moirai, black, dauntless Keres, incorruptible Charon, ruthless three-headed Cerberus, as well as all you ghosts who served in your lifetime as procurers of countless inhabitants for this black, shaded realm of mine; all you policemen, executioners, manufacturers of gas chambers, military personnel, torturers, exterminators of villages, starvers, corruptors, tyrants, mercenaries, economic ministers, landholders, bankers, heads of powerful firms, bureaucrats, traitors, fanatics and sectarians of all sorts—all of you, faithful and beloved servants.

"Behold the futile comings and goings of those three insolent Olympians as they flutter about clumsily like despicable insects amidst the well-groomed Polimnians. And once you've observed them with scorn in their activity amidst these mortals who I myself have condemned, then turn your fearless gaze back here and pause to listen to my infallible words."

And swirling his cape around his body once more, Hades, teeth chattering from the cold, went on:

"I tell you in all truth, my loyal bloodlusting servants, that the childish flutterings of those three Olympians concern me not in the least for in no way will they deter me from executing my irrevocable scheme, nor will they delay it by a single instant beyond the precise hour I've appointed for it to occur.

"On this day, December 3, 1975, a few minutes before twenty-three hours, the lives of twelve of those wretched, ill-protected mortals, now futilely accompanied by three powerful Immortals, will come to a violent end due to the action of a mysterious, untouchable death squad led by my well-loved Goat, and immediately thereafter they will enter the iron gates of this cold realm from which no soul ever returns.

"Rest assured that I've done everything for this inexorable event to occur at the precise hour, without the slightest delay, and with total efficiency and precision. I've knotted each of the invisible threads whose complex weave shapes the inevitable destiny of those mortals.

"I've foresightedly ordered the spirit of Denunciation to take fierce possession of vindictive Mrs. Frugoni, who on November 15 presented the 45th Precinct with a frightful accusation against the Polimnia Group and her legal spouse as well, the unfaithful, tormented Mr. Frugoni.

"I've instilled Diligence and the Call to Duty within Corporal Nicodemo Ramírez's well-disposed spirit in order to have him helpfully hasten the investigation that was initiated by Mrs. Frugoni's spirit of Denunciation against the individuals assembled at 2562 Teodoro Vilardebó.

"By now, Reward and Merit Promotion have ensconced themselves within the black soul of my charge Chief Officer Farías, and he in turn has transmitted this spirit to another mortal who is most pleasing to my eyes, Chief Inspector Guso, of Security Headquarters.

"By now, Cowardliness and Terror, dispatched by me, have stricken the quaking heart of Carlos Argentino Mastandrea, and he, in swift obedience to my command, has obtained a complete membership list of Polimnia for the implacable security agencies.

"By now, with three strikes of my whip against the parquet floor, I've prevented cowardly Mastandrea—who undoubtedly was under the unsettling influence of Aphrodite's breeze—from confessing his woes to simpleminded Mr. Pulicicchio, since this would have created an unforeseen hindrance to my plans.

"And in order to leave nothing to chance or sudden impulse, as do the capricious Olympians, a practice I consider unworthy of my own principles, I have proceeded to issue all the final precise details for my consummate feat of destruction and revenge.

"Loath to entrust important and delicate tasks to a servant, I took my dogskin helmet, given me by the Cyclops and rendering its wearer invisible, and calmly headed over towards the well-appointed office of my beloved charge Chief Inspector Guso, at Federal Security Headquarters.

"There, transformed into the docile messenger of a parapolice coordinator whose combat name is The Goat and who shares my lust for killing, I had myself announced, opened up the well-polished office door and introduced myself familiarly to Chief Inspector Guso, a mortal pleasing to my eyes for many years.

"Then, assuming the voice and manner of the sort of messenger who works for a murderer like The Goat, I inquired absentmindedly if there was anything new, some files maybe, to give to my boss.

"And lo and behold, beloved servants of mine, the esteemed Chief Inspector Guso opened one of the drawers of his finely contoured desk and deposited in my hand a bulky envelope containing the files, photographs, ID numbers and permanent addresses of all of the mortals who assemble punctually every Wednesday afternoon on the premises of 2562 Teodoro Vilardebó to read the poems they themselves have so enthusiastically composed, and, in addition, to escape for a while from their abject, doleful solitude. This done, Guso conveyed his cordial greetings to my chief, our beloved Goat.

"Your deity did not waste any precious time, however, in trivial social amenities, but instead, with the speed granted by my immortal rank, I vanished quickly from Chief Inspector Guso's presence and, transported invisibly by my worthy steeds, fled toward a discreet office in the luxurious Palermo quarter, where The Goat, a mortal akin to a bloodlusting Ker, has his base of operations.

"I struck the door with my black whip, and on receiving from inside the order to enter, changed once again into his obedient messenger and bowed deferentially before the mysterious parapolice coordinator whose combat name is The Goat.

"And The Goat, whose face and grim expression resemble that of Hades, was seated behind a solid oak desk reading a colorful comic book with a cover picture of Donald Duck riding a bicycle through the countryside with his three nephews. And displayed on top of the wide oak desk was a beautiful collection of Ithakas, Fals, 9-mm pistols, cartridge cases, leather straps, rope, wire, rolls of adhesive tape, ramrods, and bullets of various calibers.

"And when the godlike Goat raised his bearded face from the colorful magazine, I responded with a military click of my heels and, without uttering a word, placed in his sinister hands the bulky envelope Inspector Guso had given me.

"Then, as foreordained in my plans, The Goat laid aside Donald Duck, with his three nephews, on the solid oak desk, impatiently ripped open the envelope, spilled its precious contents next to a beautiful, painted Ithaka, whose tip stirred and rattled slightly on contact with all those names of stateless Marxists, and he shouted at the top of his voice: 'Let no one disturb me!' Then, grimly clenching his teeth, The Goat readied himself for a thorough reading of those beautifully contrived files.

"And all of this, my beloved children, has just transpired, on this very day, Wednesday, December 3, 1975, at sixteen hours and fifty minutes, barely two hours before the hour foreordained by my infallible soothsayers as the time when their terrible prophecy would be fulfilled: the violent surrender, to subversive elements, of the soul of the illustrious General Jorge Estéban Cáceres Monié, ex-chief of police and hence a man after my own heart."

XXI

Our dear president left Mr. Pasco on the platform, descended the two steps in silence, and seated himself alongside his spiritual companion, Miss Kisternmacher.

Mr. Pasco, for some reason, removed his dark glasses and seemed to be focusing his disconcerting blind gaze toward one corner of the room, waiting perhaps for total silence. Then, as was his habit, he took some gray Braille-inscribed cards from his jacket pocket, put them in order by touch, and prepared to begin. This Wednesday, as the introduction indicated, he'd be presenting a selection of some new compositions which, according to Mr. Chávez's enthusiastic announcement, were being set to music by none other than Professor María Teresa Venturini de Sicardi, a distinguished local pianist, whose absence this day, due to one of her recurrent arthritis attacks, was sorely felt by all of us. "Wakefulness," the first of Mr. Pasco's creations, was in fact dedicated to Mrs. Sicardi herself. "With gratitude and admiration on the occasion of her next eighty youthful years," he recited tonelessly and at breakneck speed, as though he'd learned the text by heart. Following this dedication of his, and still holding the gray cards in his left hand, his fingers skimming them with sureness and speed, Mr. Pasco began reading in a dull, monotonous voice, first the composition that was dedicated to Mrs.

Sicardi, and then five others, one after the other, without the slightest pause, even for titles.

They were, to my understanding, short octosyllabic quatrains, well suited for the lyrics of peasant songs, but I must confess to being unable to give them their proper appreciative due. They were, I presume, most interesting, inasmuch as Mrs. Sicardi had personally agreed to set them to music, but the almost total absence of pauses and shadings, in conjunction with Mr. Pasco's barely audible, inexpressive voice, combined often to make me miss the ends of lines, and thus part of the meaning.

I was pricking my ears, straining to understand him more clearly, when suddenly Mr. Pasco, in the same opaque manner with which he'd begun, concluded his reading. Since no one had as yet come to that realization, a few seconds of uncomfortable silence fell over the room. Luckily, the unknown young woman who had been sitting next to him broke into enthusiastic applause, and all of us followed suit. Maybe she's one of Mr. Pasco's friends, I thought, and is familiar with the poems.

Mr. Pasco, accompanied once again by Mr. Chávez, reoccupied his seat, between mine and that of the unknown young woman. She rose at the end of the row to receive him and, taking his arm, extended her lovely face toward Mr. Pasco and whispered an extended congratulatory remark in his ear. Her words must have been highly commendatory, for Mr. Pasco's face literally lit up with a broad, emotional smile of gratitude. Still smiling, and whispering, "Thank you, thank you," he sat down next to me, at which point I, too, congratulated him and shook his hand, using the opportunity to whisper a request (Mr. Chávez, you see, was about to announce the next poet), a request for a copy of those poems of his, for I was most eager, I told him, to savor them again in solitude.

He promised them to me by next Wednesday, and I somehow didn't get a chance to tell him that I preferred having him dictate them to me that very night, for I could already hear Mr. Chávez's mellow voice addressing warm remarks toward his dear friend Miss Kisternmacher. "Our dedicated Isis," I heard him say, "who is now about to lift on our behalf the merest tip of her mystical veil." And then, with an affectionate gesture, he signaled toward the spot occupied by Miss Kisternmacher in the first row and referred to her as the "Rajni of our times" and also as "a modern Kalidasa whose *tharana* will cleanse each and every one of us of our harmful auras through the incomparable beauty of her *gita.*" Once more, our president had demonstrated his vast culture, and had hinted, perhaps, through his erudite expressions, at his links with esoteric science, thus explaining his close friendship with Miss Kisternmacher.

Mr. Chávez concluded his anticipated introduction and Miss Kisternmacher, turning her wheelchair around, sat facing us. There, from her spot in the first row, she began reading her beautiful, allusive, strange compositions. Some were extremely brief, consisting merely of one word. For example, I recall one of them, which she called "Summer Love." Announcing its title, she allowed a long silence, and then slowly chanted: *"Nidagha . . . nidagha . . . nidagha . . ."* gazing at us all with her beautiful gray eyes. Other poems had to do with the transmigration of souls and the superior order of the universe, which all of us ought joyfully to participate in. She employed Sanskrit words with a certain frequency, but was gracious enough after each poem to explain their meaning to us. Despite the lecture-like tone of these explanations, the emotion elicited by her poems was, I must say, undiminished. Quite the contrary. All of us, caressed by the soft breeze of the fan and lulled, as it were, by the insinuating tone of her voice, felt an inexplicable flow of profound communication being established between each of us and the mysterious Miss Kisternmacher. The eyes of Irene and of Mrs. Giannello welled with tears, but, captivated by the sweetest of emotions, they smiled.

The last of her poems, entitled "To My Heavenly Brothers," and obviously directed to us, intensified the emotional climate. Mastandrea began sniveling, Mrs. Zimmerman stopped fanning herself, and the tip of Mr. Frugoni's chin was quivering as his hand rested tenderly on Mrs. Giannello's shoulder.

The poem, I recall, ended by prophesying the most exalted state of *samadhi* via that realm of sacred science embodied in Poetry.

And as Miss Kisternmacher from her wheelchair uttered that last word, "Poetry," she performed a gesture totally unforeseen and not at all usual amongst us: she threw kisses to us with her hands. She did this in such a spontaneous, natural manner as to arouse fervent applause and an identical reciprocated gesture from many of the members, along with their repeated exclamations of "Thank you, darling," while others rose to shake hands with her or to tenderly kiss her forehead. It was truly so beautiful that Mr. Chávez had to allow a goodly spell to elapse before he mounted the platform once again to announce the next poet scheduled for the second part.

After the applause, after the kisses and congratulations had ceased, after the handkerchiefs had wiped away the very last of the tears and Mrs. Zimmerman's fan had indicated by its renewed movement that the recitation could continue, only then did Mr. Chávez ascend the platform with list in hand. He cleared his throat and began a beautiful extended introduction to the next poet.

Before Mr. Chávez even mentioned her ineffable name, I sensed with surprise and unconcealable emotion that he was referring to Irene. The unknown young woman in our midst immediately sensed it too, for, before anyone else, she turned her sculptured head toward Irene and, with her large gray eyes, gave her an approving, knowing glance, aglow with intelligence. At Mr. Chávez's mention, in his enigmatic, needlessly long speech, of her recently assumed position as financial secretary, the entire room, realizing at last to whom he was referring, burst into spontaneous applause, and was joined by Mr. Chávez, who smilingly bequeathed upon Irene a gaze that was excessively tender for my own taste. He commented on the predictability of the literary prize that had been awarded her by the National Postal Savings Bank for her beautiful poem "Childhood and Thrift," which had subsequently been reproduced in several collections, and then, with a courtly gesture, declared: "I cede the platform to the lovely, intelligent young poetess Irene Bengoechea, on whose behalf I request a strong round of applause."

Irene, as I've mentioned, was sitting next to me, and I could tell that she was nervous. As she stood up, she gave me a smile, naive yet at the same time interlaced with a quality I might venture to describe as being mischievously sweet. At no point, it so happened, had she given me any indication of having her name on this Wednesday's list, and she was obviously taking childish pleasure in my astonishment. The unknown young woman smiled at me with a certain gay complicity. Maybe, I thought to myself, she isn't Mr. Pasco's friend at all, but Irene's.

From that moment on, it was as if I became oblivious of everything around me, and when Irene passed in front of me and moved toward the platform, with her inevitable fifty-page spiral notebook which I'd seen so often in her hands, I raised my finger unconsciously to my mouth as if to appeal for silence, leaned over to catch a better view of her, and got set to imbibe each and every one of her words.

The mysterious title of her first composition was "To X, the Unbeknowing." It was, to my renewed astonishment, an enchanting and utterly correct sonnet, whose very first quatrain, beginning "Thou who cultivateth delicate blossoms but gazeth never at the blossom by your side," betrayed if not my influence, a deliberate attempt certainly to imitate what might be called, not immodestly, my style. Her words were, in a sense, a reply to one of my own sonnets, entitled "To a Damsel," which only she was aware of, inasmuch as I'd deemed it imprudent to read in front of the group due to certain rather bold images contained in the final triplet.

One can well imagine my unspeakable agitation on listening to this poem which, to my supreme joy, had been written in the back pages of her spiral notebook, meaning that they were of recent composition. Moreover, I soon felt that I could detect amidst the carefully elaborated images in the sonnet—perhaps I was deluding myself—a secret, untranslatable message. Especially did those last two lines of hers ("Give thy word, sage gardener / I'll fear not the light should God dispatch it") strike me as an allusion to my timidity the other evening, an invitation, perhaps, to put an end to my idiotic silence. But there was even more: the following poem, which she rummaged for among the center pages of her notebook—which meant that she had written it about a week earlier—described in a tone serenely melancholic a twilight scene on a suburban street. It was a long poem in free verse, in keeping with her particular literary style, and displayed a certain boldness in its colloquial use of Buenos Aires slang. Anyhow, halfway through her reading I caught an allusion to that magnolia tree located on Marcos Sastre Street, three blocks from our headquarters. Often, while I'd escorted her to Nazca, where she catches the No. 110 bus, we paused to behold that lovely tree, ecstatic over the beauty of its form and the intense perfume emanating from its glorious blossoms. There was no longer any doubt in my mind that I, on a strictly poetic level at least, had begun occupying a considerable place in Irene's thoughts during the past week. And if there was still doubt lingering in my mind, her mention —nearly at the end of the poem—of "a lone, rakish itty-bitty / firefly" served to convince me totally. At mention of the firefly, I noticed the unknown young woman fidgeting in her seat and wrinkling her brow as if the image hadn't totally satisfied her. Perhaps, I remember thinking, the lady's a bit of a purist.

Irene proceeded to read another poem, dedicated to Gertrudis Gómez de Avellaneda, and then another, whose theme was the ascent of the soul toward God. This last one she dedicated to Miss Kisternmacher, though I'm not sure if the intent was fraternal or polemical. The two latter poems, it's interesting to note, were written in the front pages of her notebook: before our relationship had begun. But I must confess that my mind was too agitated by the concealed messages in the back of the notebook to give the others their proper due. Judging from the fervent ovation they elicited at the end of her reading, they must certainly have been excellent, like everything else emerging from her inspired pen.

I, too, applauded wildly, and was still applauding when Irene, with her graceful, timid gait, passed between the rows of chairs and sat down next to me. The unknown young woman and I were the last to stop applauding. The words "itty-bitty" and "rakish" hadn't, I was glad to see, altered her favorable opinion.

Irene's face was inflamed and her hands were trembling. I congratulated her in a hushed voice, bringing my lips close up to her ear, inasmuch as Mr. Chávez was getting ready to announce the next to last speaker of the evening.

I barely listened to the numerous qualities he attributed to Mrs. Zimmerman. It was as if I were floating on a cloud, feeling Irene's warm, close presence as I never had before, perceiving in some mysterious way the faintest of her pulsations. The breeze from the fan produced a strange sweet intoxication in me. Vaguely, I saw Mrs. Zimmerman removing from her large brown handbag a sizable number of typewritten pages, clipped together at an angle. After a few moments, I recall, she began imitating with comical gestures the movements of a children's circle game, at which point, overcoming my fear yet pretending to be natural, I suddenly rested my hand on the back of Irene's hand. She stiffened at first, as if frightened by my unexpected audacity. I could clearly sense her slender arm trembling. Then, as the revolving fan scattered its benign breeze upon us, she turned her hand and, little by little, tenderly, ardently, took mine. I remember that at that moment Mrs. Zimmerman was doing a masterly imitation of a child who'd lost a toy.

XXII

ZIMMERMAN, SARA, NÉE PRECANKSKY

Polish, 55 years old, married, journalist

A known Communist activist. Conceals activities by holding key posts in assorted cultural areas.

Member of independent theater groups, a women's union, cooperative societies, literary workshops, league for the protection of abandoned cats, cultural subcommittees, film clubs, local libraries, painting exhibitions, poetry magazines, folkloric clubs, and other agencies of Marxist infiltration and propaganda.

There is existing documentation of her participation in: *The Golden Scarab, You, Literary Gazette, For You* and various Yiddish newspapers. A specialist in children's poems, under whose innocent guise she attempts to inject the virus of atheistic and synarchical communism.

Characterized over the years as a professional agitator.

Spoke in 1954 at a pro-Guatemalan function. Spoke in 1965 at a pro-Dominican function. Spoke in 1968 at a pro-Cuban function. Spoke in 1973 at a pro-Chilean function.

Believed to be the true cell leader at Teodoro Vilardebó, with suspect Romualdo Chávez (alias The Galician) her lieutenant.

Her husband, Abraham Zimmerman, a businessman, is

a member of a Judeo-Marxist organization called Moses Berghelsson.

Her oldest daughter, Delia Zimmerman, Argentine, 19 years old, a medical student, was detained on August 22, 1973, in circumstances wherein she was painting graffiti alluding to the slaughter of Trelew in the vicinity of her school. Though freed after 48 hours without proceedings being instituted, a fingerprint file, photos, history, etc., are in our possession.

Her younger daughter, Rita Zimmerman, Argentine, 17 years of age, is a sociology student. Attends classes in body movement and guitar. Participated in ceremonies on behalf of political prisoners. Under discreet surveillance inasmuch as our informants at her school suspect her of being an important figure in the ERP.

SOSA, ROMILIO *(alias Blackie)*

Argentine, 23 years old, single, textile worker

Born in locality of Monteros (Tucumán province), like Polimnia's defunct ex-president, Brígida Urdampilleta, or Brígida Ramírez. A direct link, therefore, would not be surprising between the cell and the stateless delinquency prevalent in that province.

A worker in the Sudamtex textile factory and, most serious of all, an alternate union delegate in the Cardado section. At the assembly of 5/7/75, he voted in favor of the strike.

A militant in Peronist Youth.

Shares an apartment in the borough of Colegiales. According to one of our informants, he is an active participant in local neighborhood meetings, and gets mixed up in any demonstration, riot or petition that's organized there.

According to another informant, he's the sort you see marching way in front, carrying a flag or beating a drum.

He participated in an alleged borough festival, reciting peasant poems.

He has been seen performing clandestine masonry jobs at the residence at 2562 Teodoro Vilardebó, leading one to suspect the existence at the aforementioned residence of a "people's jail."

Regarded as highly dangerous.

FRUGONI, ANÍBAL *(alias Lefty)*

Argentine, 46 years old, businessman

No previous records.

Owner of the Flor de Lis variety store. A member of the Cuenca Street Merchants Union and the Cooperative Home guard. All of which seems to serve as a skillful cover-up maneuver.

Information reaching the 45th Precinct from the street table at the corner of Cuenca and Nogoyá streets indicates him to be a drug dealer and addict, head of an extremist organization declared illegal in 1973, a dealer in smuggled wall barometers and night-lights, a fence for stolen objects, a homosexual, a passer of bounced checks, a friend of Hector J. Cámpora, a pimp, a counterfeiter of paintings, an infiltrator, a sadist and a poet.

An avowed leftist. His writings, significantly, are signed: "Lefty Aníbal."

XXIII

And it came to pass that at 7:00 P.M. on December 3, 1975, the soothsayer's prophecy was punctually fulfilled, and the most illustrious General Jorge Estéban Cáceres Monié did indeed violently give up his ghost: the ex-chief of police, one of Hades' favorite mortals, fell beneath a volley of death-dealing bullets showered upon him by subversive elements a few miles outside the beautiful city of Parana, in the province of Entre Ríos, with its profusion of birds, and his soul then descended to Hades' lower world.

And the god's terrible wrath mounted when he learned about his protégé's bloody death. The fierce grinding of his teeth could be clearly heard in the remotest cavern of his vast realm, and it chilled the blood of his servants and made their knees quake.

But wasting no time in berating harangues or in further clenching of his teeth, barren Hades promptly mounted his black chariot, with its noble steeds, seized his awesome whip, and prepared to execute at once his long-foreseen and deadly mission.

And a cold, dim smile barely illumined his cruel countenance, for each of the necessary threads to execute his terrible vengeance had been carefully knotted, and merely lacked a few final, simple details.

Hades then cracked his swirling whip in the air, where-upon a bloodlusting Ker promptly appeared to receive his implacable orders.

And mighty Hades, ruler of the underworld, fiercely addressed the cruel Ker: "Hasten forth with all speed, O bloody Ker, to yonder building in the Palermo quarter where that idiot is stubbornly seated by the black phone, and in the guise of The Goat's aide, put a stop to those useless shouted threats of his." Whereupon, the cruel Ker did vanish from his sight.

And again implacable Hades cracked his whip, and a second Ker appeared before the god to obey his command. And Hades, bridling his restless horses with a sure hand, issued a command to the second Ker: "Go forth, second Ker, and at the exact moment when The Goat—a favored mortal of mine—is angrily reading the reports on the individuals gathered at 2562 Teodoro Vilardebó, you are to transform yourself into an Urgent Phone Message emanating from superior military ranks." Whereupon, the second Ker did vanish from his sight.

And Hades, for the third time, cracked his long whip into the icy air of Erebus, and a third Ker promptly appeared before the deity, ready to carry out his commands.

And Hades flung back his black cape with a smile and addressed the third Ker: "Go forth and penetrate the bloodthirsty soul of my beloved Goat, transforming yourself into the spirit of Prompt Execution so that his spirit becomes imbued with a desire to execute immediately the task that has been entrusted to him." Whereupon, the third Ker did vanish from sight.

And the three Keres flew swiftly toward a gray building in the Palermo quarter in order to carry out Hades' orders without delay. In the meantime, the god, swaddled in his enveloping cape which had been spun by the Moirai, waited for them in his swift chariot, whose horses were bucking and neighing in their eagerness to depart.

And the first Ker reached the gray building in the Palermo quarter and, under the guise of The Goat's aide, she harshly rebuked one of The Goat's stupid subordinates who was about to dial a number, and asked him menacingly if this idiotic habit of his was intended to enable the escape of the coveted prey.

And the imbecilic telephone threatener interrupted his call and promptly desisted from that obsessive activity of his, realizing that he would be severely punished by The Goat if the individuals at Teodoro Vilardebó became frightened by his persistent threats and well-chosen obscenities and escaped from the house.

And with her mission complete, the first Ker returned to Hades' abode.

Then the second Ker reached the terrace of the same building in the Palermo quarter and was quickly transformed into an Urgent Phone Message from superior military ranks. And in the guise of an Urgent Phone Message, she caused The Goat's phone to ring.

And The Goat did not pause in reading some reports that were in his right hand, but picked up the receiver with his left hand and in an absentminded tone said: "Coordination." Assuming the masculine voice of a superior military officer, the second Ker tersely relayed into The Goat's ear the information about General Cáceres Monié's violent death which had occurred only moments before at the hands of subversive delinquents outside the beautiful city of Parana within the province of Entre Ríos.

Having reported indignantly upon the bloody death of the illustrious General Cáceres Monié, the black Ker paused significantly, and in a forbidding tone that brooked no questions, she bluntly uttered: "Twelve." And The Goat, much beloved by taciturn Hades, understood clearly the meaning of that single word.

Then, with mission complete, the second Ker returned to Hades' abode.

And the third Ker likewise flew to the tree-lined Palermo quarter and, through the keyhole, entered The Goat's clandestine office. She hovered rapturously in front of a huge desk covered with shiny Fals, Ithakas and 9-mm Browning pistols and, transformed then into Prompt Execution, obediently pierced the soul of the parapolice coordinator, whose combat name was The Goat.

Whereupon, The Goat, smitten by Prompt Execution, felt a compelling desire to execute instantly the terse order transmitted by his black phone receiver. As it happened, he was still holding in his right hand the records of that dangerous extremist José María Pulicicchio (alias Frankie), and laid out on his table were the records of other dangerous Polimnians. Whereupon, The Goat chose the easiest, most expeditious route.

Now that day was Wednesday, December 3, and, according to reports sent by Officer Pascuali, Adjutant Covas and Chief Officer Farías of the 45th Precinct, Wednesday evenings were precisely the evenings when all those repulsive, stateless extremists met in their den at 2562, which was under present surveillance.

And before the third Ker departed, she leaned over, and in the guise of Prompt Execution whispered some suggestive words into his ear, stating that although those wretched mortals might not in fact be so extremist or stateless or dangerous, the advantage was that all happened to be congregated in one spot that very night, thus facilitating enormously his bloody mission.

Whereupon, the third Ker withdrew and returned to Hades' abode.

And the parapolice coordinator, whose combat name was The Goat, glanced at his wristwatch to see what time it was, and saw that it was exactly 1955 hours. And so, pressing a radio intercom button to contact one of his subordinates, he drew his bearded face close to the speaker and said in an urgent tone: "Motor units 25, 41, 70 and 72: to garage at twenty-four with full crew."

His door opened almost immediately and several subordinates entered his office. And the subordinates selected and carried off many of the gleaming weapons laid out on the solid oak table, as well as the rope and rolls of adhesive tape, in order to load everything into Car 25, in which Hades' favorite, The Goat, would be riding.

And a few minutes after The Goat's urgent order was whispered into that radio intercom, with all its buttons, the sirens of four sleek black Ford Falcons, without license plates and coming from different parts of the city, were startling unwary pedestrians and converging finally at a mysterious garage located in the borough of Villa Crespo.

And Hades, atop his blood-splattered chariot, observed them with great satisfaction.

And in vain did his noble steeds with their shiny flanks strive to race unbridled alongside the swift Ford Falcons, for their reins were tightly held by the god's mighty hand.

And Hades hissed at his indomitable, perspiring chargers in order to quiet them, and with soothing words bade them be still, for the proper moment had not yet arrived.

XXIV

"Beautiful . . . the firefly . . . I reacted the same . . ." I managed to stammer in Irene's ear during a pause between two of Mrs. Zimmerman's poems. But words were now superfluous. Irene, without removing her gaze from the platform, smiled. She smiled at me as our hands remained tightly united, our bodies leaning toward each other with an irresistible attraction as if attempting now to make up for the time that had been wasted due to the tormenting distance imposed upon us by my cowardliness, and now, impelled by the fan's benign breeze, were communicating in the deepest and warmest possible manner.

Mrs. Zimmerman, in the meanwhile, was holding forth without a letup. She'd been reciting for at least thirty minutes, and a goodly portion of her typewritten pages still remained to be turned. In the course of those thirty minutes, she'd imitated an old woman with a cane accompanying her grandchildren to the zoo, a drunken unemployed stevedore, a Negro mother rocking her baby and crooning, a rascal who'd battered his poor consumptive wife, a girl who spurned marriage to a wealthy man out of her love for a poor lad, and others as well, which I can no longer recall. In the pause between poems, she inhaled deeply, shut her eyes, permitted her arms to drop to her sides, and gave them a weird, rapid shaking out. Undoubtedly, this related to some effective relaxation exercise she'd learned in those distant eras when she'd been an actress. I must say, her dramatic streak really came across in the course of her recitation, and at times attained truly sublime heights. Almost forty minutes had already elapsed when she announced the title of what was to be her final poem of the evening. It was "Garment on the Grass, or, An Adolescent Couple's Trying Relationship."

Irene signaled to me significantly with her pinkie as if— I don't know why—the theme touched upon us directly. Throats were cleared, chairs shifted slightly, glances were exchanged with the sense of expectancy aroused by the provocative title. Mr. Chávez, in the first row, was smiling with rapt curiosity, his forearm resting on Miss Kisternmacher's wheelchair. Just then, Zulema, the cleaning woman, appeared at the door, probably to collect her monthly payment since it was the beginning of the month. Generally, what happens is that she signals to Mr. Frugoni, who always has the envelope ready, with her pay and the receipt inside. At which point, he usually leaves, settles everything in a matter of seconds, and then returns without further ado to the meeting room. But tonight, either because Zulema found Mr. Frugoni to be too engaged with Mrs. Giannello and dared not interrupt him, or because it was extremely hot and the fan was especially agreeable in the way it stirred the room's atmosphere, or because the poem's title kindled her interest—tonight Zulema, a plump, cheerful and extremely congenial widow with several children, entered silently and sat down in an empty chair next to perspiring Mr. Mastandrea. He shook her hand in effusive greeting and, with a gesture I'd even dare to call coquettish, stealthily removed the kerchief from around his neck.

Mrs. Zimmerman availed herself of Zulema's silent entry to prolong her relaxation exercises by a few seconds. When everything had quieted down, she repeated pedagogically the title of her composition, took a few steps back toward the rear of the platform and, with a hairpin that she'd foresightedly brought along, gathered her hair into a ponytail in imitation of a young girl's hairdo. Then, with a quaking, unsteady adolescent voice, she began recounting her heartbreaking woes.

The dramatic poem which Mrs. Zimmerman had first written in Yiddish and then translated into Spanish was about a young girl whose parents wouldn't allow her to have anything to do with a good-looking young man because their families were of different religions. Despite this, the young couple kept seeing each other on the sly. One warm spring evening, they find themselves in a forest. The young man, in despair, proposes that they commit suicide. The girl, more practical and, according to significant details, much more intelligent, suggests a more effective procedure.

"What's this attraction to death, my adored one / Leave it to me, I beseech thee," she intones in a warm, trembling voice, and then reveals her "infallible, heroic plan," which consists of the following: He was to possess her at once in order to get her with child. Under these circumstances, her parents would force them to marry. "But when, my love, where, and how?" fearfully inquires the good-looking, gentlemanly youth. Whereupon, the maiden, blushing bashfully, though prepared for any sacrifice in order to attain their mutual bliss, gazes sweetly into his eyes and, without uttering a word, gradually begins peeling off her garments. The poem concludes with the grass stirring faintly "beneath the white fluttering of her brassiere"—a phrase Mrs. Zimmerman recited lingeringly and with infinite tenderness, gazing toward the wooden boards of the floor and flinging upon its surface, with a swooning gesture, a little white handkerchief that mysteriously appeared in her hand. Just then the breeze from the fan stirred the little handkerchief and wafted it nearly to the very edge of the platform, endowing the touching scene in the forest with a hallucinatory realism.

The applause was truly clamorous, comparable to a large theater audience. Mr. Chávez had risen to his feet and was shouting, "Bravo." Mr. Frugoni and Mrs. Giannello had likewise risen, and were pushing forward to reach Mrs. Zimmerman and to congratulate her before anyone else. Irene, who had been deeply impressed by the girl's sacrifice, kept saying over and over, "Marvelous!" having flung herself back in her chair as if exhausted from such intense emotion.

Mastandrea had enjoyed the poem immensely. Apparently, it was the only one in the entire recital that he truly liked, and, tediously, he kept demanding an encore. I suddenly noticed him whispering in Zulema's ear; she seemed taken aback at first, but then, prompted no doubt by some remark that Mastandrea had made, she let out a shrill whoop of laughter which luckily got lost amidst the applause and bravos of the audience. Mastandrea conveyed the need for restraint by bringing his finger to his lips and patting Zulema's ample thigh. Zulema pulled his hand away violently, but did not stop laughing, though she muffled her squeals behind a handkerchief.

The one who seemed not to enjoy the beautiful composition very much was the unknown young woman seated at my left. When Mr. Pasco, in his enthusiasm, made some extremely complimentary remarks about "Garment on the Grass," she remarked with a knowing, magisterial expression, "Ah, yes, it's most important for you all to like it." Whereupon, she gazed in concern toward the door of the room, where I happened to notice a huge nocturnal butterfly alight, and then she added, with a sigh: "My poor children," a comment that somehow kept nagging at me.

Still, why should I care about that young woman's opinion? In addition to being a purist, she seemed somewhat petulant. So I walked toward the platform, eager to congratulate Mrs. Zimmerman personally.

At the conclusion of her poem, Mrs. Zimmerman had remained for quite a while in the middle of the platform, directly beneath the light of the little bulb, immobilized in that gesture of flinging her brassiere upon the grass, but now, finally, like a person emerging from a state of ecstasy, she smiled and gratefully bowed her head several times in response to the ovation.

When the applause finally began to subside, she didn't descend from the platform but gestured to us for silence, and proceeded on her own to announce the concluding poet of that evening's readings. "The illustrious bard, chronicler, businessman and dramatist Romualdo Chávez, our group's distinguished president," she proclaimed, and then launched at once into a most incisive cultural, social, psychological, institutional and sexual-emotional profile of our president. She spoke of the steadfast leadership that he had exercised—though if things sometimes didn't turn out so well, it was only because he refused to listen to her unflagging advice—and she spoke of his extraordinary qualities as a gentleman, as head of sales, as poet, as citizen, etc., and, in passing, even alluded wittily to his reputation as a lover.

Despite her digressions and jests, the introduction was terribly warm and beautiful, and we all listened to it with consummate pleasure, while Mr. Chávez acknowledged it by occasionally nodding in feigned anger. When Mrs. Zimmerman was through, Mr. Chávez gave her a courtly kiss, helped her to descend the steps leading to the platform, and returned by himself to begin his recitation. "Before reading some of my humble poems, however," he said, "I'd like to address a few brief words to you."

XXV

PULICICCHIO, JOSÉ MARÍA *(alias Frankie)*

Argentine, 47 years old, employed at the National Bank, in the Villa Urquiza branch

Though he reveals no penal or police records, there are sufficient indications for regarding him as a dangerous suspect, to wit:

1. His name and phone number appear in the address book of the extremist Anselmo Fernández (alias Baldy), whose accidental death due to cardiac arrest while being interrogated prevented him from providing an explanation of this detail.

2. In several of the numerous photographs obtained by this division during the funerals of extremist leaders Ortega Pena and Silvio Frondizi, both killed by unknown assailants, there appears in the background a thin, slightly bald individual with eyeglasses who, according to data disclosed by photographic research, could be none other than J. M. Pulicicchio, skillfully disguised.

3. Mastandrea's statements reveal the suspect to be a direct collaborator (second lieutenant) of the Zimmerman woman—in other words, a relevant figure in the organization.

4. According to Mastandrea, Pulicicchio's (favorable)

response to our informant's sonnet entitled "Restoration" was undoubtedly a deliberate attempt to conceal his ironic attitude toward key figures in our history, as well as his own allegiance to various non-patriotic symbols.

5. In addition: According to Mastandrea's long, garbled and contradictory statement, made under pressure from Chief Officer Farías, Pulicicchio appears to specialize in lewd, obscene and pornographic works. By means of these aberrations (and indeed others even more perverse and unimaginable), the subject has, according to Mastandrea, succeeded in corrupting Bengoechea and obtaining her total, unwholesome allegiance. Mastandrea, in addition, claims to have had an extremely warm relationship with Bengoechea prior to Pulicicchio's entrance into the organization, but it was abruptly interrupted due to pressure placed upon her by her new dominating influence.

6. It is not at all unlikely, in view of the aforesaid, that the suspect, aside from his extremist ties, is also linked to traffic in and/or consumption of tranquilizers.

KISTERNMACHER, AURELIA WANDA (alias Pupi)

German, naturalized Argentine citizen, 34 years old, single, private teacher

Connected to German-language media in various countries, among them Hungary and the German Democratic Republic.

Recipient of prolific correspondence. The subjects of these letters relate generally to occultism, astrology and states of being as communicated through mediums, proof of her strong affiliation with International Freemasonry (Synarchy), with its Marxist tendencies, which likewise explains her close friendship with Romualdo Chávez, a well-known Freemason.

An active propagandist for the organization among the

disabled and crippled (it was she who urged our informant to enroll in the organization) and someone who exercises indisputable leadership among the members of said organization. She was, it appears, an active participant in the demonstration by cripples who marched side by side with Peronist Youth down Gaspar Campos Street.

Important data:

(a) Extremist Rosa M. V. de Campos was a private pupil of hers in the year 1967.

(b) Another pupil of hers, Emma Arévalo, is first cousin of the mistress of terrorist Rafael Casas, who was shot down in the city of Rosario.

Recommendation:

Careful search of wheelchair, in the eventuality that subversive propaganda or weapons be concealed therein.

XXVI

And as the four Ford Falcons, with their slender antennas and finely tuned car radios, were assembling in a dark garage in the Villa Crespo quarter, Aphrodite, Athena and indefatigable Hermes, like solicitous mothers lovingly tending their fragile charges, were devoting themselves to the defenseless mortals who rapturously listened at that very moment to peerless Mrs. Zimmerman, and were endeavoring to gratify their every desire.

The Somber Herald of Death had by now ceased circling slowly around the house at 2562 Teodoro Vilardebó Street and, in the guise of a harmless spot of dampness, had stealthily penetrated the grooved zinc roof above the room, where it remained in order to witness the gory deeds of Hades' fierce emissaries.

And the Olympians were expecting to hear at any moment the ominous roar of motors plus the dreadful screech of brakes jamming on the cobblestones of Teodoro Vilardebó Street, for they realized that mighty Hades himself had personally completed all his final preparations and that the foreordained doom of the twelve members was therefore imminent.

Mrs. Zimmerman was busy imitating a wicked scoundrel punishing his poor consumptive wife when Aphrodite, perched amid the revolving blades of the fan, noticed plump Zulema, a woman pleasing in her eyes, signaling to Mr. Frugoni for her envelope with November's pay.

And Aphrodite wafted a welcome gust of fresh air upon Zulema's still-firm flesh and, in the guise of Sly Thoughts, whispered these winged words in Guaraní into her ear:

"Don't bother *karaí* Frugoni while he's fondling that black-haired *kuñá*. Why don't you wait for a pause from the speaker on the platform who's flailing her arms in the air, and in the meantime sit down quietly next to that very nice *karaí* with the crutches who once told you such sweet, if slightly bold, *ñeé.*"

And Zulema heeded the command of Sly Thoughts, and as Mrs. Zimmerman was pedagogically announcing the title of her next poem, "Garment on the Grass, or, An Adolescent Couple's Trying Relationship," she entered the room silently, proceeded down the aisle, and eventually settled her plump buttocks alongside Mr. Mastandrea's chair.

And Aphrodite diverted the breeze from the fan toward perspiring Mr. Mastandrea, which led him to glance to the left out of the corner of his eye and to notice Zulema's well-endowed form seated alongside him, and this made his heart rejoice.

Turning around, he shook Zulema's hand effusively, and furtively whipped the striped brown kerchief off his neck in order to make a more elegant impression on that sweet, irresistible woman.

And indomitable Athena, transformed into an unknown young woman, heard the erotic title of Mrs. Zimmerman's poem, and though she didn't especially care for the theme, she wanted the words to pierce the heart of her dear favorite, the irreproachable Irene Bengoechea, and to overwhelm her with tender emotion, which in turn would be transmitted to Mr. José María Pulicicchio, whom Athena, owing to her pact with Aphrodite, was obliged to pardon for his amorous advances on Marcos Sastre Street.

And so, when chaste Irene Bengoechea heard the words "trying relationship" and "adolescent" issuing from Mrs. Zimmerman's lips, she imagined them to be specifically directed toward her own recent and as yet unformalized courtship, and she conveyed this to Mr. Pulicicchio by wagging her pinkie finger significantly, leading him, in response, to squeeze her hand and to lean his ardent, wooing body toward her.

And just as the blushing maiden was divesting herself of her garments in front of the good-looking, frightened youth, Aphrodite, in the guise of a delicious breeze, stroked Mrs. Giannello—beautiful, goddesslike Mrs. Giannello—as well as estimable Mr. Frugoni, one of Hermes' favorites, who were seated extremely close to one another in the last row of chairs.

And Aphrodite granted them the brief, intoxicating joy of love, for since they had but a few moments left to live, Aphrodite wished those moments to be filled with sheer bliss, like goblets of inebriating wine.

And Mr. Frugoni totally forgot all the dire problems related to being a guilty husband, proprietor of the Flor de Lis variety store, treasurer of Polimnia, a Peronist of the first period, and a manufacturer of leather goods tooled in

India ink, and was thereby left free to turn his thoughts toward Mrs. Giannello's warm, silky skin, upon whose surface his trembling, loving hand furtively glided.

And Mrs. Giannello, faint with happiness, soaring toward vast multihued heavens, succumbed to a complete, throbbing orgasm, and with her head resting upon Mr. Frugoni's shoulder, she uttered the tenderest and most unmistakable of moans.

And Athena, from her spot in the fourth row next to blind Mr. Pasco, cast her gray-eyed, intelligent gaze toward her protégé, erudite, crippled Miss Kisternmacher, whom she'd infused just moments before with the irresistible Power of Persuasion.

And Miss Kisternmacher, by means of her incomprehensible poems and erudite explanations of Sanskrit words, had succeeded in persuading one and all of the compelling need for universal love, so that one and all, with surging emotion, had accepted her persuasive words, and demonstrated their universal love and gratitude through warm words and fraternal kisses upon her forehead.

But still Athena felt that her protégé ought to be granted an additional enlightened form of happiness, whereupon she transformed herself into the spirit of Tender Friendship and pierced the seductive soul of Mr. Romualdo Chávez, a mortal beloved by both goddesses, who was sitting next to Miss Kisternmacher in the front row.

Whereupon, Mr. Romualdo Chávez was smitten by an uncontainable desire for tender, spiritual friendship with Miss Kisternmacher, and just as Mrs. Zimmerman stood immobilized in that gesture of flinging the brassiere upon the grass, he impetuously kissed Miss Kisternmacher on both her hands and endearingly called her "Pupi" as he whispered some intelligent comments to her about the poem.

And Miss Kisternmacher, dewy-eyed with tender friendship and brimming with *samadhi,* gazed at him and remarked that the beautiful poem, though somewhat deficient in *tharana,* showed an abundance of *nidagha,* as evinced by the copious *krivamaha karma* that was inundating the room.

And Aphrodite waited impatiently for Miss Kisternmacher's servant, Dora, to arrive, for Dora's fiancé, young Romilio Sosa, was standing alone, rather dolefully, in a corner of the room, and the beautiful goddess was loath to have Romilio separated from his beloved during the meager time remaining for him to live.

With that in mind, Aphrodite transformed herself during the intermission into a spirit of Urgent Diligence, and under that guise lodged herself within Miss Kisternmacher's elegant mother.

And Miss Kisternmacher's mother, during intermission, recalled an extremely urgent errand that she had to attend to downtown, and therefore hurried to the room in the rear, picked up the phone, and called Dora immediately. In a few brief words, she told Dora to come by for Miss Kisternmacher at 2562 Teodoro Vilardebó, since she herself had an urgent errand to attend to downtown after the reading.

By now, however, the prolonged applause for Mrs. Zimmerman was dying down, and Mrs. Zimmerman was raising her right hand for silence in order to introduce Mr. Romualdo Chávez, and Miss Kisternmacher's maid, a brunette from Villa del Parque, had not yet arrived, much to Aphrodite's great consternation, as she gazed impatiently toward the door from the blades of the fan.

And Mr. Pasco, seated next to indomitable Athena disguised as a young stranger, was so utterly enthralled by the valiant behavior of the girl in the poem as she divested herself of her garments—his mind envisioning what his eyes were unable to see, namely the beautiful, half-naked youthful body that was reciting in a quivering voice—that his lonely heart began pounding loudly and an unconcealable enlargement arose on one side of his fly.

And since the enlargement failed to diminish, even as elegant Mr. Chávez was making his way toward the platform, Athena, with an almost imperceptible movement of her brows, appealed to Aphrodite for help.

And Aphrodite, in the guise of an Erotic Dream, swept blind Mr. Pasco up in delicious daydream, and in his fantasy he made love to the naked girl on the platform and possessed her on the downy grass, with its fluttering graceful little creatures, and he shed upon her the warm, engendering elixir of life, while Athena whispered into his ear in the disguised voice of Mrs. Zimmerman, took his hand, and magically removed the spot on his trousers.

And while all these things were happening, Hermes, disguised as a huge nocturnal butterfly with a fat, fuzzy abdomen, proceeded relentlessly in his important mission.

Diligently he circled the house, soared upward with a flutter of wings to the height of the chinaberry trees along Teodoro Vilardebó Street, scaled the plastered back wall with his little legs, and then his stiff antennas appeared above the well-repaired lintel of the front entrance.

Thus did he keep watch in all directions, waiting for the imminent arrival of the four ominous Ford Falcons, in order to notify the two Olympians instantly.

And lo and behold, in the course of the faithful performance of his mission, Hermes wearily flew toward the door of the room and alighted on its varnished frame with the intention of informing the young unknown woman that there was still no news.

And while perched atop the frame and communicating with indomitable Athena, his entire body received the full impact of a delightful puff of air bestowed by Aphrodite from the revolving fan.

And suddenly a gentle amorous titillation permeated and conquered the entire body of the gray nocturnal butterfly.

Whereupon, Hermes, trembling with irrepressible love, perched his winged body upon a well-watered mint plant which was partially concealed amidst the other little plants adorning the courtyard.

And exactly at the same time that Mr. Chávez was making a brief announcement to the well-groomed Polimnians, Hermes started up a most interesting conversation with the mint plant, one that was filled with refined and romantic words and accompanied by a tender rising and falling of his velvety abdomen upon its little perfumed leaves.

XXVII

Mr. Chávez, wearing, despite the suffocating heat, an impeccable gray suit and vest, had inserted into his buttonhole the beautiful red camellia which only moments before had adorned Miss Kisternmacher's languid bosom. I wasn't able to observe exactly when she had presented it to him, but presumably it was during the effusive outpourings of friendship that followed Mrs. Zimmerman's reading.

Clearly, this remarkable crimson flower that graced our dear president's lapel not only brought out his innate elegance but, in a way, foreshadowed the unusual festive tone which his words that evening were to have.

And that in fact was the case. As Irene motioned to me to take notice of the curious detail of the flower and was passing me secret eye signals in Miss Kisternmacher's direction, Mr. Chávez began his improvised speech.

In his well-modulated voice and agreeable Castilian accent, he began by remarking on the "productive labor accomplished by Polimnia" in the year that was drawing to an end. He spoke of the forty-eight poetry sessions that had been held that year, "including that most gratifying and on many scores unforgettable" session of today, Wednesday, December 3. And he compared that uninterrupted sequence of fruitful meetings to "a copious wreath of glittering stars magnificently traversing the black, embattled night of 1975."

He went on to say that this occasion seemed a most propitious one to single out the superior exertions of each of Polimnia's members, particularly those who shared his responsibilities on the Executive Committee. And he eulogized "Mrs. Zimmerman's generous, feverish activity as our first enrolled member, Mr. Frugoni's selfless, silent toil as treasurer, and Mrs. Giannello's orderly, indispensable efforts in keeping the minutes." And he proceeded in this vein, enumerating the members of the Executive Committee, extending to each of them his warm, gracious, eloquently expressed praise. I won't deny the near-childish joy I experienced on hearing my own name loudly pronounced from the platform as our president, pointing toward me, noted my punctual attendance at the forty-eight meetings in 1975, not having missed or arrived late for one of them, and proposed that this serve as an example to be emulated by all of our associates.

Mr. Chávez was in the midst of prophesying a happy, fruitful performance for Irene in her new capacity as financial secretary when, suddenly, the street bell rang. Young Romilio Sosa made a motion to rise, but Mrs. Zimmerman had already left the room and was crossing the dim corridor leading to the front door. We heard the jangle of keys, the grating of the latch, the familiar groan of the old hinges, and immediately a gay, chiming, feminine "Hello," which obliged Mr. Chávez to interrupt himself in order to await the newcomer with manly curiosity. A quick patter of steps in the corridor, and then there appeared at the door of our room, a few steps ahead of Mrs. Zimmerman, our familiar Dora, Miss Kisternmacher's maid.

Unabashed by the somewhat ceremonial tone of the meeting and showing not the slightest concern over the disturbing clatter of her heels, Dora, who was dressed rather daringly and was carrying a large bunch of acacia blossoms, chimed out, "Good evening, everyone." With heels tapping against the parquet floor, and flaunting her beautiful, provocative body, she approached Miss Kisternmacher's mother, exchanged a few brief words with her, said, "Yes, of course," and then once again, with her resounding and distracting little heels, she briskly crossed the length of the room, in order to seat herself quite happily next to her fiancé, young Romilio Sosa. She kissed him loudly, and familiarly hooked her arm through his. Then, crossing her shapely legs, she raised and lowered her long, dark and, I believe, false eyelashes several times, tilted her head with a slightly scholarly air, and turned her radiant gaze toward Mr. Chávez as if waiting for him to continue, or granting him permission to continue, or perhaps conveying that she failed to understand why he'd interrupted himself in the first place.

Mr. Chávez, who'd been gazing at Dora with smiling raptness (slightly spellbound, I must add) during all her bustling about through the length and breadth of the room, tipped his head majestically and, clasping his hands, proceeded with his promised but as yet unfulfilled words.

Having concluded the portion devoted to the society's functioning, he then embarked upon the theme of Polimnia's specific poetic activity in the course of 1975. With his innate expressive skill, he enumerated what he called zenith moments in that area. He cited in rapid succession the most felicitous readings and the most memorable poems of each of the Polimnians. This brief recapitulation (in which I had the supreme honor of being cited for some sonnets about autumn which I'd read at the beginning of the season) concluded with the presentations made by Mrs. Giannello and Mrs. Zimmerman on that very evening, that truly extraordinary evening, December 3, 1975.

Having spoken, Mr. Chávez lowered his head and paused at length with the obvious intention of creating a special air of expectancy. When he deemed the entire audience to be in an appropriately receptive state, he raised his eyes and proclaimed: "Furthermore, I cannot refrain from mentioning tonight something which, like the fragrance scattered by an exquisite flower, reaches out to each of us with a palpitating message of bliss and beatitude."

Another pause while the expectancy kept mounting, until finally he came out and said what he'd been building up to from the outset, which was apparently the true purpose of his unexpected discourse.

He began with a profound exegesis of Miss Kisternmacher's poem "Summer Love," explaining the total significance which the mysterious term *nidagha* held for him. He then moved on to "universal love," which he termed "an axis around which the infinite universe spins," and improvised then and there a series of exceedingly beautiful metaphors on love. When the general suspense had reached its limit, he concluded: "Love, which has impetuously traversed the long road of history and life, transforming vast expanses of indifferent matter along its way, has today, in our beloved little room, been reborn." With a sweeping gesture toward the blue-wallpapered walls, he undertook his peroration with a metaphor that struck me, despite its having originated with estimable Mr. Chávez, as being somewhat farfetched. "In this hospitable, well-ventilated room," he said, "the miraculous reconciliation between Venus and Minerva has enabled love to flourish beautifully amidst the rigors of mental exertion."

His original intention had been, I think, to allude merely to the freshly divulged relationship between Giannello's ex-wife and Mr. Frugoni. But then, as his long disquisition advanced, as his gaze encompassed the entire room, he probably noticed Dora next to Romilio; and Mastandrea, taking by now considerable liberties with Zulema; and Irene, whose hand was linked with mine; and thus concluded with that image drawn from classical mythology, which I personally found rather unconvincing.

The one who seemed particularly pleased by the allusion to Venus and Minerva's reconciliation was that unknown young woman seated next to Mr. Pasco, for she broke into instant applause, obliging us to follow suit. This confirmed the notion I'd formed about her being a purist, insensitive to mundane affairs, and a trifle pedantic. Anyhow, this is a mere digression and hasn't the slightest importance, and perhaps it's best to leave it at that.

A halting gesture from Mr. Chávez brought the applause to an immediate end. Irene, sensing that many eyes were focused upon us as a result of Mr. Chávez's significant words, attempted modestly to untwine her hand from mine. But I, with an audacity unrecognizable even to myself, emboldened by the ardent impulse inexplicably aroused in me by the delicious breeze from the fan, held on to it firmly. Triumphant and smiling, I openly returned the glances, and in so doing couldn't help but realize that many were the smiles and nods giving happy approval to our incipient, unexpected idyll. Even Mastandrea was precipitately inspired to wink at me and to point with an ill-concealed gesture of his thumb toward Zulema, whose color seemed to have risen considerably.

Dora and Romilio felt alluded to not in the least. Dora even ignored the orator for a few moments in order to whisper something into her fiancé's ear and to offer him some anise drops.

Mrs. Giannello, in the last row, was contemplating all this with a gentle, weary smile. But suddenly, taking a moment to smooth out her dress, she greeted Irene with a gracious gesture of her hand. It's no exaggeration to say that her face was radiant, as if now, after the critical moment that she'd undergone, she found herself plunged into an iridescent cloud of happiness which would protect her from all worldly reversals.

I tried to catch a glimpse of Mr. Frugoni, to determine whether he, too, had left his grave problems behind, but Mr. Chávez, having savored the effect of his flowery, mythological remark, once again resumed the thread of his speech.

He said something quite lovely about the brevity of our

passage through life, and about never rejecting the wild challenge of love, which, according to Mr. Chávez, was an unappealable dictate from the gods. "That is, of God," he corrected himself, in response to an involuntary vexed glance from Irene.

And concluding his improvised speech, he slowly articulated, in his melodious, unmistakable Castilian accent, the following brief, simple and moving words:

"And now, as love vehemently deposits the illusory kiss of immortality upon so many beloved faces, it is for me an utmost honor to read some of my humble poems, knowing that those I am reading to, owing to their own tender, blessed state of being, will, I have no doubt, receive them with fraternal benevolence."

Whereupon, adjusting the cuffs of his impeccable shirt, he prepared to deliver his reading. But much to our surprise, we promptly noted that he wasn't holding any sheets of paper in his hands, and hence would not be reading but would be reciting his poems from memory.

XXVIII

"Fuckin' heat."

"Looks like it's goin' to rain."

"It's even worse inside. Outside, there's a little breeze at least."

"What time you got?"

"Not quite twenty past."

"Eighteen past."

"Everyone here?"

"Car 41 is missing."

"Son of a bitch, always late."

"Here he comes."

"What the fuck happened to you?"

"Why?"

"It's seventeen past."

"Oil change."

"Don't give me that baloney."

"Say, maybe it'll cool off if it rains."

"Who knows."

"Were all the tanks filled up?"

"Hey, schmuck, the butt of your Ithaka is sticking out."

"So what?"

"Okay, but ya better cover it up."

"Follow my car. I'll follow the chief."

"Give me the address."

"One sec. 2562 Teodoro Vilardebó."

"Hmm? Where's that?"

"Around Villa del Parque, more or less."

"Did you get to see *That's a Laugh* on TV?"

"It was fantastic."

"Say, what's eatin' ya?"

"Sleepy, man. Didn't sleep a wink last night."

"An assignment?"

"Nah. It was that chick from last week."

"Tell her to bring around a little friend."

"Then you'll have some fun, eh?"

"That way I get you to bed early, dummy."

"Fuck off."

"Gettin' close to Villa Devoto, I think."

"It's somewhere around here."

"What happens after that?"

"How should I know? I guess it'll be some spot near Ezeiza Airport."

"Did you ask?"

"What for? We'll see soon enough."

"Careful with the cars. No blood inside."

"Where's the chief?"

"He went to take a leak."

"Hey, pass me some of that stuff."

"Look at him, that asshole. First he gets here late; then, to top it off, he forgets his stuff."

"Don't be a prick. Pass it to me, 'cause I left mine in the other car."

"One of these days, this jerk is gonna forget his pistols."

"Give it to me and stop fuckin' around."

"Hey, what're you doin'?"

"A hunk of adhesive tape and a bunch of rope . . . Goddamn!"

"Get going to your car."

"These wagons are already pretty messed up."

"They gotta be changed."

"Ya gotta know how to take care of them, man."

"Drop dead."

"I hope we finish up early."

"Why?"

"The old lady. She's got a fever."

"Anything serious?"

"No, just a cold. But still."

"I figure we'll finish by four."

"Won't be hitting the sack before six."

"What can you do? That's how it is with this work."

"It's ten of."

"Here comes the chief."

"He's getting in. Follow me and don't screw up."

"Okay, those by the door. On the move."

"Get going, get going, dammit. Move, I tell you."

"That guy sure got the pants scared off him."

"Almost got killed."

"Everything in order?"

"Everything in order, Chief."

"Let's go."

"Got the list, Chief?"

"Yup."

"Everyone on it?"

"How should I know?"

"Are there a lot of them?"

"Twelve."

"Jeez!"

"Car 25 to Headquarters: Everything in order."

"Shall I take Jorge Newberry Street?"

"No, better take Juan B. Justo."

"Car 25 to Headquarters: We're heading for Villa del Parque. Anything new to report?"

"Nothing new. Proceed to operation."

"Ain't it a little early, Chief?"

"At ten, everyone on the double. Hurry."

"Do we nab 'em according to the list?"

"Any twelve, I told you."

"I hope the guys from the 45th don't screw up like the other time."

"Bevilacqua was warned. He's not going to show up."

"I'd remind him, just to make sure. Not to fuck around."

"Don't worry. He was cured after what happened last time."

"Do we turn at Warnes?"

"No, keep going till Avenue San Martín. Then along Jonte till Teodoro Vilardebó. Signal Car 41 when you're ready to turn."

XXIX

"Ah, feckless, craven, resigned Olympians! Unable, by your own admission, to combat invincible Hades, buried as you are in a mire of inertia, concealing your cowardliness by a few niggling morsels of happiness strewn upon those hapless mortals you so unjustifiably claim to be under your protection!

"Onward in your hypocritical zeal, devoting yourselves to the minuscule span of life that those poor, forsaken Polimnians still have left, for in truth, there's nothing you can do to save them from Hades' emissaries!

"Hasten to grant them little inane pleasures, like part-time wet nurses paid for their service, or like someone handing a weeping, frightened child an improvised, and perhaps shoddy toy in order to distract him and temporarily allay his fear and his tears!

"Bestow upon those mortals your frivolous and easy generosity—those secret hand-claspings, wet-eyed declarations of tender friendship, empty proposals of universal love, burning and furtive caresses, and silent orgasms— since, in fact, you're incapable of bestowing upon them the only gift that genuinely ought to be exacted of you: life itself.

"Onward, intriguing Aphrodite, with your meaningless efforts, hidden behind the blades of the fan, dispersing the gentle titillation of love upon those gathered at 2562 Teodoro Vilardebó, whose lives at this very moment can be calculated in terms of minutes.

"What a fine idea, I avow, to shed plentiful doses of it upon lame Carlos Argentino Mastandrea, who, while listening to Mr. Chávez, in that circumspect vest, reciting a poem by memory, was suddenly reminded that he, Mastandrea, was widowed, just like Zulema, with whom he happens to have fallen madly in love, and is simply waiting now for a pause in the recital in order to make her a rather foolish, ill-timed marriage proposal.

"And now, proceed with utmost caution and shift the solid base of the fan so that its breeze is directed toward the rostrum, where Mr. Chávez, with spare gestures, is holding forth, and have him desist from boring everyone with his high-sounding poems about rustic Castilian peasants and launch once and for all into the recitation of a long, descriptive and somewhat salacious poem which will arouse high tides of eroticism among the serene members of the Polimnia group.

"Onward in your course, O frigid, disdainful, irascible Athena, vain daughter of Zeus! Remain stiffly seated beside blind Mr. Pasco in order to capture a goodly armful of the Universal Love exhaled by Miss Kisternmacher into the blue-wallpapered room and to waft it secretly toward Dora, Romilio Sosa's fiancée, an attractive, chatty resident of Villa del Parque.

"Whereupon, Dora's only wish will be to have this rather silly reading come to an end so that she can spring nimbly from her chair and snip stems of acacia from the bouquet she's holding on her lap and distribute them to each of the nice people at the meeting as a demonstration of the deep universal love she feels toward them.

"Prompted, however, by Aphrodite's ceaseless revolving motions, she will at the same time have a desire to make love to Romilio, as God commands, and the sooner the better. Thus, she'll want everything brought to a speedy conclusion in order to push Miss Kisternmacher's wheelchair back home, a bit on the fast side perhaps, and then catch a convenient taxi and race toward the Hotel Lilies, since Blackie has been acting especially affectionate tonight.

"As for you, O negligent Hermes, wretched protector of thieves and a thief yourself, it was sensible of you to forsake your futile, deranged mission, for what benefit would it serve that defenseless congregation on Teodoro Vilardebó if the Olympians were to learn, merely seconds before the members themselves, about the ominous arrival of the vehicles of doom, those four Ford Falcons?

"You were quite right to ignore Aphrodite's request, and to abandon your watchful lookout over the street in favor of engaging that well-watered little mint plant in beguiling conversation. And she, by the way, happens to be none other than Mintho, the underworld nymph who was metamorphosed by Persephone, Hades' lawful wife (though only four months out of the year), due to the spiteful—and unfounded—jealousy Persephone felt toward Mintho.

"Proceed, O gods, in shedding your soothing balm of oblivion. Mend, darn, distract, apply urgent patches of ephemeral bliss, for there's little else, despite your immortal rank, that you're capable of doing.

"Lavish your transient pleasure and unjustified joy upon this cluster of unprotected mortals, for at this very moment four black Ford Falcons, led by Car 25 with The Goat inside, have just speeded across Juan B. Justo Avenue and General Rodríguez Street, and are now approaching Villa del Parque in order to punctually execute Hades' bloody command! O indolent, ambrosia-loving creatures! O abject, foolish, craven, insufferable Olympians!"

But the truth was that no one dared to express these admonishing insults to the gods, and thus they continued blithely in their futile task of rendering the last moments of those doomed mortals as pleasant as possible, while, in the meantime, icy Hades, utterly contemptuous of the Olympians' exertions, proceeded to execute with implacable fury his final preparations for the slaughter.

No sooner did the third Ker depart from The Goat's office in the Palermo quarter and cross the metal gates of Hades' dark abode to inform the taciturn waiting god of the punctual fulfillment of her mission, than Hades cracked his whip upon the steaming flanks of his majestic steeds and at last allowed them full rein.

With hot breath issuing from their nostrils, the three black chargers raced forth, goaded by the hissing whip, guided by the bloodlusting deity who kept them at firm rein. And soon the gloomy realm was left far behind in the distance, and the creatures were galloping through the air, speeding toward Juan B. Justo Avenue, a well-paved street with many traffic lights.

And at the exact spot where Juan B. Justo Avenue crosses the cobbled pavement of Cucha Cucha, Hades, from atop his chariot, spied the four Ford Falcons, and in the lead, with motor roaring, was Car 25, commanded by The Goat, a mortal who in a sense could be likened to one of the bloodlusting Keres, armed with deadly weapons.

And Hades, in order to keep close watch on his emissaries, transformed himself into a fine white sticky filament, a plant commonly known as devil's spittle, which soared with the invisible breeze and flew a few feet above the gleaming hoods of the cars. This gave Hades a fine vantage point for surveying the faithful execution of his commands.

Yet not one of the numerous mortals heedlessly passing at that very moment along the broad avenue of Juan B. Justo was able to detect the wispy filament, which, on reaching the corner of Avenue San Martín, stopped flying in the direction it was going, turned right, without straying an inch from the swift cars, and then continued on in silent flight along Avenue San Martín.

And Cars 25, 41, 70 and 72 advanced at great speed along Avenue San Martín, sounding their ominous screeching sirens from time to time in order to force all buses, wine trucks, station wagons, and cars of various models to move fearfully to one side, giving them the right of way.

On reaching the beginning of Avenue San Martín, where the numbers are in the 2800 range, the four vehicles, without waiting for a green light, spun around the corner, one behind the other, into Álvarez Jonte Street, their tires loudly screeching. And Hades did rejoice, for this screeching was most pleasing to his ears.

And Car 25 advanced without obstruction along Álvarez Jonte Street and reached the intersection where Álvarez Jonte and Argerich cross, at which point the skilled subordinate seated at the steering wheel turned sideways to The Goat and uttered these significant words: "How many blocks?"

And The Goat, with one elbow propped on the window ledge, drew his cigarette to his lips, and, exhaling bluish smoke slowly, he replied: "Five, pal; and when you reach Teodoro Vilardebó, three to the right."

And Hades, from his fluttering observation post overhead, heard each of his beloved Goat's words perfectly, and his heart brimmed with joy.

And as the four vehicles, one behind another, turned down Teodoro Vilardebó Street, and the occupants took hold of their impeccable weapons, the ominous click of their safety latches being released reached Hades' ears, and his joy peaked in intensity like a voluptuous orgasm.

XXX

Mr. Chávez hadn't personally participated in a recitation for quite some time, due to his absorption in the multiple tasks related to the organization. Especially in the last few months. As a result of transactions on the property which we were renting (and which was managed by our unwearying president through Delos Real Estate), plus the as yet unsuccessful negotiations to obtain a bank loan that would enable us to acquire the old house on Teodoro Vilardebó, Mr. Chávez had little time at his disposal to devote to his most cherished vocation.

He was esteemed in our circle as a most refined and sensitive poet, in the romantic vein, and needless to say, our expectations at hearing him were great. As his lovely introductory remarks were ending, Mrs. Giannello and Mr. Frugoni sneaked out of the last row and raced up two rows closer so as not to miss a single word of what promised to be an utterly brilliant recitation. Miss Kisternmacher gazed at the platform with an air of ecstasy, and Mrs. Zimmerman gestured for silence, even though not a soul had spoken or uttered a sound.

No one was better suited than eloquent Mr. Chávez— many of us, I'm sure, were thinking—to bring the evening's recitation, with its very special tone, which I might venture to describe as being warm and romantic, to a glorious conclusion. Especially after Mrs. Zimmerman's composition, and that beautiful interpretation of hers, you could sense amongst the members a certain desire (wafting in the air, as the saying goes), a desire to maintain that tone, to intensify it and transport it, upon the wings of our president's refined poems, his melodious voice and natural grace, toward luminous and keenly resonant realms. Or, to put it another way, toward that magnificent finale of deep, prodigious communication which all of us sensed would indeed be unforgettable.

Some of his earlier beautiful poems remained clear in my memory, especially a short one about a kiss which I found extraordinary in conception and perfectly realized in form. There was no doubt in my mind that the poems he'd be reading to us tonight would be worthy peers of that other one, and assuredly perfect examples of his romantic and amorous inspiration. Thus, all of us, with genuine reverence, were in total readiness to listen to Mr. Chávez.

It is not without pain, therefore, that I find myself obliged to recount what follows. The very title of what was to be Mr. Chávez's first poem caused us considerable surprise, and though, I repeat, I find it painful to say, the title in a way betrayed our high expectations. I wish to speak quite frankly: a poem with a title of that sort was not the type of thing one would expect of Mr. Chávez. I shall try to explain, for otherwise my interpretation may be regarded merely as a personal evaluation. The poem was called "To a Peasant from Castile," and was dedicated to his deceased father.

Mr. Chávez began reciting his very Castilian, rustic poem by heart. He was solemn, intense, ruminative, seemingly untouched in the slightest by all that had taken place that evening. The rigorous, echoing verse, its pronounced rhythm marked by the author's foot—a would-be attempt to imitate the monotonous beating of the hoe against the dry earth—depicted vivid memories, from his childhood assuredly, in a small village in Zamora. Thus, instead of the suggestive, courtly images all of us were anticipating, there paraded before our weary attention and scant enthusiasm something which could be of no possible interest to anyone at that moment: the curved backs of laborers over arid fields, sturdy women accompanying their menfolk in the harsh tasks of the plow, in spare meals at rustic family tables, and in brief rests; clusters of farmers marching off at the first flicker of dawn, and the hiss of scythes, the shouts of "giddap," the peal of Angelus bells, and the prayers of solemn villagers over a freshly dug grave. Well!

I began thinking that this was a clever way to begin so as to strike a contrast with the tone of his next poem, which undoubtedly would conform to his more familiar beautiful, romantic vein. But much to our disenchantment, a second poem followed entitled "The Hoe," and then a third, "Sheaves of Ripe Wheat," and a fourth, "A Sower's Death." With the resumption of hissing scythes, and peasants' curved backs, and sturdy women, and clusters of farmers marching off to the harvest, and Angelus bells, and prayers, and muted death.

The audience began showing unmistakable signs of fatigue. One must not forget that this was the last poet of the evening, after more than two hours of readings. People began squirming in their seats, fingers were drumming on knees, eyes wandering off on the trail of some insect fluttering in the courtyard. And suddenly, from the seats at the rear, came a loud, deep yawn which could only have emanated from Mastandrea. I cursed him soundly under my breath, but felt certain that even Mr. Chávez had heard it from the platform.

Just at that moment I noticed that the pleasant breeze of the fan extended into the audience, but that somehow, despite its brisk, sweeping movements, it failed to reach the platform where our president was standing, and that he must certainly be suffering from the heat more than anyone else. I then recalled that Mrs. Zimmerman, on descending from the platform, had bumped into the base of the fan and had unwittingly shifted its position. As soon as I realized this, I waited for Mr. Chávez to conclude "A Sower's Death," and since no one else in the front rows had noticed the problem, I stood up to correct it. I was obliged once again, therefore, to disturb Mr. Pasco, the unknown young woman and Miss Kisternmacher's mother. I hadn't gotten even two feet down the aisle, however, when something truly comical occurred.

Due to some unevenness in the floor, perhaps, or to a thump of the hoe more resounding than the others, the base of the fan moved—on its own, it seemed—and veered about an inch to the right. Enough now to allow the air to reach Mr. Chávez fully. And so I turned around, and once again disturbed Miss Kisternmacher's mother, the unknown young woman and Mr. Pasco. I reached my place and took my seat, somewhat embarrassed (for I could offer no explanation now for having so impulsively risen), although Mr. Chávez, having guessed my intention perhaps, smiled at me as if sharing my surprise about that inexplicable jolt of the fan.

Anyhow, as a result of the breeze which now stroked his entire body, wresting him with its delightful coolness from the parched fields of Zamora, the stooped peasants and hissing scythes, or perhaps due to Mastandrea's loud yawn, which alerted him to his listeners' fatigue, the fact is that Mr. Chávez, from that moment on, underwent a complete change of attitude and, as will be seen shortly, of repertory as well.

He rubbed his hands gleefully, as if the evening were just getting under way, and then, glancing at the audience with an open, irresistible smile, asked to be forgiven, but he was going to introduce, if allowed to do so by the Executive Committee, a small change in the program. Instead of "The Master's Wheat Field," which had been announced and which those of us who cared to do so could read, at a later time, in the minutes, he felt an urge, if we would forgive him, "to recite some other little thing."

XXXI

And as impeccable Mr. Chávez was doggedly reciting "To a Peasant from Castile," beating out the rhythm with his foot in the old-fashioned way, Hermes, garrulous, forgetful, negligent Hermes, had meanwhile abandoned his important mission of surveillance without a twinge of remorse, and had surrendered happily to the lighthearted task at hand.

Thus, the wily Messenger was hovering no longer over Polimnia's well-tended headquarters, nor keeping a sharp lookout on both sides of Teodoro Vilardebó Street, as the goddesses had enjoined him to do, nor did he appear overly concerned about the imminent arrival of four Ford Falcons with their slaughterers of men.

Instead, Hermes, his heart swelling with love and urgent desire (due, surely, to the gust of air unwittingly blown upon him by golden Aphrodite), astutely exercised his ancient, dauntless, conquering wiles upon a humble, timid and trembling mint plant, who responded with secret pleasure to the amorous discourse of the eloquent god.

Hermes, well under way by now in his seductive mission, and still in the guise of an attractive nocturnal butterfly with soft, caressing wings, began eulogizing the plant's dark, straight, graceful stems as well as her scent, which was reminiscent of Aphrodite's breath, and emanated from her leafy body at the slightest touch.

As usual, Hermes was shamelessly deceitful in his infinite wiles for seducing unwary maidens, having learned from long experience how to soften a maiden's heart, irrespective of her rank.

And so, as he was delicately rubbing the plant's tender little leaves with his velvety abdomen—at the same time that Mr. Chávez was launching into a second poem about peasants and sturdy family tables—Hermes began to speak, and dolefully he informed the plant that he was an immortal youth and the son of a mighty deity, but that, despite this, no one, no goddess, nymph or mortal woman, had ever commiserated with his loneliness or bestowed upon his forlorn heart the tender warmth of love.

And the chaste little plant, hidden amidst the many well-watered plants surrounding the courtyard at 2562 Teodoro Vilardebó, believed Hermes' skillfully forged lies, and in fact Hermes generally found the ruse of the lonely, misunderstood youth to be quite infallible. And the little plant felt seized by a desire to be the one appointed by Destiny to allay the sufferings of such a handsome youth.

And in order to overcome the shyness of the lonely, misunderstood young man and to gain his confidence, she gently fluttered her festooned leaves and, in turn, recounted her own luckless tale, addressing her sincere, fragrant words to wily Hermes.

"Ah, illustrious youth, so cruelly pursued by solitude and sadness, you must truly believe me when I tell you that

I, too, am the loneliest and most unjustly punished of the nymphs.

"Mintho is my name, and before I acquired this vegetal guise so lavishly and gracefully praised by you, I was a young underworld nymph, whiling away her time in carefree play beneath the fragrant soil of the forest.

"But once, as I was resting alone by the deep root of a murmuring poplar, repulsive Hades caught me unawares and attempted to violate me.

"Of course, he did not succeed, for as you must certainly know, kind youth, he, unlike you, I'm sure, is quite awkward in this form of combat and, according to what my sisters have told me, rather impotent as well.

"Nevertheless, his lawful wife, divine, spiteful Persephone, the only woman whom Hades has known (perhaps) in his entire, barren life, became enraged with me.

"And on that very day, blinded by her absurd, unfounded jealousy, she trampled upon me in great fury, and transformed me forever into this fragrant mint which now adorns the shaded courtyard at 2562 Teodoro Vilardebó, and upon which you, O divine youth, are presently perched."

So spoke the hapless little mint plant, while Hermes gazed at her covetously, and while at the same time the doomed Polimnians were squandering their last, precious moments of life amidst the utterly tedious chiming of Angelus bells and of peasants lumbering off to their harsh toil.

And while Hermes, smitten with amorous desire, was listening attentively to the tale that the beautiful mint plant told, his delicate nocturnal butterfly ears were suddenly assailed by the loud poundings of the hoe so enthusiastically discharged by Mr. Chávez upon the resounding wooden platform.

And as it happened, those sudden jarring blows jolted negligent Hermes back to reality, and brusquely reminded him of the doomed Polimnians and their imminent bloody fate at the hands of the fierce parapolice in the four Ford Falcons, and also of the important surveillance mission he'd so negligently abandoned.

But most jarring of all to Hermes was the sound of Hades' abhorrent name upon the lips of the beautiful little plant, and gradually he found himself emerging from his amorous trance and, with customary speed, began wondering if that deplorable happening Mintho had so movingly recounted might not in some way be turned to their advantage.

And so, without relinquishing his graceful demeanor or the well-dissembled guise of a melancholy, misunderstood youth, Hermes posed an astute, seemingly innocent question while stroking the ingenuous little plant with his velvety abdomen.

"O gentle Mintho, surely the purest and most beautiful of nymphs, whose fragrance drives Immortals to the madness of love and mortals to yearning for the delightful freshness of the forest.

"Your story has moved me to shedding hot tears, and I believe truly, after hearing your tale of woe, that the two of us were created to provide one another consolation and pleasure.

"But there is only one question, O beautiful nymph, that I'd like to ask of you, out of sheer curiosity, if you are willing, at this special and enchanting moment, to reply."

And the well-watered mint responded: "Speak, handsome youth, whose name is as yet unknown to me, and I shall indeed answer your question, since from this day on, there is nothing that I shall ever hide from you."

Tripping along the slender stem, his butterfly wings flapping amorously, Hermes, ever resourceful, spoke up.

"O beautiful, hapless Mintho, tell me, since you've agreed to reply: How does mighty Hades regard you and what has been his treatment of you after that forced and futile attempt of his to possess your immaculate body?

"Does the impotent deity detest you now and long only for your extinction because of your haughty refusal to yield to his licentious desire?

"Or, on the other hand, is he abjectly humiliated because of his bungling and ineffectual behavior, and feel perhaps beholden to you and ready to gratify most solicitously any wish you may have, providing that you inform no one about his humiliating defeat?"

And precisely at that moment when Mr. Pulicicchio stood up to adjust the position of the floor fan, the well-watered plant blushed and uttered these winged words:

"How wise you are, O handsome youth, in having so quickly divined Hades' loathsome behavior.

"Indeed, it is true that Hades, after his thwarted attempt to violate me, has been beleaguering me with near servile solicitude, quite unbefitting a powerful god.

_____

"His manner toward me ever since the occurrence of that foolish episode by the murmuring poplar has been rather ashamed, abject and guilty.

"And since I, unwittingly, know his innermost secret, namely his unpardonable awkwardness and humiliating impotence in amorous encounters, he wastes not a single opportunity to visit me secretly, despite his wife's awful jealousy, and to persistently ask if there's anything he can possibly do to gratify some wish of mine.

"It is quite possible, as you may surmise, that this ridiculous comportment of Hades is intended simply to purchase my silence and to prevent me from informing the Immortals of that secret which undoubtedly plagues his nights in that nether world of his damp and shaded abode.

"But tell me, O handsome youth, is my reply not by chance to your liking? Why have you so abruptly ceased fondling my leaves with your silken abdomen? What accounts for that motionless, distant gaze, as if your mind were preoccupied with grave thoughts totally removed from the two of us?

"Tell me, I beg you, fearing not that you will hurt me with your admonishing words, the thoughts that are racing so dizzily through your mind at this very moment."

157

XXXII

... a turbulent situation which the country is undergoing ... in the month of November, the cost of living . . . with a monetary inflation of . . . the economic minister and provincial governors signed a bill . . . in opposition to the executive power on parliamentary investigation . . . yesterday, four more corpses in Greater Buenos Aires . . . a denunciation revealed the grim discovery . . . according to subsequent findings . . . a group of heavily armed individuals . . . identifying themselves as policemen . . . belonging to the factory's private security force . . . River, San Lorenzo and students are winning . . . the goals of Pasarella, Scotta and Vernon . . . a trout meet at San Carlos de Bariloche . . . a fine specimen weighing nine kilos was caught by . . . and that other lovely participant confessed that she . . . today is Artillery Day . . . on which occasion the army high commands . . . a good piece of news . . . confirmed: there will be a first-class race . . . the announcement made in the press office . . . telex, urgent . . . last-minute . . . has the painful duty to inform . . . on this day and date . . . at approximately nineteen hours . . . in the outskirts of the city of Paraná . . . subversive elements murdered . . . the press secretary divulged . . . agents of chaos and criminal violence . . . victim of this vandalistic assault . . . cowardly attack from the rear . . . collapsed in a pool of blood . . . undoubtedly the work of disturbed, perverted minds ... presumably drugged ... this criminal wave which assails the nation ... subversive delinquency ... mercenary, stateless extremism ... contemptible, Godless murderers ... a suitable punishment ... sixty-two organizations communicate ... once more, the repellent counternational forces ... whose atheistic Marxism has unleashed its murderous fury ... acts of supreme barbarism ... misfits whose base instincts ... who have disavowed their human condition ... of the sinister antinational, synarchical plot ... our solidarity with the glorious Armed Forces ... whose copious blood ... against stateless subversion ... and spurious interests ... your valor, integrity, manly worth ... the brave soldier in you ... because they are incapable of fighting in the open ... of showing their faces ... shielded by cowardly anonymity ... we vow to fulfill our patriotic mission ... to annihilate definitively ... and streams of blood will run....

A brief pause for a commercial, and we shall return at once with more news.

XXXIII

Mr. Chávez, following his apologies, went on to clarify something about the poem he was about to declaim, the one that would be concluding the reading on that memorable Wednesday, December 3, 1975.

With utmost solemnity and composure, he informed us that it had been inspired by the woes and follies of a certain friend of his who, unfortunately, was in love with a certain lady who was, you might say, a bit . . . He pretended to be searching laboriously for the correct adjective, imitating the gestures of a long-suffering parish priest, and finally he came out with it: a bit featherbrained. We all smiled, and some of us even broke into open laughter, primarily, I think, because of his reference to "a friend of mine." Most of us knew full well that Mr. Chávez had no need to resort to other people's experience when it came to composing a poem about a woman, especially a certain type of woman. . . .

He then proceeded to clarify the subsequent need for indulgence on the part of his distinguished audience toward a certain expressive license he'd found himself obliged to introduce into his composition, which was intended simply to be a faithful interpretation of his unhappy friend's ardent thoughts and strange dissipation. "This poor friend whose suffering and inflamed desire—thus do I hope, and thus must we all hope—will be reciprocated by the tender surrender of that beautiful lady and by her dubious fidelity." As he spoke, you could hear an occasional nervous feminine twitter. Irene inhaled deeply and gave me a few little pats on the back of my hand, as if to convey that I, with respect to her own fidelity, might remain completely at ease. Mastandrea found it necessary to translate our president's entire prologue to Zulema, and I overheard him quite clearly saying "a little whore"—in other words, the gist of the explanation, which Zulema received with a kind of yelp, stifled by a handkerchief.

Mr. Chávez went on to explain that the composition still lacked a title, and thus he wished to make the following proposal to Polimnia's enlightened members: that each of those assembled, upon hearing the poem, jot down on a slip of paper the title he or she regarded as most apt, and hand it over to him after the meeting. He would then select the one he believed most fitting, and would announce his choice at next Wednesday's meeting. The winner, male or female, in this form of competition, as it were, would be awarded a book with an acknowledgment, in Mr. Chávez's very own script, of the invaluable aid that had been received. Miss Kisternmacher promptly raised her hand and declared that she'd be glad to donate the prize for such a significant occasion, and that it would consist of a clothbound book by the great Krishnamurti.

We all applauded, and Mr. Chávez bestowed a delicate remark of gratitude upon his cherished friend. And then he lapsed into silence, waiting for the last sighs to subside, whereupon, very softly, with a slow, measured rhythm and in an emotional tone, he began reciting that as yet untitled poem.

The beautiful composition told, as the author had previously indicated, of what you might call a woman of the world, someone, in other words, who was a bit on the loose side. Endowed with ravishing beauty and seemingly with unflagging sensuality, the lady received her reproaches upon certain extremely painful occasions with a luminous, bewitching smile that totally disarmed her betrayed lover.

Mr. Chávez, now luckily receiving the breeze from the fan, conveyed an utterly beautiful and detailed description of the beloved woman, all through the words of her lover. He began an extended sensual enumeration, akin to a modern Song of Songs (I already had my title for the poem), of each of the provocative regions of that splendid body, which in his fevered fantasy he compared, as in biblical song, to wondrous and resplendent objects: a river in its winding course, a slender column of marble, a mother-of-pearl shell, a shaded garden amidst snow-white mountains, two little rosy-beaked doves which the poet's mouth longed to consume, soft hills bounded by deep, dark vertiginous abysses, etc.

The poet did not pause at any region of his beloved, and thus he'd be alluding at one moment to a certain "hidden rose with palpitating petals," where he, like an indefatigable bee, would alight to sip "the perfumed love-steeped nectar," or perhaps to a certain shell, warmly oozing (the beloved woman's tongue), which in turn he explored inch by inch until coming upon the sacred red monolith "from which emanated the twelve cabalistic routes of desire."

At this point, Irene, totally collapsed upon my shoulder, began breathing arduously. Dora was patting Romilio on his knee to calm him down. I turned around discreetly and noticed Mrs. Giannello passing her lips over Mr. Frugoni's neck, and Mastandrea waging stubborn battle with Zulema's hand. Mrs. Zimmerman began having unexpected trouble with a band on her corset and kept trying to adjust it. For some reason, Mr. Pasco, seated at my left, requested my legal-size portfolio, the one containing my sonnets, and placed it on his knees. Just then, I tried to observe the unknown young woman seated next to me and, to my surprise, noticed that her chair was empty. She'd vanished, as though miraculously. Scandalized, no doubt, by the sheer boldness of certain words in the composition, she had made a hasty departure, without my so much as seeing or hearing her. I'd previously sensed her to be rather formal and purist and had a feeling that certain poetic forms would offend her circumspect nature.

The fact is, however, that never before in our little blue meeting room had there ever been heard images of such descriptive audacity and, at the same time, such captivating communicative force. Suffice it to say that I myself at this point was starting to feel quite aroused, and experienced a sudden fervent desire to kiss Irene on her eyes and her lips.

Unwittingly, and not without a twinge of guilt, I gazed upward from the corner of my eyes at Mrs. Urdampilleta. There she was, observing us gravely and even admonitorily from eternity, at that precise moment when Mr. Chávez mentioned the palpitating rose hidden amidst dark shrubbery.

I quickly withdrew my gaze from the portrait and continued listening with infinite pleasure to Mr. Chávez. It was impossible to escape the enchantment of that beautiful poem, seeded as it was with ever more daring images, ever more ardent and flaming repressed desires.

And to think that I personally hadn't even dared to read a certain sonnet to the group because of a couple of images in the second triplet which I regarded at the time as being a trifle bold. Naturally, I now felt remorseful for my scruples, and vowed to overcome my timidity. I made an absolutely firm decision: I would ask to have my name included in next Wednesday's recital, and without any excuses would divulge my sonnet (along, perhaps, with the triptych dedicated to Irene, if I could manage to complete it by then). Considered impartially, my own suggestive, though moderate, images were evangelical sermons in comparison with the impetuous metaphors that surged forth unrestrained from this man heretofore a stranger to me: Mr. Chávez.

In the last lines particularly, where the wakeful lover has been waiting several hours for his beloved's delayed return (presumably from one of her immodest adventures). At that point, the images attained their maximum audacity and outright eroticism. The lover, sick with desire, resolves not to rebuke her at all this time, but, on the contrary, announces his intention to smother her with impassioned kisses and electrifying embraces "the moment she opens the door." While reciting that last line, Mr. Chávez pointed vehemently toward the door of the room, whereupon all of us turned in that direction, as if truly expecting to see at any moment a beautiful woman turning the latchkey and gracefully crossing the threshold. Our eyes remained fixed in that position as though hypnotized in their yearning gaze toward the door, while the poet went on proclaiming unto all the spirits of the night that he would lie down alongside his beloved and their bodies would intertwine "in an oft repeated embrace" until, wearily, they would succumb to "the gentle slumber of dawn."

XXXIV

Futile was your attempt, O estimable José María Pulicicchio, to observe the unknown young woman seated in
your row, and in vain, O lustful Mr. Pasco, did you grope
furtively for her beneficent hand, while Mr. Chávez, inspired by blond Aphrodite, kept reading, with great fervor
and without opposition, his untitled aphrodisiacal poem.

For Athena, alarmed by lack of news from the Messenger, Hermes, and worried about the lateness of the hour,
has decided to vanish abruptly from her position in the
fourth row of that blue-wallpapered room, and, once more
in the guise of a chattering belfry owl, has gone off impatiently to search for the wayward immortal youth.

Yet, despite her endless circling around the old house
on Teodoro Vilardebó Street, despite her clever scrutiny of
the strategic spots where the wily god might be found, her
great, peering owlish eyes have been unable to detect diligent Hermes, hidden away as he was amidst the scented
foliage of a virtually invisible little mint plant.

And so, convinced that the feckless Messenger had forsaken his mission for good, Athena resolved that she herself would act as sentinel, and at this moment is perched,

in the guise of a motionless belfry owl, with feathered feet, hooked bill and fixed, piercing eyes, upon the uppermost part of the garden gate, statuesquely waiting for the four Ford Falcons.

Hermes, meanwhile, having just been informed by fragrant Mintho's own lips of her heretofore undivulged relationship with Hades, is nervously waving his delicate antennas back and forth, hastily contriving all sorts of ruses.

It was true, as sensitive Mintho had surmised, that the thoughts of the handsome youth had strayed far away from her and from that peaceful nook in the courtyard, and were wandering off into realms completely removed from their fervent, loving conversation.

In truth, the mind of the wily god was racing at a dizzying speed, and in less time than was needed for a nervous flick of his antennas, it had shifted quickly from the shaded courtyard at 2562 Teodoro Vilardebó to the shadowy realm of unnamable Hades, and then from the lofty peaks of resplendent Olympus to a discreet office in the Palermo quarter, stacked with lethal weapons.

At the exact moment in which Mr. Chávez was talking about snowy white hills and hidden palpitating roses, Hermes reached the acute realization that the fragrant, humble little mint could be of greater use to the luckless Polimnians who'd been condemned by Hades than could any of the powerful, haranguing Olympians, their presumed protectors.

And so, once again tenderly wending his way up toward the delicate tip of a little stem, he uttered these words to Mintho, words that were partially true and partially false.

"Your reproach, O delightful, fragrant Mintho, is quite just, for, in truth, my mind has been working without respite these past few moments, though I tell you sincerely that in all its vertiginous flights I have been unable to forget you.

"Listen, and you will understand the cause of my concern, since hereafter I shall conceal nothing from you.

"I shall begin by telling you why I am here, the reason why I, a young Immortal, descendant of mighty Olympians, transformed into a harmless nocturnal butterfly, find myself now in this well-tended courtyard in Villa del Parque.

"The ones responsible for my knowledge of your existence here in this courtyard, the ones whose comradely words impelled me to assume this winged guise, were twelve magnanimous mortals, and that is the reason, O most understanding and most tender of nymphs, why I've vowed to protect them.

"There they are now, seated in that room in parallel rows of chairs, listening to the sweet, enticing words of love pouring forth eloquently from Mr. Chávez's mouth.

"But Hades, jealous of our bond of love, has decided, O dearest Mintho, to avenge himself upon those twelve magnificent mortals protected by me, and he has decided upon their irrevocable death.

"Within the scantest of moments, four sinister Ford Falcons, led by a parapolice coordinator called The Goat and dispatched by the bloodlusting god, will be performing an ominous mission of extinction.

"With a chilling squeak of rubber tires on pavement, they'll come to a halt in front of this well-established residence, and then a trained group of untouchable, murderous parapolicemen, whom the morning newspapers will hypocritically refer to as 'a group of strongly armed individuals,' will descend from the cars.

"No one, god or mortal, will dare to oppose those fierce emissaries, inasmuch as they're under the protection of Hades himself and of high government security systems. And thus, tomorrow, my twelve dear comrades will be found murdered amidst the pasturelands near Ezeiza Airport. I was advised of all this in Hades' own realm, from the very lips of an illustrious former colonel.

"Their bodies, O sweetest Mintho, will reveal signs of having been tortured, their hands will be tied behind their backs, their benign mouths will be sealed with adhesive tape, and several high-caliber bullets will have pierced those bodies that once knew love.

"Now, beautiful Mintho, do you understand why my mind, so oppressed by the terrible fate awaiting my charges, has strayed momentarily from our delightful conversation?"

And just as the four Ford Falcons were leaving the traffic on Avenue San Martín and turning onto Álvarez Jonte Street, scented Mintho, trembling with indignation, replied.

"Ah, vindictive, unjustifiably jealous, idiotic, impotent Hades. Not only have you beleaguered me with servile advances, but envious of those virtues which you yourself do not possess, you are now trying to harm this romantic, lonely youth by wreaking horror and icy doom upon his magnanimous charges.

"Truly well-earned are the names given you: Hades the Fierce, the Hated, the Detested, the Bloodthirsty. Your sole pleasure is in cutting down magnificent lives, since you yourself are forever incapable of properly loving a fecund woman and engendering life in her.

"No one in this whole vast universe do I detest and disdain as much as you, O cold, cruel, barren, shivering Hades."

Upon hearing these words, Hermes, ever resourceful, fluttered his ashen nocturnal wings in a pacifying manner and spoke.

"Calm yourself, I beseech you, O beautiful Mintho, and desist in these ranting, futile, ignominious insults against unyielding Hades.

"It is commonly known that everyone, even the mighty Olympians, fears the devastating power of invincible Hades, and that no one, god or mortal, is so brave or foolhardy as to challenge him or sway him from his schemes."

And wily Hermes went on in a remorseful voice: "Let us therefore be resigned, O beloved Mintho, for you too, owing to your size and fragility, can do not a thing, and so we must be prepared to accept with resignation and fortitude the preemptory doom of our beneficent charges."

And just as Car 25, with The Goat inside, turned into the tree-lined street of Teodoro Vilardebó, the fragrant little mint plant, quivering with justified rage, uttered these heartfelt words:

"What you have just said, O handsome youth, is exactly so: everyone, gods and mortals alike, fears invincible

Hades, and even Zeus himself, with his awesome rages, prefers not to intervene in the schemes of his powerful brother.

"But I tell you truthfully and beg you to believe me, O youthful and fairest of strangers, if there's any creature in existence in the entire vast universe utterly unafraid of that loathsome dweller of Erebus, any who, on the contrary, feels uncontrollable contempt for him, that creature is this humble little mint plant upon which you are now perched.

"Hades is quite aware of this, and I'd even venture to say, amiable youth, that after his embarrassing failure and the unjust punishment inflicted upon me by his wife, he's the one who feels a certain deference toward me, combined with craven fear."

But as valiant Mintho was ranting on about terrible Hades, eager to besiege him with a fresh tirade of infamous insults, Hermes' ears happened to catch the terrified screech of an owl.

Realizing instantly that this could be none other than dauntless Athena performing the important mission he himself had so negligently abandoned, Hermes turned to Mintho and, heartstricken by gloomy presentiments, uttered these agitated words:

"Wait but a moment, O beautiful Mintho, for unless it be a false alarm, that cry of terror which has just issued from Athena's mouth means that fierce Hades is about to arrive, or that perhaps he has already arrived, at that dearly loved house at 2562 Teodoro Vilardebó."

And as beautiful Mrs. Giannello was passing her lips over Mr. Frugoni's coarse neck, and as Mr. Pasco was urgently asking to borrow a portfolio, Hermes the Messenger shook his nocturnal butterfly wings, soared upward and flew swiftly around the house in order to locate bronze Athena.

And he spied her above the front gate, in the guise of a nocturnal belfry owl, her wings outspread and her feathers all ruffled, as she issued hoots of anguished, lugubrious warning, for at last she'd spied the first of the four Ford Falcons approaching along Teodoro Vilardebó Street.

Swiftly Hermes flew toward the well-maintained lintel, and barely had he exchanged silent greetings with frightened Athena when a single glance toward one end of the street informed him of what had rightly aroused her alarm.

Four sleek Ford Falcons were speeding down the paved street, and hovering but a few feet over the car in front, disguised as a white filmy thread of devil's spittle, was dreaded Hades.

Numbed by icy Fear, dauntless Athena was powerless even to give warning to golden Aphrodite, who was still engaged in wafting her gentle breeze over impeccable Mr. Chávez and the entranced Polimnians.

And at that moment, as the sleek Ford Falcons were crossing Marcos Sastre Street, and barely seconds before the doors of the vehicles burst open, discharging their occupants, Hermes, in hasty flight, returned to the little concealed mint plant and uttered these words of alarm:

"O precious Mintho, who alone has brought consolation to my lonely heart, the bloody murder of those twelve magnificent comrades who were instrumental in leading me to you is now about to be committed.

"At this anguished moment, Hades' implacable emissaries are approaching the gate of this fine house. And flying above them, in the guise of devil's spittle, is Hades himself, the purpose of his arrival undoubtedly being to witness the punctual execution of his sinister commands."

Valiant Mintho, stirred by these words and the knowledge of Hades' loathsome proximity, addressed the stricken, frightened youth:

"O handsome youth, son of two happy Immortals, if it is indeed true, as you say, that Hades in person has just arrived at this tranquil site where the two of us, owing to your twelve splendid comrades, have miraculously met, then go without fear and hide behind the velvety leaves of yonder beautiful geranium, allowing me to talk alone to that vile and bungling god of darkness."

Then, in order to communicate her seductive presence to the unnamable Hades, Mintho rubbed her dark little stems against one another, and a fresh, inviting aroma of whispering forests wafted over Polimnia's entire well-established premises.

Whereupon, Hades, from his combat post a few feet above Car 25, in which The Goat was riding, experienced an instant awareness of Mintho's unmistakable enticing summons.

And still innocently disguised as a filmy thread of devil's spittle, he hastened toward the little plant so unjustly punished due to him, and attached his sticky filament to her uppermost stems.

And the soft twilight breeze rocked the taciturn god, and his gauzy body resembled a frayed white flag of truce waving conciliatorily on top of a mast.

But despite appearances, invincible Hades spoke up gruffly, addressing fragrant Mintho with these surly, impatient and uncouth words:

"By the guardian dog of my barren dwelling, how pleased I am, I vow, O aloof, elusive and indifferent Mintho, to find you of all people at this old house on Teodoro Vilardebó Street, and I would not be at all unwilling to hold a secret little chat with you, as we used to.

"But to tell the truth, I haven't much time to spare tonight, and bring no costly gifts as I did in the past, for you might as well know, O seductive nymph, that I've journeyed here from my vast abode simply to perform a most splendid, pitiless and bloody deed.

"Gaze yonder, and with your own eyes you'll be able to see my implacable emissaries, on the verge of halting their black, sleek Ford Falcons in front of that doomed residence. Already the safety catches on their sinister weapons have been released and the men are happily and faithfully preparing to fulfill my command.

"Tell me then quickly, little Mintho, what has made you release your arousing perfume, inviting me, for a change, to join you."

Lowering her little leaves with seductive grace, clever Mintho replied to those brusque words of his.

"O fearsome Hades, how I'd love to see where you're pointing, and to observe your most faithful purveyors of death with my own eyes.

"But as you can see, I've been transformed, as a result of your ridiculous advances—you don't mind recalling that, do you?—by your lawful wife into this little plant, and my eyes are unable to view whatever may be happening behind that balustrade.

"If you've no objection, O relentless violator of chaste maidens, I'll consult with dauntless Athena, whose unmistakable screech I heard but a moment ago, and implore her most earnestly to carry me in her hooked beak to the top of the front gate.

"From there, enjoying a comfortable vantage, I shall be able to admire the bloody deed of extermination which you and your fierce emissaries are about to perform.

"But in order, of course, to persuade chaste Athena to grant my request, I shall naturally have to inform her, without the omission of a single detail, the reason that led to my being so unjustly transformed from a lighthearted, agile underworld nymph into this immobilized, scented mint plant. You have no objection to that, do you, O mighty Hades?"

XXXV

"Ah, blissful fatigue, ah, sweet death. / Defeated at last, we shall succumb / to the dark stealthy chariot / of dawn's warm slumber. . . ." These, I believe, were the last four lines of text which all of us suspensefully listened to, holding our breath, gazing entranced toward the door, awaiting (and in my case, due to a very special frame of mind, almost detecting) something that sounded like footsteps in the dark corridor, and even a slight movement in the worn lock.

The end of the poem produced a brief, mysterious silence. I can unhesitatingly state that we actually seemed to be expecting a beautiful woman to make a radiant entrance, so caught up were we by charismatic Mr. Chávez, his spellbinding words and his yearning gestures. But after a few magical, interminable seconds, all of us, for equally inexplicable reasons, returned abruptly to reality, and the entire little room suddenly and unanimously burst into thunderous applause. This was then followed by a phenomenon indeed most unusual for us prior to that evening: an outcry of bravos and other sorts of exclamations more befitting, to tell the truth, an opera hall than a sedate little meeting room in Villa del Parque. Virtually all of us had risen to our feet, and many—Irene and myself included—were attempting to reach our president. Literally squeezed into the narrow aisle, we were on the brink of actually accomplishing this when Mr. Chávez, beckoned imperiously by his crippled lady friend, Miss Kisternmacher, leaped from the platform and practically raced toward her. Standing in front of her wheelchair, he gave her a loving, courtly bow, whereupon Miss Kisternmacher wound her languid arms around his neck and gazed at him with infinite tenderness as she uttered incomprehensible words in Sanskrit.

Irene and I decided to wait till some of the others had gone over first to our dear president to convey their congratulations, and then to do so ourselves, with greater ease. We moved aside from the dense group surrounding Mr. Chávez and Miss Kisternmacher's wheelchair. Almost all the members, in fact, were there, except for the unknown, rather lackadaisical young woman who had disappeared a while ago, without even bothering to say good-bye to the people in her row, and the only ones to remain slightly apart from the rest of the group were Irene and myself, Mastandrea, Zulema, and Mr. Pasco, who still had my portfolio on his knees. We were soon joined, however, by Miss Kisternmacher's elegant mother, who had already congratulated Mr. Chávez and was merely waiting, it seemed, to arrange something with Dora before departing.

While Irene and the rest of us were commenting on some of the details of this beautiful meeting, we approached Mr. Pasco and offered to escort him up to Mr. Chávez. But the author of folklóric verse capriciously declined, claiming that he needed to take some notes on a field laborer that had just occurred to him, lest the ideas be forgotten. From his pocket he took a pencil and one of those Braille cards, and using my portfolio as a support, he began scrawling something on the gray cardboard. Though it remained unclear how he'd be able later to read what he was writing, at least his urgent request for my portfolio was now clarified.

At that point, we approached stout Mr. Mastandrea, intending to help him as well, since both of his crutches were propped against the wall and it might be hard for him to stand up. But the moment he saw me, he began making urgent, unmistakable and rather grotesque signs for me to move away from him. At first, I didn't catch on, but everything soon became clear to me. He was obviously transacting matters of great importance with Zulema, for she kept gazing fixedly and solemnly at the parquet floor, and I couldn't help but overhear the following illuminating words from my impassioned rival in the sonnet: "Give me your answer next Wednesday, will you, dear?"

In order to avoid disturbing the good fellow, we drifted off toward the others and patiently waited for an opening so that we could get to Mr. Chávez. We were finally able to do so. Irene, with a slight flush embellishing her delicate face, endowing it, in my eyes, with incomparable grace, shook our president's hand, praised the classic structure of his poem, and concluded with some erudite allusions to Ovid, the Archpriest of Hita and, I believe, San Juan de la Cruz. I merely managed to stammer: "Extraordinary, Mr. Chávez," as I embraced him with sincere admiration.

Mastandrea, by now, had concluded his important transactions with Zulema, and they, too, approached Mr. Chávez to congratulate him. Unfortunately, I couldn't quite catch Mastandrea's indubitably encyclopedic congratulations. But I remember Zulema's sweet remark quite clearly, as well as her charming provincial accent. "Oh, how precious," she said, and Mr. Chávez thanked her emotionally and embraced her tightly for several prolonged moments.

The recital had reached its conclusion. The only thing actually remaining to be done was for us to draw up next Wednesday's list of poets. But unlike previous meetings, no one—not even Miss Kisternmacher's mother—seemed disposed to retreat from the room. It was as if each of us— surely for diverse reasons yet essentially out of the same vague and inexplicable desire to remain together—wanted to prolong, under any pretext, that warm gathering in which so many truly prodigious events had but recently transpired. We continued, therefore, commenting in detail on everything that had taken place that Wednesday, as well as improvising new, intriguing topics of conversation, or remarking simply, as a childish subterfuge, on how the fan made the atmosphere of the room so much more pleasant than that of the street. In truth, no one dared to sever that marvelous, rare spiritual communion which we had so beautifully and almost unintentionally achieved.

Miss Kisternmacher was chatting with Mrs. Giannello, Mr. Frugoni and young Romilio Sosa on her favorite topic: universal love. And behind them stood Dora, holding her large bunch of acacia, ready to propel her mistress's wheelchair, but then, suddenly, as if moved to the core by the theosophic remarks of the wise woman, or perhaps inspired by the hospitable, fraternal atmosphere pervading the room, she began plucking off sprigs of acacia flowers, and in an unforeseen gesture, one that was imbued with spontaneity and camaraderie, she began offering them, with a smile, to each of the members. Dora moved quickly and gracefully from one end of the room to the other, so that within a few moments, all of us, men and women alike, were each holding in our hands a little yellow spray. Some, like Mastandrea, promptly stuck it into a lapel. Mrs. Zimmerman and Zulema fastened theirs to their bosoms (one with the blossoms facing up and the other with the blossoms down). Beautiful Mrs. Giannello fastened hers gracefully amidst her tinted tresses and began, with waggish charm, imitating a gypsy dancer. Mr. Pasco, who had finally risen to his feet and returned my portfolio to me, slid the diminutive spray along his face with an expression of infinite pleasure. Irene and I exchanged blossoms and vowed to preserve them between the pages of a book throughout our entire lives, as a souvenir of that blessed evening of December 3, 1975.

We all felt truly content, serene, blissful. Mrs. Giannello

and Mr. Frugoni, having overcome their painful predicament thanks to the good offices of Mrs. Zimmerman and also—why not say so?—to the fraternal support they'd received from us, were smiling, brimming with good fortune, their eyes now gazing clearly toward the future. As for me, after the long, torturous moments produced by my timidity and lack of confidence toward Irene, I suddenly and miraculously found all my old difficulties resolved. Irene loved me. Irene, for some time, had been thinking of me. What else could I desire of life? We were united at last by a sweet, indolent joy, and perhaps it is no exaggeration to state that, despite our other obligations, we could have remained that way all night, chatting, commenting, recalling beautiful moments, making plans for the next meetings, feeling a surge of plenitude within ourselves, an unforeseen love related perhaps—I remember thinking—to that mystical, wondrous, universal love so fervently described by Miss Kisternmacher.

The one who displayed a certain urgency to leave, despite her gesture of solidarity in the distribution of flowers, was restless, exultant Dora. She may have had some pressing appointment, for she whispered something into her fiancé's ear, glanced at her watch for the time—it was already a quarter to ten—and signaled to Miss Kisternmacher to hurry up (a signal, to tell the truth, not especially appropriate for a lady to give in company). Miss Kisternmacher, an understanding woman, smiled and responded—through signals as well—that Dora wait just a moment, and then began bidding farewell to her friends. As I recall, she was taking leave of Miss Zimmerman when the screech of a nearby owl reached our room. All of us, I must confess, were a trifle taken aback, and Mr. Mastandrea, with his usual bad timing, did not waste this opportunity to remind us of the bad-luck omen usually associated with an owl's screech. Mr. Frugoni, who was knowledgeable in country ways, pursued the theme, more in order to keep talking than out of any genuine interest, and he remarked on how nice owls were and how helpful also in the cultivation of fields, and that at the next meeting, coincidentally, he was planning to present a brief, illustrated poem in which one of those little white owls that you see on posts appeared. Mr. Frugoni was corrected by erudite Miss Kisternmacher, who delicately explained to him that judging from the sound of the cry, the place, and particularly the present hour, the creature that had just been heard was not one of those little barn owls mentioned in his poem, but undoubtedly a larger, darker specimen, known as a belfry owl (she mentioned its name in Latin), that probably had its nest nearby. Another screech sounded, louder and more prolonged, leading Miss Kisternmacher to confirm her classification with absolute certainty. She went on to elaborate that in all likelihood some creature, perhaps a cat, was roaming near the bird's nest, inasmuch as this particular screech tended to be emitted only in the presence of danger. Now, indeed, her vast zoological knowledge was conclusively demonstrated.

Mrs. Giannello, seated cozily upon the platform, was meanwhile performing her duties as recording secretary: she, Mrs. Zimmerman and Mr. Chávez were hastily drawing up the list of readers for the next Wednesday. Mastandrea was the first to volunteer. In accordance with our institution's practice, he provided his first and last names, plus the titles and approximate length of the poems he'd be reciting. After him came a rejuvenated Mr. Frugoni, and immediately after him, an eager and fecund Mr. Pasco. Irene was scrutinizing me intently. I made a sudden and prompt decision, and, in view of my natural disposition, a hazardous one. Stepping up to Mrs. Giannello, and in the calmest voice I could muster from my constricted throat, I asked to have my own name included on the list. When she smilingly inquired, with pencil in mouth, about the titles of my compositions, I gazed at Irene and replied: " 'To a Dream Converted into Reality.' A triptych of sonnets." I was, of course, referring to my as yet uncompleted work. No one, I believe, managed to detect my nervousness.

Mrs. Zimmerman, in a loud and half-joking tone, declared that she couldn't stand having such a masculine preponderance at next Wednesday's meeting, and without further ado, virtually forced Irene and Mrs. Giannello to be included on the list.

Dora now began propelling Miss Kisternmacher's wheelchair toward the exit. Mrs. Zimmerman took Mr. Pasco's arm. Mr. Chávez extended farewell embraces to Mr. Frugoni and Mrs. Giannello. Young Romilio, ever concerned with the upkeep of our headquarters, had gone to turn off the lights and close the doors. He returned to the room and had, in fact, just disconnected the floor fan, when we heard from very nearby the loud, disagreeable screech of tires.

XXXVI

And it was precisely as Miss Kisternmacher was expounding upon the two different classifications of screeching owls, and explaining most eruditely that the hoot that had just been heard belonged to a large, beautiful belfry owl, that barren Hades, perspiring profusely for the first time in his life and trembling in ill-concealed dread, remonstrated with the delicate, fragrant mint plant:

"I vow by the countless souls perambulating in my vast abode, and by the incorruptible boatman who has transported each of them at the proper time across the swampy Acheron, that I see no need, O disrespectful little nymph, for you to divulge to any of those indolent, prating Olympians certain best-forgotten events pertaining strictly to my private life.

"I command you, therefore, to remain here in this well-protected, moist corner of the courtyard and not to ask either Athena or any other Immortal to transport you elsewhere. You are absolutely forbidden to wag your indefatigable tongue, but are to wait here patiently until my mission is complete. And then I shall return, and we shall resume discussion once more of this disagreeable matter. Is that clear, Mintho?"

Responding to these brusque words with feigned surprise and childish rage, Mintho brushed away some nonexistent tears and cleverly gave Hades her reply.

"O mighty Hades, why do you take such advantage of my size and weakness to mistreat me as you do? Didn't you but a moment ago invite me to admire in ecstatic contemplation the doings of your fierce emissaries? Are you perhaps ashamed of this poor nymph and disinclined to allow her to join the defeated Olympians in observing with awe your prodigious feat?

"Ah, how clearly do I see that you've quickly forgotten the flaming love you once professed toward me! Well, so be it, O powerful deity, but I can truthfully say that your insulting forgetfulness does not in any way mitigate my ardent desire to watch you in action.

"And so I must tell you that, despite your cruel indifference, I shall indeed be observing your memorable, bloody deed, on my own, from the top of that venerable lintel.

"But since I am merely a plant and unable to climb up there on my own, I shall ask assistance of obliging, dauntless Athena. It is futile, O Hades, to try to conceal anything from me."

And from its perch at the uppermost tip of the fragrant mint, the frazzled thread of devil's spittle trembled with rage, and irate Hades blurted out:

"O stubborn, obdurate, disobedient nymph! How can I explain to you and make you understand that you are not to speak to any of the contemptible Olympians?

"The order that I've issued is quite clear: You are to remain where you are, without opening your dangerous mouth. Ask anything else of me, and I promise to grant it at once.

"But by the three heads of my fierce dog, do not ask permission, O tattling Mintho, to speak to that frigid, gossipy Athena, for I know all too well what the subject of your conversation will be, and that my heart cannot bear."

And since the words "ask anything else of me" were precisely those which astute Mintho had been hoping to hear, she stirred her little leaves with enchanting grace, exhaling as she did a fresh, intoxicating perfume, and then, still appearing to sulk, responded quickly to faltering Hades.

"Very well, O implacable Hades, I shall, in the end, as always, obey your sovereign will. Sad and forlorn, I'll remain in this distant, solitary corner, resigned to not seeing you, or engaging in conversation with anyone, be it god, mortal, winged insect, leafy plant or fluttering bird.

"But since you have so kindly invited me to request something of you in exchange for the harsh sacrifice so strictly imposed, allow me, though shedding profuse tears of disappointment, to humbly accept your offer and to frame a small request. You do not mind granting that to me, do you, O powerful deity?"

Somewhat reassured, for the moment at least, by tattling Mintho's promise to observe a discreet silence regarding his intimate life, Hades, ever shivering and with ears focused on the motors of the nearby Ford Falcons, then spoke:

184

"I agree. Make your request, little one, and I shall grant it at once. But, by all the Keres and Moirai combined, hurry and say what you wish to say, for the appointed hour of my bloody revenge is near, and I have scant time to waste.

"Already my beloved Goat has cocked the safety latch of his loud Ithaka, the four black vehicles—I can hear them from here—are about to come to a halt in front of that odious residence at 2562 Teodoro Vilardebó, all the indispensable elements of those frequent and unpunishable kidnappings are in the hands of my capable emissaries. And in fact, I ought to be there myself to oversee the fatal deed.

"Twelve consecutive voyages are in store for my tireless boatman, for there are twelve occupants in that blue-wallpapered room presently engaged in drawing up a pointless list of poets for a nonexistent forthcoming Wednesday; instead, they will, on this very night, be transported to my icy realm. So speak up, little Mintho, for I am urgently pressed."

And as indefatigable José María Pulicicchio was giving beautiful Mrs. Giannello his first and last names to be included on her list of poets for Wednesday, December 10, 1975, and as Hermes, concealed behind a velvet-leafed geranium plant, was listening attentively to that entire conversation, the clever little mint plant at last proposed to bloodlusting Hades her carefully weighed request.

"I shall indeed speak up, O impatient Hades, since that is your command. And, though still tearful over your unloving manner toward me and your shabby treatment, this is the request I shall resign myself to make. Listen attentively and heed me well. And, above all, remember that you must comply at once, as you have promised.

"You are surely aware, O invincible Hades, that in the course of my long sojourn in this well-tended courtyard, I've grown quite attached to several of the kindly occupants in that blue, illumined room, for unlike certain crass Immortals, they've always, in one way or another, looked after me.

"Plump, cheerful Zulema never neglected to sprinkle an abundance of water upon my fragrant leaves and delicate roots. Able, diligent Romilio would frequently pull out oppressive and destructive weeds that were growing near me.

"Elegant Mr. Chávez fervently defended this little strip of moist soil surrounding the paved courtyard whenever someone impulsively sought to place some horrible cement benches upon it.

"And beautiful Mrs. Giannello, who resembles a goddess, displayed on more than one occasion a fragrant spray of mint amidst her tinted tresses.

"Circumspect José María Pulicicchio did not neglect to mention me in his sonnet to gentle spring. And even the ineffable, chaste Irene Bengoechea generally carries in her handbag some white, heart-shaped mint candies, which she offers to the refined Polimnians.

"In short, each of the members of this well-governed society has, through the years, shown me delicate and memorable consideration.

"And so I beseech you to desist from this bloody mission you're about to perform, and to allow the twelve mortals whom you've condemned—perhaps with justification, I shan't deny—to continue pursuing the hazards of life.

"Allow them, despite the displeasure this may cause you, to persist in cultivating their foolish vocations in that old house at 2562 Teodoro Vilardebó. That, O mighty Hades, is my request. Now you will grant it to me, will you not?"

And just as Dora was pushing Miss Kisternmacher's wheelchair rather quickly toward the door, Hades darkly uttered these dreadful words.

"No! I will not accede to this absurd request of yours, nagging, opportunistic Mintho! You may as well know, once and for all, the motive behind the bloodthirsty revenge which I've been plotting for days. It is all due to the violent death of one of my dearest purveyors of souls, namely the illustrious General Jorge Estéban Cáceres Monié, whose murder took place in Entre Ríos, a province abounding in birds.

"Yonder, in my shaded realm, all preparations are complete. Charon has skillfully caulked his much-used boat. Those souls who were, during their lifetime, faithful servants of mine are already waiting impatiently, since I myself have announced the imminent arrival of those twelve nefarious, vile subversives.

"On this very eve, they will be crossing the black waters of the swampy Acheron. And since all of them are now assembled at the same time inside that little room, the task should prove to be quite easy for the able parapolicemen entrusted with kidnapping them, first, and then torturing them and riddling them with bullets. And so, luckless Mintho, you must ask for something else. But speak quickly."

XXXVII

"Hey, this is it, ain't it?"

"That house over there, the one with the guard."

"Yeah, and then people bitch about Security not working."

"It's a perfect hideout."

"Even has a people's jail."

"Cut the bullshit."

"Park over here."

"I'll go in shooting, what the hell."

"No, man, the arrest comes first."

"Whadaya mean?"

"I mean cool it. There ain't gonna be no resistance."

"How d'ya know?"

"The chief is real sure. He said so, didn't he?"

"Okay, but still, you can never be too sure."

"If you're all hung up on that, you better stay in the car. We gotta do things today just like they're spelled out."

"Same baloney all the time. Nobody gives a fart about the risks we slobs gotta take."

"Did ya get paid yet?"

"Payday's on Friday."

"A guy's dough ain't worth a piss nowadays."

"The orders we got are real clear: dig 'em out, then stick 'em in the cars. Three in each. The fun comes later."

"We'll see. We're gonna dump 'em at Ezeiza, not far from the airport. Right?"

"Yep."

"Whenever you give the word, Chief."

"Cars 41, 70 and 72: exercise caution. I don't want no screw-ups."

"What if they resist, Chief?"

"Then we'll pump 'em with bullets, of course. But they won't resist. All this, you know, is because Cáceres Monié got killed. A warning to everyone, that's what this is. Just evening up the scores, that's what we're doing tonight."

"Twelve, right?"

"Twelve, dammit, I told you already. You deaf or something? Get behind Car 41."

"Shall I stop the traffic?"

"You don't have to. Wait for me to get out. Cars 41, 70 and 72: commence operation when I get out. Everyone ready?"

"Can you see 25?"

"Yeah, I see it from here. When the chief gets out, so will we. All set?"

"All set."

XXXVIII

And desperately realizing that she was wasting an opportunity to save the lives of her handsome suitor's twelve magnanimous friends, the sensitive nymph, though suffering inwardly, played her last foresighted hand on their behalf.

"O mighty Hades, are twelve mortals the price exacted by your harsh vengeance? Very well. If that is what you have decided, I accept it. But why must my kind friends be the victims of your fury? Why do those who've lavished so much attention upon me necessarily have to be the ones to enter your icy realm this very night?

"Is it not possible for you to choose twelve other souls? Some distant place, perhaps. In the interior province of Córdoba, for example, you might find twelve other mortal enemies of yours, all conveniently assembled, as these are, beneath one roof so that your beloved parapolice need waste no time tracking the streets in search of them.

"And if for some unforeseeable reason you fail to locate exactly twelve, the number you're so stubbornly determined to slay, aren't there enough mortals in Rosario or La Plata whom you mortally hate to round out your appointed quota of revenge?

"Please grant what I'm asking of you in order to save my friends and without hindrance to your own plans, and rest assured that my gratitude will prove most gratifying to you. Tell me, O implacable Hades, what is your reply?"

Indifferent to Mintho's grievous tears, grim Hades angrily detached his sticky, buoyant filament from the slender little stem and answered in a deafening and ominous voice:

"I've already told you no, disrespectful and persistent Mintho, and command you not to insist. Neither you nor anyone else will sway me from my ineluctable schemes! And stop pestering me, for I'm about to leave at this very moment to execute them at once."

And Hades, in the filmy guise of devil's spittle, began drifting away from the little plant in order to resume his strategic observation post, whereupon valiant Mintho, seized by uncontainable fury, spoke up:

"O false, perjuring, stupid, impotent Hades. Only a moment ago you promised to satisfy any request of mine, and now you treacherously refuse to keep the promise you're obliged to keep!

"Do what your icy heart dictates, and waste not a single second of your time listening to me.

"But listen carefully to what I'm about to tell you: Inasmuch as you have broken your recent vow to me, I shall not, like a fool, remain bound by mine.

"Thus I want you to know that this humble little chastised plant will not remain silent. Of that, O Hades, I assure you.

191

"There will be mortals and Immortals aplenty, satyrs, nymphs, naiads, centaurs and small winged gossiping creatures, who will be informed by my very own lips of what did happen—or, rather, what failed to happen—by the roots of that murmuring poplar.

"Go then to your task, without wasting time, for I, too, am in haste to fulfill mine. Good-bye, O mighty Hades, until we meet again."

Confronted by these menacing words, the solitary dweller of Erebus, his hovering body trembling with terror and his voice punctuated with absurd moans, replied.

"Oh, cruel, extortionate Mintho! What terrible means you do employ to attain your capricious ends! You know, O pitiless one, that I'd die of humiliation yonder in my dark realm if any of those indolent Olympians were to learn my innermost secret!

"Do not behave so spitefully toward me, fair Mintho. Has it not occurred to you that if mortals were to lose their respect for me and jeer at me in frivolous conversation, the entire universe and its laws would be in great disarray?

"No one, then, O heedless maiden, would fear irreparable death, and the memorable deeds of men would lose the supreme value incurred by the risk of death.

"Ah, little Mintho, I'd like very much at this point to grant this request of yours in payment for your precious silence, and as you've so sensibly suggested, to exchange those twelve doomed mortals for an equal number of inhabitants of Córdoba, Rosario and La Plata.

"But, sadly, that is now impossible: the intricate machinery for my revenge has been set in motion, and everything is proceeding in accordance with a well-laid plan.

"Following a well-timed though rather stupid accusation, every police move has been skillfully manipulated by me and has unfolded today, step by step, into this beautiful parapolice procedure.

"No one, not even the swiftest of Olympians, could manage in one split second to reach a certain secret office, whose exact location it is senseless for me at this point to indicate, and from which the order to suspend the murder would have to be issued to my well-loved Goat.

"Ask something else of me, gentle Mintho, and I vow, by the illustrious sires of my black stallions, to grant it to you."

And then, speaking very loudly in order to assure that her words be heard by the youth hidden behind the velvet-leafed geranium, clever Mintho asked her question.

"Well, since there isn't enough time, O Hades, to transmit a message of this sort, nor anyone, besides, who can transmit it, tell me, if you don't mind, merely to satisfy my feminine curiosity, what the text of such a lifesaving message might be and the exact place where it would have to be delivered?"

And just as diligent Romilio Sosa was turning off the lights and closing the doors at 2562 Teodoro Vilardebó, grim Hades, in a much-beleaguered tone, replied.

"I've no objection to answering your futile questions, gracious Mintho, for that will prove to you that ill will is not what prevents me from exchanging those twelve luckless mortals for twelve others, as you so kindly request.

"But please, I beg you. Do not allow your anger to blind you. Do not reward my sincere attitude with spiteful retaliation. Remember, you are to tell no one what only you and I know.

"The fact is, O delicious nymph, that even if there existed an Immortal as swift as thought itself (which is clearly impossible), in order for him to be able to reach a certain Security Headquarters, at 1425 Moreno Street, he would need to be leaving this shaded courtyard in the time it takes me to finish this brief sentence.

"Then, once there, he'd have to be transformed into an Urgent Phone Call and to say only one thing: Suspend Operation Teodoro Vilardebó.

"One of my most efficient servants, who's in constant radio contact with The Goat, would receive the call and would transmit the immediate order to him to suspend the operation, which is now virtually under way.

"But since everything that I've just told you is totally unfeasible, and since there is no one in existence who could possibly transmit this message so quickly, I repeat, O Mintho, resign yourself to the inexorable end of these twelve doomed souls, and make some other request."

But lo and behold, diligent Hermes, having been alerted by clever Mintho, was listening from behind the geranium to Hades' unwary and illuminating words.

And as Hades kept talking, Hermes, transformed once again into the graceful Olympian Messenger, did not delay a single moment, even to inform Aphrodite and Athena, but flew swiftly toward Security Headquarters on Moreno Street.

And gentle, fragrant Mintho saw him ascend from behind the geranium, fleet and resplendent in his beautiful winged hat and golden sandals, and she immediately realized that her handsome, lonely suitor was none other than divine Hermes.

But her tender heart did not grieve on this account, and on the contrary she greatly rejoiced, for with a woman's wisdom she knew that in time, and with God's help, she would contrive to tame the seductive, deceitful Messenger and transform him into a faithful husband and the loving father of numerous progeny.

And Hades, too, saw the ascent of the winged Messenger, but only later did he realize that he had been most cleverly tricked by incorrigible Mintho.

And though Hades was bursting with hatred, restored in a trice to his true nature, his hands fiercely clenching his black whip, he found himself compelled to restrain his terrible impulses, for Mintho's presence was a silent reminder that she would know exactly how to proceed if he did not.

And flying as fast as he'd ever flown in all his life, the winged messenger streaked across the Buenos Aires sky like a luminous unidentified flying object.

And before one could finish a sentence, he arrived, and halted on the guarded roof of Security Headquarters on Moreno Street.

Then, proceeding in accordance with the words he'd just overheard, Hermes converted himself instantly into an Urgent Phone Message and sounded the bell near the radio speaker where one of Hades' brutal servants was in communication with Car 25, the vehicle commanded by the murderous Goat.

And Hermes, in the firm voice of a division commander, his tone much like Chief Inspector Guso's, contacted the brutal radio communications officer and whispered into his ear merely the following words: "Suspend Operation Teodoro Vilardebó."

And the radio communications officer, with surprise and disgust, communicated that same message to The Goat, Hades' bloodlusting servant: "Suspend Operation Teodoro Vilardebó," but on his own, he added: "For the time being."

And just as the brakes of Cars 25, 41, 70 and 72 brought them to a sinister screeching halt, and as The Goat's hairy hand was reaching out to open the door so that, at last, he could embark upon that long-awaited gory mission, he heard those terrible words emanating unexpectedly from his well-tuned radio: "Suspend Operation Teodoro Vilardebó—for the time being."

The Goat, not even bothering to cover his own speaker, reacted to the awful meaning of that statement with a volley of horrible oaths against the government, God, and superior security, as well as the loving mothers of numerous functionaries.

Then, in a great rage, he issued the order to leave, whereupon the four shiny black Ford Falcons, with their crew of skilled murderers, departed and, accompanied by an ominous wail of sirens, traversed, once again, the boundless city.

XXXIX

"Goddam it."

"This is a disgrace."

"Some helluva nerve."

"They'll hear from us, those sons of bitches. It ain't fair. Those shitheads ain't gonna fuck me again. Keep driving."

"Where do we go now?"

"Back to the garage. Bunch of lousy rats."

"What do you think it's all about, Chief?"

"Orders from the top. Didn't you hear, you dummy? I swear I'll get that shithead Guso."

"Was it Guso?"

"Who else?"

"Strange, ain't it?"

"Not so strange."

"What did you say, Chief?"

"Nothing. I got my own thoughts."

"All that work pissed away for nothing."

"Yeah, nothing. Attention, Cars 41, 70 and 72: returning to garage."

"Did you hear?"

"Sounds like an order from the top."

"Who do those fags think they're dealing with?"

"That's how the whole country works."

"No respect for nothing these days."

"What respect can you expect?"

"The chief must be fucking mad."

"You know what? We shouldn't of paid attention to them."

"Oh, sure, and then what? Go fight city hall."

"Get that Fiat out of my way."

"Open up, goddam it. Open it, I say."

"Strange that the chief . . ."

"I wonder if somebody mixed in."

"Some punk soldier boy."

"Who knows? Hand me a butt."

XL

"Ah, these youngsters, these youngsters nowadays," exclaimed Mr. Chávez, wagging his head tolerantly, whereupon Miss Kisternmacher added that it wasn't their fault, but that in a world bereft of *samadhi,* young people lacked true spiritual guides.

I preferred to hold my silence. But I remember unwittingly comparing my own sad, lonely youth (filled with dreams, anxieties, unfulfilled loves, and long walks in order to save a few coins) with today's loose, freethinking youth drawn irresistibly to violent emotions and danger.

I was just about to comment on this to Irene when Mrs. Zimmerman, who was ready to leave, suddenly turned back, took my arm and said to me: "Do you know why they run around? Do you know why they take their parents' cars and make mincemeat out of them? Rebellion, my dear, nothing more than rebellion. And it's all because of their irrational upbringing, what did I tell you?"

Mastandrea, apparently in disagreement with Mrs. Zimmerman's point of view, and puffing from the heat and the recent scare, declared that they were all simply "a band of loafers" who should be put in jail, and "skip the psychology."

Indeed, this rather spontaneous, totally unintellectual outburst from incorrigible Mastandrea provoked general hilarity, and in a way served to reduce the tension that had been briefly aroused among us by an admittedly insignificant event, a childish prank, let us say: the nearby disagreeable screeching of brakes.

No one mentioned the little incident again. There was, I'd almost say, a kind of tacit agreement, after Mastandrea's glorious remark, not to bring up the subject in any way. It was as if those noisy, shrill sounds which assailed our cozy room were representative, so to speak, of a violent, brutish, aggressive world bereft of beauty, lurking perhaps in the immediate vicinity of our dear Polimnia but with which we neither had nor wished to have anything in common. And so we, very promptly and quite effortlessly, dismissed the matter totally.

We continued wending our way into the street, bidding each other fond farewell until the following Wednesday. Irene smilingly showed me her sprig of acacia pressed between the pages of her spiral notebook. The sound of a piano drifted forth from a nearby house. The night was warm and balmy. Through the chinaberry trees you could see a beautiful diaphanous, starry sky.

XLI

And Hades, cracking his fierce whip upon the sleek backs of his horses, withdrew in a rage from 2562 Teodoro Vilardebó, abandoning for the time being his twelve long-coveted prisoners.

And Aphrodite, Athena and the diligent Messenger Hermes decided that the mission which had wrested them from Olympus and brought them to the well-established quarter of Villa del Parque had drawn to its end.

And so they, too, like barren Hades, withdrew from 2562 Teodoro Vilardebó and, flying swiftly, reached within seconds the summit of Olympus, with its plumage of clouds.

And from a high, solitary peak of Olympus, the three Immortals watched helplessly as irascible Hades proceeded in his brutal roundup of individuals to substitute for the twelve rescued Polimnians, covering in his hunt the entire vast territory of the Argentine Republic.

And they saw Hades gnashing his teeth as he headed toward the interior province of Córdoba, where the shadowy deity had other emissaries, akin in every respect to The

Goat and his brutal subordinates, who were performing the death mission which, as a result of clever Mintho's intervention, they had been unable to accomplish in that house under surveillance in Villa del Parque.

And the Olympians mournfully watched the ominous parapolicemen of Liberators Commando of America: Cáceres Monié Squad rapidly taking off in their Ford Falcons and driving to a spacious home on Hipódromo Avenue and Tacuarí.

Entering violently, with merciless blows, foul insults and powerful, menacing weapons, they handcuffed, gagged and sequestered in their black automobiles twelve students who were occupying the house.

But neither Hades nor his parapolice emissaries were able to get their required number of twelve victims, for three of the occupants of the beautiful residence on Hipódromo Avenue and Tacuarí managed to escape the brutal kidnapping and to elude the skilled murderers.

And so, furiously cracking his swirling whip, implacable Hades was forced to head for the industrial city of Rosario, and then to the well-planned city of La Plata, in order to complete in those two cities the roundup of the twelve victims exacted by his revenge.

And in Rosario there were other sinister parapolicemen, counterparts of The Goat, who kidnapped a union delegate from the Acindar steel factory, and still other parapolicemen who kidnapped, handcuffed and gagged a married couple who lived in the beautiful city of La Plata.

And from their inaccessible Olympian peak, the three Olympians witnessed how twelve sequestered individuals, who, as a result of clever Mintho's intervention, were substituting for the designated Polimnians, got driven in speeding automobiles toward prearranged outdoor sites.

And with eyes blindfolded, they were forced from the vehicles on out-of-the-way roads and pasture grounds, where they were then harassed, savagely beaten, tortured, and in the end mercilessly slain and riddled with countless high-caliber bullets.

And a shudder of fear pierced the three Olympians, for they instantly thought of the horrible ending that had been in store for the twelve occupants of the house on Teodoro Vilardebó, had clever Mintho not intervened.

XLII

(December 4, 1975)

Further details: Córdoba, Argentina. Today, at approximately 8:30, an anonymous phone call informed Security forces that they would be able to find four dead bodies seven kilometers along the road to Molinos Dam. The report was confirmed by police authorities upon arrival at the aforementioned site. On a dirt road running parallel to Route 5, four corpses were stretched out, face down, hands and feet tightly bound. Said bodies revealed numerous impacts from high-caliber bullets. It was further noted that they had been previously subjected to brutal punishment.

As preliminary investigations on the macabre discovery were being made, the owner of a brickworks located in the Piedra vicinity—an unpopulated area with a road edged by low shrubs—disclosed that he'd found five other bodies. These, as was subsequently confirmed, revealed the same features as the other four—that is, numerous bullet wounds, signs of torture, and extremities tightly bound.

Police authorities did not conceal their initial bafflement over this fresh outbreak of violence (particularly in light of the number of victims). Police technicians estimated that an operation of this nature would have had to require the mobilization of numerous individuals. Furthermore, the fact of not having lately received any accusations related to kidnappings or disappearances made preliminary investigation difficult.

At one point when all speculation at the investigation desk seemed plausible, local newspapers received an early-morning private communication from a group that goes under the name of Liberators Commando of America: Cáceres Monié Squad, giving the details of the multiple slayings and imputing subversive activities to the victims. The communication gave clear indication that the occurrence was intended as a retaliation for General Cáceres Monié's death.

According to what could be ascertained, the victims—nine young students, nearly all of them foreigners—lived in a luxurious house located on Hipódromo Avenue and Tacuarí, in the residential Botanical Quarter of this provincial capital. Said residence was raided on the night of Wednesday, December 3, by a group of heavily armed individuals driven in several vehicles.

According to one version, three of the residents in the house had managed to escape when the band of strangers who kidnapped and killed their companions arrived. The victims' names are as yet not officially known. More news will follow.

Further details: Córdoba. Urgent. Seven of the nine victims in the Córdoba slaying seem to have been unofficially identified. They appear to be: Ricardo Rubén Haro, Argentine, 20 years old; Luis Radney Salinas Burgos, Bolivian, 21 years old; Luis Villalba Álvarez, Bolivian, 26 years old; Alfredo Saavedra Alfaro, Bolivian, 24 years old; Jorge Raúl Rodríguez Sotomayor, Peruvian, 29 years old; Américo Ricardo Apertile, Argentine, 21 years old; and Jaime Sánchez, Argentine, 21 years old. More news will follow.

———

206

Further details: Rosario, Sante Fe province. The body of Francisco Rodríguez, 28 years old, was found in this city on Route 9. The murdered man, who showed numerous bullet wounds, was employed by the Acindar factory.

La Plata, Buenos Aires province. The bodies of a woman and a man, approximately 40 years of age, were found in an open lot in Berisso. The victims, whose names are as yet unknown, revealed numerous high-caliber bullet wounds, had their hands tied behind them and wide bands of adhesive tape on their mouths. According to unconfirmed sources, both the man and the woman had been kidnapped a few hours earlier by a group of heavily armed individuals who, pretending to be policemen, had burst into their home.

These nine victims bring the number of dead bodies found by the police in the Argentine Republic in the last 24 hours to twelve. Further details will follow.

XLIII

Aphrodite, her heart repelled by the spectacle of that gruesome slaughter and her beautiful cheeks moistened by hot and anguished tears, was the first of those atop Olympus to speak.

"Ah, cursed, vengeful, fierce, bloodlusting Hades! Now you can indeed be proud of your terrible deed!

"Bereaved mortals may still rightly continue to refer to you as Hades the Omnipotent, the Cruel, the Invincible, the Insatiable.

"For only on condition that your wretched appetite be sated by twelve other victims did you give your consent, though temporarily, to allow the twelve magnanimous Polimnians to continue savoring the warm, joyful multifarious breath of life.

"But as always, O implacable Hades, there is not one single ambrosia-imbibing Olympian who can rightfully boast of having obtained your temporary pardon, through either threats or pleas.

"Only gentle, fragrant Mintho has succeeded—through arguments totally unknown to us mighty Immortals—to deflect your bloodlusting hand even for the time being.

"How long, O shadowy, barren Hades, shall we allow you to use your vast power, time and again, in bringing all those splendid mortals, conceived and reared only for sweetest love, to your cold abode?

"What inadmissible cowardliness prevents us Immortals from all rising in rebellion and plunging you forever into the depths of Erebus, thus gaining for desirable men and fair-bosomed women the divine gift of immortality?"

But indomitable Athena, shaking her tresses from her gilded helmet, interrupted Aphrodite and rebuked her sternly.

"O weepy, impulsive Aphrodite, why are you lamenting in a manner so unbefitting an Immortal?

"Why all those harsh and futile imprecations directed against that invincible god who has been empowered since the beginning of time to cut down at will the lives of all mortals?

"Rejoice that we have contrived, for the present, to deflect Hades' hand, since it is an illusion to imagine that those men and women whom both of us protect, though for different reasons, will be generously granted life by Hades.

"And, in your hasty judgment, you might do well to consider that though it was a nymph, clever Mintho, who contrived through mysterious means to obtain an unforeseen pardon from relentless Hades, it was an Immortal, diligent Hermes, whose cunning reasoning persuaded Mintho to proceed as she did.

"And it was you, O beautiful, seductive Aphrodite, with that ridiculous titillation of love that you scattered profusely from the twirling blades of the fan, who induced womanizing Hermes to approach fragrant Mintho so winningly and to engage her in fruitful conversation.

"And was it not perhaps I who, transformed into a screeching belfry owl, announced the arrival of sinister Hades and of his fierce emissaries?

"And were my vigilant screeches not responsible, after all, for providing Mintho with ample time to contrive a clever plan and, after calm and prudent reflection, to devise arguments—to us unknown—for prompting Hades to restrain his destructive hand, and to force him into furious retreat from that dear house on Teodoro Vilardebó?

"The lives of our protégés have thus been spared, O Aphrodite, but not indefinitely, as you so rashly expressed as your desire, for that would be an utterly naive and futile expectation. Our mutual efforts, however, have at least achieved the temporary retreat of Hades.

"And at long last, the awaited moment for each of us to fulfill our plans for those splendid mortals has arrived.

"Which means, O unrepentant rival of mine, naked, resplendent daughter of Uranus, that from this moment on, each of us separately will employ her individual powers to enable the irreproachable Polimnians to proceed, in keeping with our own particular divine interests.

"The pact we made under oath while threatened by implacable Hades is therefore severed from this moment on, O scheming, seductive, fretful Aphrodite.

"You may return to your unscrupulous intrigues, your sharp arrows poisoned with desire, your palpitations, blushes, languid glances, caresses, fornications, silly words and tender, insipid little love poems.

"For we Immortals are all well aware that those petty, insignificant and secondary matters are the only ones to arouse your frivolous interest.

"And as for myself, I shall once again engage, as I always have, in the rigorous pursuit of the intellect, war, manual labor and virtue, all worthy occupations for an Immortal who sprang without maternal intervention from tempestuous Zeus."

And as proof of her acceptance of the broken pact, golden Aphrodite turned her beautiful back upon Athena and, released from all bonds, diverted her flashing gaze with renewed interest toward the old house on Teodoro Vilardebó, which was completely empty since it was now half past eleven, close to midnight, and the magnanimous occupants had all departed.

But lo and behold, divine Aphrodite spied Mintho in a dark corner of the tiled courtyard, and the nymph was shedding profuse tears of love on behalf of a handsome, deceitful Immortal.

For the unscrupulous Messenger, having gotten what he wanted from her through her astutely proposed scheme, had promptly forgotten all his tender avowals of love and had heedlessly abandoned the fragrant little mint plant.

And so Aphrodite, greatly indignant over Hermes' wicked behavior, and filled with compassion for enamored

Mintho, ordered one of her many personal servants to shoot a sharp arrow impregnated with unrestrainable love into Hermes' womanizing heart.

And Hermes, pierced straight in the heart, suddenly recalled the tender little mint plant and felt an immediate desire to return to the shaded courtyard at 2562 Teodoro Vilardebó in order to be at her side and to resume that amorous conversation which had been so absurdly interrupted.

And from the heights of golden Olympus, Aphrodite smiled as she observed how Hermes flew swiftly toward the tree-lined quarter of Villa del Parque and how he stopped at Teodoro Vilardebó Street, and reappeared with his winning ways before forlorn Mintho.

And Aphrodite also observed how Mintho, with ancestral skill, ensnared the winged Messenger in her subtle, fragrant net, eliciting from him, without even asking, a vow of eternal fidelity before both of them happily surrendered to the pleasurable fray of love, all of which gladdened Aphrodite's heart exceedingly.

But as it happened, Zeus' indomitable daughter, chaste and warlike Athena, was also gazing foresightedly toward Teodoro Vilardebó and the surrounding vicinity, in order to guide her magnanimous charges toward pursuits of a more serious nature, and therefore more to her liking.

Glancing downward into the shadows of Marcos Sastre Street, Athena was shocked to see Irene Bengoechea, her irreproachable charge, a woman adept in rigorous intellectual pursuits, on the verge of succumbing to that dreadful nonsense of love, and this due to the bold and ardent advances made by José María Pulicicchio.

The temerity of that excellent installment loan manager, a member in good standing of Polimnia, was approaching the most dangerous of limits, as indomitable Athena, with unconcealable displeasure, could well observe.

For under the pretext of taking a leisurely look around the dark garden, where last Wednesday they'd encountered a fabulous, romantic firefly, Pulicicchio was obviously drawing closer and closer to chaste, unwary Irene Bengoechea, his evident intention being to kiss her.

And so Athena, once again, decided to resort to her virtually infallible emissaries, Timidity and Indecision, so that they might instantly pierce José María Pulicicchio's tumultuous, impassioned heart and curb his enslaving impulses.

And precisely at that moment when beautiful, chaste Irene Bengoechea was parting her delicate, cosmetic-free lips and awaiting with trembling emotion her suitor's impassioned kiss, then Timidity and Indecision effortlessly grasped ineffable José María Pulicicchio in their clutches. Whereupon his throat knotted up, his hands began perspiring profusely, and his knees began quaking as if he'd suddenly contracted malarial fever. Paralyzed by this fit of timidity and tormenting indecision, he totally restrained his impulses and dared no longer pursue the operation that had begun so promisingly.

But, ah! Athena, foresighted Athena, how soon would you be obliged to admit your failure, for despite your lucid intelligence, you overlooked the power of that sweet titillation of love that had spread over Irene Bengoechea's skin for over two hours.

And so, as Polimnia's financial secretary sensed that her suitor, the excellent José María Pulicicchio, author of perfect sonnets, was turning pale and hesitant and dared not, out of fear, bring his lips to hers as he properly and rightfully ought, Irene Bengoechea, virginal, enamored and suddenly emboldened Irene Bengoechea, brought her beautiful cameolike face toward the face of indecisive José María Pulicicchio, whereupon both members of Polimnia's Executive Committee merged, there beneath the sheltering bougainvillea, in a long, moist, quivering lingual kiss.

Frightened and scandalized by this dreadful contact, Timidity and Indecision took hasty flight and, humiliated by their defeat, appeared, crestfallen, before indomitable Athena.

And Athena, on seeing them, realized that her well-intentioned intervention had been totally futile, and that from that moment on, no one, not even tempestuous Zeus, the king of all Immortals, could prevent the delirium of love from overpowering peerless Irene Bengoechea.

And Athena, from her position on golden Olympus, sighed with resignation and her gaze slowly swept over the tree-lined quarter of Villa del Parque at half past eleven that night, and the wise goddess must have realized that it was perhaps also too late to prevent love with its stupefying effects from imprisoning several of her protégés.

From the heights of Olympus, Zeus' indomitable daughter could see Carlos Argentino Mastandrea, that limping, harassed informer, seated in the private section of

214

a bar on Avenue San Martín, whispering tender, naughty remarks into plump Zulema's ear.

And she could also see beautiful Mrs. Giannello and the previously tormented Mr. Frugoni inside Mr. Frugoni's automobile, which was parked on a dimly lit street near a convent, lavishing all sorts of caresses upon one another and vowing eternal love.

And she saw beautiful, impulsive Dora and diligent Romilio inside an air-conditioned room, No. 22 at the Hotel Lilies, embarking on their third erotic bout, and judging by the great enthusiasm that both were investing in that foolish game, it would seem that they were prepared to continue all night long.

And so Athena was obliged, with a frown, to acknowledge the partial but indisputable triumphs of her eternal rival, seductive Aphrodite.

And as compensation for this, Athena resolved to employ her powers to the utmost so that she might at least compel some of the Polimnians to perform that night certain important acts which she herself looked kindly upon.

And as a result of Athena's resolution, indefatigable Mrs. Zimmerman found herself temporarily forgetting all her maternal and conjugal obligations, and that very night she shut herself up in her edifying library to consult countless tomes on Psychology, Marxism, Talmudic Law, Sexual Relations After the Age of Fifty and Home Economics, and to prepare, moreover, a clever strategy for the following day, when she would confront and surely convince irascible Mrs. Frugoni to curb her ugly, irrational impulses and to rationally agree to divorcing tormented Mr. Frugoni.

Having accomplished this, Athena turned her far-darting gaze toward a solitary room in a boardinghouse in the Villa Urquiza quarter, where lonely Mr. Pasco dwelt in the company of a cat and an encased guitar, and she authoritatively ordained that he be smitten at once by Creative Fever.

Seized by sudden Creative Fever, blind, folkloric Mr. Pasco took a sheet of grocery paper and, at one fell swoop, penciled the lyrics of a beautiful *chacarera* song, clearly inspired by the naked girl on the platform—that flinger of brassieres—and the inspired title of the ballad was "The Buxom Lass," which he would be sure to recite with great success at the next Wednesday meeting.

This done, dauntless Athena meditated wisely for a while, and then silently uttered these wise words:

"Since I'm clearly unable to prevent the upright José María Pulicicchio from being loved by my protégé chaste Irene Bengoechea, or in fact to vouch any longer for the virginity of my excellent financial secretary, I shall therefore delegate a task to the installment loan manager at the Villa Urquiza branch of the Argentine National Bank, a long, arduous and meticulous intellectual labor, which will find great favor in my divine eyes."

And so Athena enjoined irreproachable José María Pulicicchio, who at that moment was preparing for bed in his venerable house in Villa Devoto, to take a fat, barely used accounting ledger out of his desk.

And she commanded him, as future assistant director of the bank, with power of attorney, to begin recording in it, with his small but beautiful handwriting, all the intensely interesting events that had taken place at Polimnia in the course of that unforgettable evening of December 3, 1975, as well as his wise personal opinions and impressions regarding the magnificent members of that meritorious group.

And though José María Pulicicchio obediently acceded to Athena's command, one can only lament that the extensive account inscribed in his own handwriting over a four-month period, in painstaking though rather corny wording, fell into the hands of a certain unknown second-rate novelist who unscrupulously developed it with the wild intention of constructing a silly, absurd and barely credible account around it, involving gods, evil policemen, and splendid mortals over whom death inexorably and ceaselessly hovered.

XLIV

FROM: Anon. Coordinator of Special Groups
TO: Anon. Federal Security Headquarters
December 5, 1975

STRICTLY CONFIDENTIAL

To Whom It May Concern:

Deeply concerned over the security of the precinct which it is my honor to supervise, and about the lives of the self-sacrificing men who constitute it, the object of the following communication to the above division chief is to call attention to the strange behavior of one of the commanding officers who performs his duties in the above division.

In effect: On the night of December 3, just past 2150 hours, under circumstances wherein I was in command over eight of my subordinates, members of Special Operations Units 3 and 4, preparing for Operation Teodoro Vilardebó, of which you are informed, I was unpleasantly surprised by an ill-timed countercommand transmitted by radio communications officer Arístides Fernández.

Said countercommand called for immediate suspension of the operation, which had been mounted at such great expense, and for the return of our four motor units to their usual point of concentration.

Though extremely annoyed by such an unforeseen countercommand, I proceeded in accordance with my unblemished concept of discipline and, obeying it immediately, ordered my men to suspend action of any sort.

Nevertheless, it must be pointed out that given the advanced nature of the operation, one can safely assume that the individuals assembled in said premises at 2562 Teodoro Vilardebó may to some extent have detected our movements. And furthermore, that as a result of mistaken actions based on a superior officer's decision, we have alerted said suspects, hence making it harder in the future to perform the anticipated operation.

In any event, the next day, to wit December 4, at 1117 hours, I appeared at the office of Chief Inspector Guillermo Guso, the only superior officer, I deduced, who could have issued such a suspicious countercommand.

When questioned with respect to the aforementioned, Chief Inspector Guso denied (after certain hesitation) having issued any countercommand, and adduced, with visible signs of nervousness, that it must have been simply an error.

In order to eliminate any trace of suspicion on my part, I pretended to accept his explanation and to consider the matter closed.

But I immediately presented myself before Officer Fernández, who, as previously mentioned, was in charge of radio communications during the aforesaid circumstances. The event that ensued is responsible for the present confidential note. When Officer Fernández was questioned about the superior officer who had issued the order to suspend Operation Teodoro Vilardebó, he replied quite frankly that the superior officer, oddly enough, had failed to identify himself, but that he personally believed it was probably Chief Inspector Guso, inasmuch as the latter's voice was all too familiar.

The foregoing leads one to deduce, and it is my hope

that the division chief concurs, a certain suspicious, or at least contradictory, attitude on the part of Chief Inspector Guso, whose service file, which has already been obtained by me, contains references to several "educational" trips abroad.

Hence, I do suggest that said officer be placed under discreet but strict surveillance, and that each of his movements be recorded.

It is my duty to remind this office of recently disclosed instances of subversive elements infiltrating our glorious ranks and of the great harm that this sinister infiltration has occasioned. I insist, therefore, that the Guso case be taken with due seriousness, and that no effort or resource be spared in order to clear up the matter with utmost dispatch.

Anticipating the decisions that the division chief will adapt, I would like to indicate my personal determination, for the sake of expediency, to take this delicate matter into my own hands: Two of my most trustworthy men have already commenced surveillance of Chief Inspector Guso. If it is deemed necessary (and should I be expressly requested to do so), I can inform the division chief of the proper moment for subjecting said subject to interrogation and/or appropriate punishment. Given the grave risk that the presence of a traitor incurs upon all of our lives, particularly those of my subordinates, I am of the opinion that it is essential to proceed with utmost expediency and without the slightest hesitation.

I wish, moreover, to add further significant details. Our experience gained in the two previous grave instances has taught us that an infiltrated element never acts alone, and that once the principal figure is discovered, the existence of one or various accomplices can always be detected. And in this particular instance, Guso's excessively favorable reports concerning Arístides Farías, the chief officer, and Corporal Nicodemo Ramírez of the 45th Precinct, convert both *prima facie* into accomplice suspects. I therefore suggest that a watch be placed on both, and most particularly that any form of communication between them and Chief Inspector Guso be recorded. In anticipation of the afore-mentioned, I have been able to substantiate with evidence that on Monday, December 1, at exactly 1005, Corporal Nicodemo Ramírez did appear in Guso's office, with no existing reason pertaining to duty to justify this visit.

I likewise regard as highly suspicious Officer Guso's request to me "to remove from circulation as soon as possible" suspect C. A. Mastandrea, an occasional informant at Bevilacqua's headquarters. On the contrary, I believe that as a precautionary measure, Mastandrea should be granted adequate protection. It is evident that, for reasons still unknown to us, Guso wishes to eliminate the aforementioned and will therefore, in all likelihood, attempt some drastic measure against him in the near future. The man obviously knows a good deal more than he claims, and it is important to us that no one lay hands on him now.

With nothing further to report, and hoping that each of my suggestions be given due consideration, I convey my most respectful salutations.

XLV

Thus draws to a close this account of the sundry events, for so many reasons unforgettable, which transpired on the evening of December 3, 1975.

I began writing it on that very night when, inebriated with happiness after my walk with Irene along Marcos Sastre Street, I returned to my old house in Villa Devoto. The basic idea sprang, as I remember, from a sudden, inexplicable impulse: the simple need, perhaps, to keep alive, to prevent from fading into oblivion, so very many beautiful things that had happened to us all in the course of that Wednesday's remarkable meeting.

I naively imagined, owing to my total lack of experience in this area of endeavor, that the account would be finished within a few hours, or at most a few days. In fact, its slow and sometimes laborious execution has consumed me for over four months. Four long months, night after night, reminiscing and meticulously transcribing on paper, in strict chronological order, each of the wonderful moments of that evening. It was a slow task and, I repeat, not bereft of difficulties, inasmuch as I never would allow my imagination to substitute for something which my memory, for some reason, failed to retain.

Still, I can't deny my satisfaction with the work accomplished. Without claiming in the remotest that this modest, sincerely felt account constitutes a genuinely literary work, I do believe that the story itself, as well as the hours devoted to its writing, have been and will continue to be useful in various senses. Let me try to explain what I mean. In the first place, I can't conceive of a better way to relive, whenever one should so desire, that compressed succession of memorable events (some of which forever altered the course of our lives) than by leaving a minute record of those events in this old accounting ledger, under the guise of an objective account.

In the second place (and I hope I'm not branded as conceited), this unpretentious but serious, painstaking and responsible prose exercise will probably one day yield its reward. Without, of course, neglecting my impassioned pursuit of the sonnet, I've poured myself into it, as I mentioned, for four long months. Anyhow, the ongoing execution of this task has led me to believe that literary endeavors in prose may not be totally alien to my true vocation. What I mean to say is that I'm not discounting the possibility of embarking seriously, in the not very distant future, on the writing of a piece of fiction, a short story, or—why not?—a novel. At least I've proven to myself a certain capacity for description, of which I was hitherto absolutely unaware.

These, however, are for the moment mere projects. At the beginning of this folio, I indicated that the story was reaching its end, but since I'm not in the habit of leaving things up in the air (in this instance, the events relating to our dear members of Polimnia plus a befitting epilogue), I wish to add a few brief lines.

A quick summary, then, especially of the meeting on Wednesday the tenth, in other words, the meeting following the one which occasioned this narrative. It was truly an interesting session, and how could I refrain from mentioning some of the happenings which were, in a way, corollaries of the previous meeting.

The title of Mr. Chávez's poem, for example. It was

announced by our president with considerable protocol at the beginning of the meeting, following a few tense moments of expectation. The title selected was "Crucifixion for Love, or, Martyrdom of a Swain Whose Beloved Fails to Reciprocate His Ardent Sentiments." And the author's name: Irene Bengoechea. Flushed with emotion, Irene received Mr. Chávez's congratulations and gratitude, as well as abounding applause and a beautiful book by Krishnamurti donated by Miss Kisternmacher.

Nor could I neglect to mention that Mr. Frugoni, utterly transformed by happiness and optimism, was the first to mount the platform and to recite at long last, in an appealing rustic accent, his much postponed poem, "Phantom of the Wagon." It was an utterly beautiful composition, inscribed in India ink upon the canvas of an actual miniature wagon, drawn by four oxen of polished wood. Nor could I fail to mention that subdued Mr. Pasco surprisingly struck the light and joyful note of the meeting by mounting the stage with a guitar and accompanying his well-tuned voice in the words of a gay and saucy *chacarera* folk song dedicated "with the greatest of respect" to Mrs. Zimmerman, thereupon winning for himself a most enthusiastic ovation from the room.

The incredible Mastandrea read to us "in the way of exclusive first fruits," as he put it, the four famous sonnets, printed on a brochure of orange oak tag, which he was having sent to each member of the organization, along with a "disinterested and sincere" New Year's greeting.

Irene and Mrs. Giannello, virtually compelled by Mrs. Zimmerman in order to counterbalance "an unfair male preponderance," read short but extremely successful compositions. And I, the last to occupy the platform that evening, read, as I'd promised our recording secretary that I would, my triptych of sonnets to Irene, as well as the romantic "To a Lady," which I hadn't until then dared to present publicly. Irene, visibly moved, asked me for a copy that she could read when she was alone. And upon adjournment, Mr. Chávez approached me for the specific reason of telling me that those four sonnets were the best to have emerged from my pen, and among the most perfectly realized works ever to have been heard at Polimnia.

In short, the recitation on Wednesday the tenth, though lacking the magical, fervent note of our previous meeting, was by all lights a most congenial and positive encounter with Poetry.

Now before placing the final period, I ought to say something about the current situation of our organization and about some of its members, since nearly four months have almost imperceptibly elapsed following that indelible evening.

As a result of Mr. Romualdo Chávez's active transactions (and to some small extent, my own position at the bank), we have finally been granted the mortgage credit we so long wanted. The beautiful site at Teodoro Vilardebó will therefore become the exclusive property of Polimnia.

Another felicitous event, which in a way concerns us all, is that Gianello's ex-wife, now Ms. Mastrocarbone, and Mr. Frugoni have, thanks to Mrs. Zimmerman's invaluable assistance, overcome their former problems. Much to our joy, moreover, they're now living together in a charming little house on Gaigorria Street, a few blocks from headquarters. Frequently, after meetings are over, Irene, some other friends, and I go over there to have coffee with the dear couple.

Irene and I will become engaged in July. We've already announced it to our friends, and it's quite likely, if Irene's family doesn't object, that we'll be celebrating our official engagement at our cherished headquarters at Teodoro Vilardebó.

I also happen to know that Mastandrea continues enjoying excellent relations with Zulema, and that Romilio and Dora, on Mr. Chávez's advice, are in the process of taking a small apartment on Cuenca Street, which leads one to deduce that they'll probably be announcing their marriage at any moment.

To summarize accounts, I can assert that in the wake of that memorable evening of December 3, 1975, happiness has entered our midst and there seems no reason for it ever to abandon us.

Every now and then we get newspaper accounts or reports on acts of violence, and even crimes, which stem apparently from matters of a political nature. Clearly, a certain disorder and intranquillity pervade the country. It has even been insinuated that Polimnia, due to the intense cultural activity which it encourages, could eventually run into some trouble with the police. Mastandrea is the most wary and fearful in this respect. I, frankly, don't believe in such things. Those virtually forgotten telephone threats which Mr. Chávez smilingly informed us of have never recurred. It was, therefore, as Miss Kisternmacher so sensibly suggested, a random joke in bad taste.

I firmly believe, on the other hand, that our headquarters, independent of government fluctuations, will continue to remain a peaceful haven for us and an utterly secure oasis of protection in the face of any sort of chaos. And that certain news items, exaggerated perhaps, concerning raids, kidnappings, murders, etc., ought not to affect us to any appreciable extent. Any victims that there might have been in certain instances were undoubtedly individuals with conspicuous political activity, and hence, because of the trying moments which this country is undergoing, vulnerable to those violent and perhaps unjust forms of repression.

But, fortunately, none of this is likely even to graze Polimnia. None of us participates in political activities, and it would be ridiculous to imagine Irene, or Mr. Frugoni, for example, having anything to do with what's known as subversion. Furthermore, any political activity within headquarters is expressly prohibited by our statutes.

Our sole interest, I wish to reiterate once again, is the spiritual pursuit of Poetry. Our sole longing is to continue meeting week after week at our venerable house on Teodoro Vilardebó—that dear, sheltering haven where so many beautiful encounters have lately come to pass, and where we have long found a propitious means for developing our vocations, as well as a warm, untouchable spiritual refuge for our afflictions and loneliness. May God, watching over us from Heaven, deign that it remain that way forever.

XLVI

And so ended the unequal battle in which three powerful Olympians, united by pact, confronted grim, invincible Hades on behalf of a handful of people in the tree-lined quarter of Villa del Parque that was so conducive to love.

In which luminous Victory—following the final moments of harsh combat—suddenly shook her resplendent wings and ascended in majestic flight toward one of the combative factions, thereby siding with the rejoicing Olympians.

And grim Hades was compelled to flee in defeat toward his shadowy realm, abandoning the battlefield and his long-coveted spoils.

And this signified that the twelve doomed Polimnians were not destined that night to enter Hades' abode, but were to continue awhile longer to enjoy their peaceful lives in the midst of minutes, diaries, lovemaking, applause, painstaking poems and Mr. Chávez's flowery introductions.

Nevertheless, it irremediably behooves the honest chronicler to add that the Olympians would have been unforgivably flippant to celebrate their recent victory with vainglorious hymns, banquets or copious libations.

For implacable Hades, as everyone knows, does not readily forgo his spoils or forget the wrongs inflicted upon his awesome pride.

On the contrary, spiteful and relentless, he promptly begins to devise his bloody revenge whenever a coveted spoil must be temporarily abandoned in the hands of his loathed enemies.

And indeed, before even a single day had elapsed following his humiliating defeat, it came to pass that insatiable Hades commenced plotting with renewed fury the fierce destruction of the irreproachable Polimnians.

Toward this end, he penetrated The Goat's bloodthirsty soul in the guise of an Uncontainable Desire for Revenge, and imbued that mortal with an unbridled longing to wreak vengeance upon his detested superior, Chief Inspector Guso, of the Security Headquarters.

Whereupon, The Goat secretly accused Chief Inspector Guso of treason, on the basis of a mysterious phone call which had stupidly called off the carefully planned Operation Teodoro Vilardebó.

And by means of this wily ploy, the forbidding deity once again began spinning impatiently the invisible threads of his postponed revenge.

And thus, soon afterward, as a result of an insidious and skillfully worded confidential report, ominous security agents began strict surveillance of Chief Inspector Guso,

Officer Arístides Farías and efficient Corporal Nicodemo Ramírez.

At the same time, sinister parapolicemen, subordinates of The Goat, were again posted around 2562 Teodoro Vilardebó, and secretly observed each and every movement of all the dangerous individuals who infallibly attended Wednesday meetings.

And as it happened, several weeks after this round-the-clock surveillance was in operation, the Heralding Shadow of Death appeared upon the clear sky over Villa del Parque.

And once again disguised as a huge vulture, it hovered overhead, slowly tracing wide, endless circles around a certain condemned group of unsuspecting mortals:

Inasmuch as all of the well-groomed Polimnians, and even the peaceful residents who dwelt in fragrant Villa del Parque, as well as the countless inhabitants of vast Argentina, a land under military siege, had become highly suspicious to the military rulers of the nation and to the secret parapolice who happily assisted them . . .

And also due to the fact that splendid mortals are destined to pass sweet life beneath the everlasting threat of death . . .

Which endows each of their acts with singular value and imbues the gods with deep respect toward even the smallest and most insignificant of men.

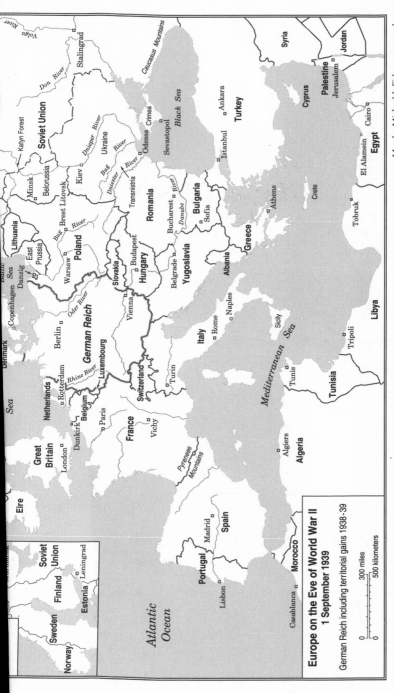

**Europe on the Eve of World War II
1 September 1939**

German Reich including territorial gains 1938-39

0   300 miles

0   500 kilometers

Map by Michael J. Fisher, cartographer

WAR & GENOCIDE

WAR & GENOCIDE

A Concise History of the Holocaust

DORIS L. BERGEN

ROWMAN & LITTLEFIELD PUBLISHERS, INC.
Lanham • Boulder • New York • Oxford

ROWMAN & LITTLEFIELD PUBLISHERS, INC.

Published in the United States of America
by Rowman & Littlefield Publishers, Inc.
A Member of the Rowman & Littlefield Publishing Group
4720 Boston Way, Lanham, Maryland 20706
www.rowmanlittlefield.com

PO Box 317
Oxford
OX2 9RU, UK

Distributed by National Book Network

British Library Cataloguing in Publication Information Available

Library of Congress Cataloging-in-Publication Data

Bergen, Doris L.
    War and genocide : a concise history of the Holocaust / Doris L. Bergen.
      p.   cm.—(Critical issues in history)
    Includes index.
    ISBN 0-8476-9630-8 (cloth : alk. paper)
    1. Germany—History—1933–1945.   2. National socialism.   3. Antisemitism—
Germany—History—20th century.   4. Holocaust, Jewish (1939–1945)—Causes.
5. World War, 1939–1945—Causes.   I. Title.   II. Series.
DD256.5 B3916   2002
943.086—dc21   2002008963

Printed in the United States of America

♾ ™ The paper used in this publication meets the minimum requirements of American
National Standard for Information Sciences—Permanence of Paper for Printed Library
Materials, ANSI/NISO Z39.48-1992.

CONTENTS

FOREWORD

Neither the experience of mass murder of civilian populations nor the concept of war crimes was new to human experience at the start of the Second World War; however, the discovery of the Nazi German systematic annihilation of 6 million Jews and millions of others, including non-Jewish Poles, Gypsies, homosexuals, and physically and mentally disabled people imparted tragic meaning to our modern understanding of genocide and new urgency to the protection of human rights following the war. The implications of the Holocaust—the murder of Jews by Nazi Germans and their collaborators—were so profound, as Doris Bergen observes at the outset of her study, that we still have not fully come to grips with the entirety of this horrific calamity. That the Holocaust occurred in the first place raises fundamental questions beyond historical analysis to deeper philosophical and theological issues concerning, among other problems, the purpose and ultimate fate of humankind.

The escharotic effects of the Holocaust on the modern mind are not easily removed. Yet perhaps a peculiar lesson is found in the very acknowledgment that the Holocaust left such deep scars on peoples and nations—that is, an awareness of calamity acknowledges evil in the world, and through such knowledge, however abhorrent, morality is derived and justice found.

The word "genocide" did not enter into common usage until after the Second World War, when the full extent of the Holocaust became known to the modern world. The word was coined by a Polish émigré lawyer, Raphael Lemkin, who, after learning of the Turkish slaughter of Armenians in the First World War as a young boy, set out on a lifelong quest to introduce into international law protections against the annihilation of innocent people. During

World War II, Lemkin sought desperately to warn public officials and Jewish leaders in the United States about atrocities being committed by Nazi Germans against the Jews.

Lemkin's warnings were dismissed. Samantha Power, in *A Problem from Hell* (2002), found that Lemkin became so distraught by officials' unwillingness to heed his warning that he seriously contemplated suicide. Other reports were also brought to the attention of British and U.S. officials. For example, Jan Nowak in his dramatic memoir of a resistance fighter in Poland, *Courier from Warsaw* (1982 reprint), tells of his frustration in trying to convince Winston Churchill and Downing Street of the Jews' annihilation in Poland, only to fail for reasons he leaves the reader to induce. Whether the western Allies could have slowed the Holocaust through bombing of train tracks remains a question of debate among historians, but there is no doubt that many people during the war turned a blind eye to atrocities being committed by the Nazi Germans.

Recognition of the Holocaust and measures to prevent mass murder on this scale in the future led to adoption of the U.N. Genocide Convention in 1948. Raphael Lemkin played a direct role in the drafting of this convention and in lobbying for its adoption. Although this convention, in the end, did not prevent later campaigns of genocide in Cambodia in the 1970s or in Rwanda in the 1990s, this convention articulated an awareness that this evil existed within nations and among humankind.

Any speculation of the full meaning of the Holocaust must begin with an understanding of its history. Without an understanding of these events, any consideration as to the larger meaning of the Holocaust becomes nugatory.

Doris Bergen provides a concise account of the Holocaust in this volume, yet her study is more than a brief narrative of events. She shows how the Holocaust became possible only within the context of the Second World War. She begins by setting the preconditions for the Holocaust, then traces the rise of Adolf Hitler, the Nazi revolution, the outbreak of war in Europe, and the early "Euthanasia" programs that ultimately led to the killing frenzy of 1941–1945. Along the way, she offers keen insights and a subtle interpretation of these events that will stimulate both students and general readers alike.

Donald T. Critchlow
General Series Editor

Preface

WAR AND GENOCIDE:
RACE AND SPACE

The Holocaust was an event of global proportions, involving perpetrators, victims, bystanders, beneficiaries, and rescuers from all over Europe and elsewhere in the world. Any effort to grasp it in its entirety must begin with recognition of that massive scope.

This book attempts to address the enormity of the Holocaust by situating it in the context of the Second World War, the largest and deadliest conflict in human history. War and conquest delivered into Nazi German hands the Jews of eastern and southeastern Europe—Poland, Ukraine, Belorussia, Hungary, Yugoslavia, Greece, and elsewhere—as well as the smaller Jewish populations of the west: for example, France, Belgium, and the Netherlands. Approximately 95 percent of the Jews killed between 1939 and 1945 lived outside Germany's prewar borders. At the same time, war—in particular the Nazi war of annihilation to Germany's east—exponentially increased the numbers and kinds of victims, as brutal programs of persecution, expulsion, and murder, bloated on carnage, demanded and created even more enemies. Mass killings of non-Jews were also part of the Nazi German war effort, a war launched for the related goals of race and space: so-called racial purification and territorial expansion. War provided killers with both a cover and an excuse for murder; in wartime, killing was normalized, and extreme, even genocidal measures could be justified with familiar arguments about the need to defend the fatherland. Without the war, the Holocaust would not—and could not—have happened.

Since the 1960s, the term "Holocaust," from the Greek for "a burned offering," has been used to refer to the murder of approximately 6 million

European Jews by Nazi Germans and their collaborators during World War II. Sometimes the Hebrew word "Shoah"—catastrophe—is used as a synonym. There is no doubt that hatred of Jews constituted the center of Nazi ideology. Hitler and his associates preached what the scholar Saul Friedländer calls "redemptive antisemitism": the belief that Jews were the root of all evil and that Germany could be saved from collapse only by total removal of Jews and Jewish influence. Jews were the main target of Nazi genocide; against the Jews Hitler's Germany mobilized all its resources: bureaucratic, military, legal, scientific, economic, and intellectual.

Nevertheless, it was not Jews but the mentally and physically disabled who became targets of the first large-scale, systematic killings in Nazi Germany, under the euphemistically labeled "Euthanasia Program." This program, like the assault on European Gypsies (Roma), shared with the genocide of the Jews personnel, methods of killing, and goals of so-called racial purification. At the same time, Nazi Germany persecuted, incarcerated, and killed millions of Slavic people—Polish gentiles, especially members of the intelligentsia; Soviet prisoners of war; and others—and attacked Communists, homosexual men, Jehovah's Witnesses, Afro-Germans, and other people considered unwanted in the "new European order." Whether or not one considers members of any or all of these groups to belong under the label "victims of the Holocaust," their fates were entwined in significant ways with that of the Jews targeted and murdered in the Nazi quest for race and space. This book seeks to identify and explore connections between and among victim groups, not in the interest of establishing some kind of hierarchy of suffering but with the hope of coming to understand how state-sponsored programs of violence and atrocity function.

These are ambitious aims for a short book. Indeed, although this book is concise, it will not necessarily make dealing with the Nazi era, the war, and the Holocaust easy. That history is complex, and I have tried to present it honestly and as fully as possible in a brief survey. Nor do I promise that this small book will resolve the big questions that might be on your mind as you approach this topic: Why did such horrible things happen? If there is a God, how could such atrocities have been possible? What are human beings that they can inflict such agony on other people? Finding answers to those kinds of questions is a lifelong challenge, not something you can accomplish with one book or one class.

Nevertheless, this book will help you address some more modest yet important questions regarding the history of Nazism, World War II, and the Holocaust. Who was involved and in what ways? What motivated those people to behave as they did? How—through what processes—did large numbers of people, some of them "ordinary," some less so, become murderers of larger numbers of other people? If you care enough about the past to try to understand these matters, perhaps you will also discover some insights that help you think about brutality and suffering in our own world.

What follows here is only a brief introduction to a subject so broad and multidimensional that you could probably read for the rest of your life and never get through all that has been written about it. I hope that you will read this book in conjunction with some of the many excellent studies that go into more depth on specific topics. A list of sources for each chapter and some suggestions for further reading are included at the end of the book. Any synthesis such as this relies heavily on the work of other scholars, and I am indebted and very grateful to all of those people whose research and interpretations have shaped and challenged my own.

Many people helped make it possible for this book to appear. My thanks go to Jim Harink and Christine Bergen, who loyally and critically read the first draft. I also appreciate the students and teaching assistants in my courses on the Holocaust at the University of Vermont and the University of Notre Dame. In particular, feedback from my class in the fall semester of 1999 has been invaluable, and Kristin Kobes provided especially detailed suggestions. Professor Margarete Myers Feinstein of Indiana University, South Bend, Daniel S. Mattern, and Professors Gary Hamburg, Laura Crago, and Robert Wegs of the University of Notre Dame commented on chapters, as did Glenda Regenbaum, formerly of the Holocaust Museum Houston. My friends Linda H. Pardo, Patricia Blanchette, and Catherine Schlegel—a scientist, a philosopher, and a classicist—always came through with insight and encouragement. Emily Elizabeth Fleming and Annamarie Bindenagel read the manuscript and gave me many useful ideas; I especially appreciated Emily Elizabeth's astute judgments regarding photographs. Thank you as well to Sharon Muller and Judith Cohen at the United States Holocaust Memorial Museum Photo Archives, whose assistance was indispensable; to Nicole and Karly Bergen for proofreading; and to Nicole Thompson, who did a superb job of preparing the manuscript for press. Notre Dame's Institute for Scholarship in the Liberal Arts generously funded a summer assistantship for the project. Steve Wrinn and subsequently Mary Carpenter and Erin McKindley at Rowman & Littlefield Publishing Group were patient and supportive, and Donald Critchlow offered wise editorial guidance.

Without my two scholarly mentors, Annelise L. Thimme and Gerhard L. Weinberg, I would never have come to work in this field in the first place. They have influenced me in ways that continue to surprise me, and I am deeply grateful to them both. Of course, all errors and shortcomings in the book are my own responsibility.

1

PRECONDITIONS: ANTISEMITISM, RACISM, AND COMMON PREJUDICES IN EARLY-TWENTIETH-CENTURY EUROPE

In order for a house to burn down, three things are required. The timber must be dry and combustible, there needs to be a spark that ignites it, and external conditions have to be favorable—not too damp, perhaps some wind. Hitler's Nazi regime in Germany provided the spark that set off the destruction we now call the Holocaust, and World War II (1939–1945) created a setting conducive to brutality. However, without certain preconditions—the dry timber—mass murder on such a scale would not have been possible. People had to be prepared to accept the identification of other members of their society as enemies. In other words, a substantial part of the population had to be ready to consider it desirable, acceptable, or at least unavoidable, that certain other people would be isolated, persecuted, and killed.

Hitler and his National Socialist German Workers' Party, now commonly referred to as the Nazis, came to power in Germany in 1933 and remained in place until the military defeat of Germany in 1945. More than half a century later, Nazism has become synonymous with the mass murder of millions of innocent people: Jews, above all, and also handicapped people, Gypsies, political opponents, and others.

In their choices of target groups the Nazis reflected and built on prejudices that were familiar in many parts of Europe. Hitler and the Nazis did not invent antisemitism—hatred of Jews—nor were they the first to attack Roma (Gypsies) or people considered handicapped. Their hostilities toward Europeans

1

of African descent, Slavic people, Jehovah's Witnesses, and homosexuals were not new either. The Nazis were extremists in the lengths to which they went in their assaults, but they were quite typical in whom they attacked.

Long-standing hatreds alone did not cause the Holocaust. Sadly, the world is full of old prejudices; fortunately, only rarely do they erupt in genocide. Leadership, political will, and manipulation of popular sentiments are needed to fan hostility into organized killing. Widespread negative attitudes on their own do not create a holocaust, but they are a necessary condition for mass persecution—that is, the rest of the population must regard certain groups as legitimate targets in order for them to participate in or tolerate open assault. Nazi leaders could not simply have invented a category of enemies—for example, people who weighed between 130 and 145 pounds—and then have expected the majority of the population to turn against them. Such a group would have been incomprehensible to most people. The identities of those targeted for destruction during World War II were no coincidence; these people were already victims of prejudice.

This chapter surveys some of the widespread attitudes toward Jews and other groups in Europe prior to the Nazi rise to power in Germany in 1933. It outlines some ideas already in place in Europe by the early twentieth century that provided the ground in which the Nazi ideology of race and space— "racial purification" and territorial expansion—could take root and grow.

A NOTE ON VOCABULARY AND
SOME WORDS OF WARNING

The Holocaust originated in Nazi Germany, but it was by no means uniquely German in terms of its perpetrators, victims, bystanders, beneficiaries, or heroes. They came from all over Europe and even farther away, swept into the deadly force field of developments with worldwide repercussions. By the same token, many of the ideas and attitudes that fed into the Holocaust had roots and branches outside Germany, particularly elsewhere in Europe. Although much of the discussion in this chapter focuses on Germany, it is important to keep in mind that scholarship, publications, opinions, and prejudices flowed freely across national borders throughout the modern era; most Germans of the 1920s and 1930s were more typical than they were atypical for Europeans in their time.

Discussing the Nazi era raises some thorny problems of vocabulary. Should one say "Nazis" or "Germans" when referring to the people of Hitler's

Germany? Some scholars have argued that using the term "Nazis" in this general way is misleading. It implies that Hitler's supporters were not themselves Germans and that the "real Germans" were somehow untouched by Nazism. On the other hand, simply saying "Germans" suggests that all Germans marched in step behind Hitler. That was not the case either. German Jews were excluded from the Nazi movement by definition—that is, they were not permitted to join the Nazi Party or its affiliates—and the same was generally true of Germans deemed handicapped, Gypsies, and other outsiders. Nevertheless, those people too were Germans. Moreover, some Germans also opposed the regime and tried to distance themselves from it. Throughout this book, I try to be as precise as possible in my use of terms, while recognizing the impossibility of avoiding overgeneralization.

A final introductory word of caution: prejudices always reveal more about the people who hold them than they do about those at whom they are directed. You will not learn much useful information about Judaism or Jews by studying antisemitism, but you can learn quite a lot about antisemites, their insecurities, and their fears. By the same token, examining the lives of Jews in Europe before World War II is important in its own right, but it will not answer the question as to why antisemites hated Jews any more than studying African American history will explain why white supremacists hate black people. Prejudices are habits of thought; they are not reasoned responses to objective realities. When you read the descriptions of common prejudices that follow, keep in mind that these attitudes were based on imaginings about people rather than on who those people really were.

To illustrate this point, it is useful to observe that Nazi prejudices against all of the target groups followed similar patterns. Proponents of Nazi ideas focused their attacks on people who were already suspect in the eyes of many Germans. They then echoed and enlarged familiar hatreds and linked them to current anxieties and concerns. For example, in the 1920s and 1930s, many Germans were distressed by Germany's defeat in World War I. So, no matter which of their supposed enemies they described—Jews, homosexuals, Communists, Jehovah's Witnesses—Nazi propagandists accused them of causing Germany to lose the war. Similarly, many Germans in Hitler's time were worried about decadence, criminality, and supposed racial degeneration. Nazi thinkers charged every enemy group with promoting immorality, spreading crime, and polluting the bloodstream. Whether they were talking about Slavic people, Gypsies, Jews, Afro-Germans, or homosexuals, Nazi propaganda used similar slurs.

ANTISEMITISM

Why begin a discussion of preconditions with the topic of antisemitism? Hatred of Jews was the center of Nazi ideology. Nazi propagandists labeled all of Germany's supposed enemies as "Jews" or judaized: they depicted Jews as deformed and criminal and compared them to handicapped people and Gypsies, whom they also described as monstrous and dangerous. Nazi ideologues linked Communists, capitalists, and liberals with a purported Jewish conspiracy; they described homosexuals, eastern Europeans, the British, and the Americans as nothing but cover groups for alleged Jewish interests. So by studying the history of antisemitism and Nazi uses of it, we can begin to get a sense of how other Nazi ideas functioned and built on older traditions.

The term "antisemitism" was coined in the 1870s by a German journalist who wanted to contrast his supposedly scientific hatred of Jews with religious forms of anti-Judaism. As a label, "antisemitism" is misleading, because the adjective "Semitic" describes a group of related languages, among them Hebrew, Arabic, and Phoenician, and the people who speak them. Often you will see the word written with a hyphen—"anti-Semitism"—a spelling I avoid in this book. Use of the hyphen implies that there was such a thing as "Semitism," which antisemites opposed. In fact, no one who used the term in the nineteenth century (or since) ever meant it to mean anything but hatred of Jews.

Antipathy toward Jews in Europe dated back much further than the 1800s—as far as the ancient world. Roman authorities worried that Jewish refusal to worship local and imperial gods would jeopardize the security of the state. At times such unease, coupled with political conflicts, turned into open persecution and attacks. In 70 C.E. the Romans destroyed the Jewish temple in Jerusalem, the focal point of Jewish life up to that time; sixty years later they dispersed the Jews of Palestine, scattering them far from the region that had been their home.

The rise of Christianity added new fuel to anti-Jewish sentiments. Christianity grew out of Judaism—Jesus himself was a Jew, as were the apostles and important figures such as Paul of Tarsus. Nevertheless, early Christians tried to separate themselves from other Jews, both to win followers from the gentile (non-Jewish) world and to gain favor with Roman imperial authorities. Some early Christians also stressed their loyalty to the state by pointing out that the Kingdom of God was not of this earth and therefore did not compete with Rome. Such efforts paid off: in less than four hundred years, Christianity went from being a persecuted branch of Judaism to being the dominant religion of the Roman Empire. It is significant that some early Christian accounts blamed Jews for Jesus' death even though crucifixion was a specifically Roman form of punishment commonly practiced during Jesus' time. The version of events that had Jewish mobs demanding Jesus' death while the Roman governor Pontius Pilate washed his hands allowed later Christians to emphasize their difference from Judaism and downplay the hostility that Roman authorities had shown toward Christianity in its early stages. All of the false accusations against Jews associated with the Roman imperial period—that Jews were traitors and conspirators, that they killed Christ—remained familiar in Europe into the twentieth century.

In many ways the Middle Ages—from around the ninth to the sixteenth centuries—were difficult times for Jews in Europe. Often crusades against Muslims and Christian heretics started off or ended up with violent attacks on Jews. Such attacks, known as pogroms, were also common responses to outbreaks of plague or other disasters. For example, in many parts of Europe, the Black Death of 1348 sparked brutal pogroms, as Christians blamed Jews for somehow causing the epidemic of bubonic plague. Mobilized by such accusations, Christian mobs—sometimes spontaneously, sometimes urged on by state and church leaders—attacked Jewish homes and communities, plundering, destroying, and killing. The scale of pogroms varied wildly, from brief local incidents to weeklong massacres that swept through entire regions. In their wake they left among Christians a habit of using Jews as scapegoats, and among Jews, a sense of vulnerability and a repertoire of defenses, such as paying protection money, sticking together, and keeping a low profile.

In addition to sporadic waves of violence, Jews faced harassment and restrictions of various kinds from governments across Europe. In some cases, regulations forced Jews to live in certain areas or ghettos; sometimes Jews were required to wear identifying badges; elsewhere, state authorities drove Jews out of their territories altogether. In 1492, for example, King Ferdinand and Queen Isabella of Spain expelled all Jews and Muslims from the Iberian Peninsula except those who agreed to convert to Christianity. Throughout the Middle Ages, Jews everywhere in Europe faced limitations on the occupations in which they could engage as well as the kinds of property and titles they could hold.

Some church leaders and secular rulers tried to convince or coerce Jews to abandon their religion and convert to Christianity. But even conversion did not necessarily solve the problems of intolerance. Converts from Judaism to Christianity in sixteenth-century Spain found that they were still viewed with deep suspicion and regarded as somehow tainted by supposed "Jewish blood."

So even the notion of Jewishness as a "race" was not entirely original to the Nazis.

The Protestant Reformation did not improve the lot of European Jews. At first its leader, the German monk Martin Luther, hoped that his break with what he considered the corrupted church of Rome would inspire mass conversions of Jews to Christianity. When the anticipated wave of baptisms did not occur, Luther turned against the Jews, whom he derided as stubborn and hard necked. In 1542 he wrote a pamphlet called *Against the Jews and Their Lies*. That tract, with its vicious characterization of Jews as parasites and its calls to "set their synagogues and schools on fire," would later be widely quoted in Hitler's Germany. Other medieval images—the association of Jews with the devil; charges that Jews used the blood of Christian children for ritual purposes—also survived into the modern era. Even those Nazi leaders who hated Christianity and mocked it for its historical ties to Judaism found it useful to invoke these powerful, traditional notions about Jews. In other words, Nazi antisemitism was different from older religious forms of anti-Judaism, but its proponents still drew on those traditional hostilities. Ancient associations of Jews with deadly evil gave modern antisemitism a virulence that set it apart from other prejudices.

Antisemitism after the Emancipation of European Jews

In the seventeenth, eighteenth, and nineteenth centuries, European society became more secular, but bigotry toward Jews did not disappear. Instead, social, economic, and political prejudices grew alongside and sometimes in place of older religious resentments. Enlightenment thinkers in eighteenth-century Europe favored religious toleration and mocked the rigidity of institutionalized Christianity. But even such a self-consciously progressive thinker as the French writer Voltaire labeled Jews with contempt as "vagrants, robbers, slaves, or seditious." In the nineteenth century, Napoleon and other rulers introduced legislation to repeal old restrictions on Jews in Europe. This process is usually referred to as the emancipation of the Jews. Nevertheless, formal and informal limitations often remained in place.

Like every minority group striving to better its position while hampered by obstructions, European Jews ended up overrepresented in some occupations and underrepresented in others. Hostile non-Jews made much of the fact that in Germany by around 1900, the field of journalism included a higher percentage of Jews than did the population as a whole. However they never mentioned the fact that Jews were almost completely excluded from the higher ranks of the government bureaucracy and the military. By the late 1800s, political parties that openly championed antisemitism had sprung up in various parts of Europe. Vienna's popular antisemitic mayor Karl Lueger would make a deep impression on the young Adolf Hitler. In particular Hitler noticed how Lueger played on widespread anti-Jewish sentiments to whip up enthusiasm in the crowds he addressed and to boost his own support.

Modern antisemites claimed that their views were scientific, based on the biological "facts" of blood and race. In reality hatred of Jews was no more scientific than were European attitudes of superiority toward Africans, Asians, or native peoples in the Americas. Moreover the notion of "Jewishness" as a race was invented, as were the concepts of "blackness," "whiteness," and "Orientalism" that became so central to how many Europeans and North Americans viewed the world. Still, Social Darwinist ideas about struggle between rival "races" and survival of the strongest provided fertile ground, not only for Nazi notions about Jews but for an entire, interlocking system of prejudices against people deemed inferior. In medieval Europe, religion had served to legitimate and justify hatreds. In the modern era science and pseudo-science played a comparable role.

THE DIVERSITY OF JEWISH LIFE IN EUROPE

Never more than a small minority—at most 1 or 2 percent of the entire population of Europe—Jews existed alongside Christians for centuries. Judaism was and is a religion and a living community. Despite pogroms, massacres, and expulsions, Jews survived in Europe. They thrived as individuals and as a community in different places at different times—in Spain before the Inquisition, later in the Netherlands, at times in Poland and Germany. Ever since ancient times the Jewish contribution to European life has been enormous.

European Jews, like European Christians, were and are a diverse group. It is important not to oversimplify or let studies of persecution distort our understanding of Jewish history. By the early twentieth century many were highly assimilated; neither from appearance, habits of daily life, nor language could they be distinguished from their gentile French, German, Italian, Polish, Greek, or other neighbors. Some attended religious services several times a year; others, never. Some maintained a strong sense of Jewish identity; others, very little or none at all. Many Jews were intermarried with Christians; often Jews in intermarriages converted to Christianity, and usually they raised their children as Christians. Karl Marx, the founder of Communism, is frequently described as a Jew, but in fact he was the son of a couple who converted from Judaism to Christianity. Nazi law would not recognize such conversions but considered converts to Christianity, as well as the children and in some cases grandchildren of such converts, to be Jews.

In Europe in the early 1900s there were also more visible kinds of Jews. In some parts of eastern Europe many Jews lived in small communities known as shtetls. Forced by the Russian tsars to remain in an area in the west of the Russian empire called the Pale of Settlement, these Jews developed a lifestyle of their own based on shared religious observance, the Yiddish language, a diet following kashrut—the Jewish dietary laws—and predominance of certain occupations. For example, many were small traders and craftspeople. Those lines of work did not require them to own land, something from which they were restricted and in some places prohibited altogether.

Jews in southern and southeastern Europe tended to come from what is called the Sephardic tradition and to speak a language called Ladino rather than the Yiddish of the Ashkenazic Jews of northern and central Europe. By the twentieth century, there were many strands of European Judaism. Some Jews were strictly Orthodox, so that their mode of dress, adherence to dietary laws, and other religious observances set them apart from the gentiles around them. Others were Reform, part of a branch of Judaism that emerged out of early-nineteenth-century Germany and emphasized adapting rituals and practices for modern times. Some Jews embraced the tradition of Hasidism, a movement that started in Poland and emphasized joyous mysticism; others were more austere. Some dressed distinctively, with the adult men wearing beards and earlocks; other Jewish men might be distinguishable only by the physical marking of circumcision.

In short, there were wealthy Jews in Europe around 1930 as well as middle-class and very poor Jews. There were Jewish bankers and Jewish shopkeepers, and Jewish doctors, nurses, actors, professors, soldiers, typists, peddlers, factory owners, factory workers, kindergarten teachers, conservatives, liberals, nationalists, feminists, anarchists, and Communists. Nazi propaganda would create the category of "the Jew," a composite based on myths and stereotypes. In reality there was no such thing as "the Jew," only Jews who often differed as much, and in many cases much more, from one another than they did from the Christians around them.

Three Jewish Lives in Prewar Europe

Perhaps the best way to capture the diversity of Jewish life is to look at several individuals who experienced the assault of Nazism as young people in

The Jewish proprietor of a kosher butcher shop in Danzig (Gdansk) stands behind the counter with his son. The photograph was taken sometime in the 1930s.

Europe. One example comes from a memoir by Peter Gay called *My German Question*. Gay was born in Berlin in 1923 to a middle-class family named Fröhlich, which means "happy" in German. (After moving to the United States, the name would be changed to the English translation "Gay.") Peter's father bought and sold glassware; his mother worked part-time as a clerk in her sister's sewing notions store. Committed atheists, Fröhlich's parents officially left the Jewish community. They had their son circumcised but showed few other signs of Jewish identity.

Fröhlich's father fought in World War I and was wounded and decorated. An avid fan of all kinds of sports, Fröhlich Sr. had many close friends who were not Jewish. Young Peter was one of a handful of Jewish boys at his school; he does not remember ever being ridiculed or harassed. He and his family considered themselves thoroughly German. Gay and his parents managed to get out of Germany before the Second World War began in 1939. Gay eventually moved to the United States, where he became an important historian of modern Europe and a professor at Yale University.

As a young girl in Hungary, Aranka Siegal lived a rather different Jewish life in Europe before the Holocaust. She describes it in her book, *Upon the Head of the Goat*. Siegal, whose name at the time was Piri Davidowitz, was an observant Jew like her parents and her four sisters. Born in 1931, she went to a public school, where her friends included Catholic, Protestant, and Russian Orthodox as well as Jewish children. Some of her fondest childhood memories are of the months she spent each summer on her grandmother's farm. It was from her grandmother that Piri learned the most about Judaism. With her grandmother she lit the Sabbath candles, recited the blessing for the new year on Rosh Hashanah, and prepared traditional foods.

Siegal's grandmother also taught her about Jewish history. Old enough to have vivid memories of pogroms in Ukraine and Hungary in the 1910s and 1920s, she told her granddaughter how Christians had often used Jews as scapegoats in times of trouble. She also warned the little girl about a "madman" called Hitler, who was terrorizing Jews in Germany and Poland. Aranka Siegal's grandmother was right to be afraid. Almost everyone in the family would be killed in the Holocaust. Miraculously Piri and one sister survived being sent to the Nazi killing center of Auschwitz. After some time in Sweden, Aranka Siegal moved to New York. She speaks to many students every year about her experiences during and after World War II.

A third, very different Jewish life is that of Jack Pomerantz, which is recorded in his memoir *Run East*. A native of Radzyn, a small town near Lublin in Poland, Pomerantz was born in 1918 during a pogrom, a violent attack on the Jewish community by their Christian neighbors. His mother was hiding in a barn when she gave birth to Yankel, one of eight children. (He would later anglicize his first name to "Jack.") Yankel's father was a peddler; he wore a long beard, dark clothing, and often a prayer shawl. Although the family was desperately poor, Yankel's mother still always tried to have a special meal for Shabbat, the best day of the week. Like all married Orthodox women she wore a wig. For the Jewish holidays most of the women in the shtetl made wonderful food, but sometimes Pomerantz's mother had nothing to cook. She would boil rags just to steam up the windows of their shack and create the impression that they too were preparing a feast.

Pomerantz spoke Yiddish at home and was very conscious of himself as a Jew. His town was about half Jews and half Polish Christians, and there was considerable tension between the two groups. As a boy Yankel heard people say they hated Jews because they "killed Christ." Once, in a fight, a Polish Catholic boy cut Yankel's cheek with a knife, right through into his mouth. Pomerantz was no stranger to antisemitism.

Like Peter Gay and Aranka Siegal, Jack Pomerantz survived the war and came to the United States, where he worked as a builder and contractor in New Jersey. He died a few years after publishing his memoir. Gay, Siegal, and

Pomerantz are only three of millions of examples of the immense range of living situations experienced by European Jews before the Holocaust.

EUGENICS AND ATTITUDES TOWARD PEOPLE DEEMED HANDICAPPED

When one considers the long history of anti-Jewish attitudes and actions in Europe and the dramatic, destructive ways that Nazi antisemitism disrupted the lives of people like Peter Gay, Aranka Siegal, and Jack Pomerantz, one might conclude that Jews must have been the first targets for systematic murder in Hitler's Germany. That, however, was not the case. Instead, the first category of people slated for mass killing were individuals deemed handicapped. Perhaps Nazi leaders believed they would encounter less opposition to attacks on that segment of the population; perhaps they thought it would be easier to keep such a program secret. Certainly initiatives came from within the scientific and medical communities, whose members played key roles in carrying out the killings. These are all matters open to research and discussion. What is clear is that attitudes toward people with disabilities in Europe developed in a manner rather different from what we have seen with regard to antisemitism. Nevertheless, here too Nazi ideology and practice built on existing prejudices in ways that were extreme but not unique.

It is hard to know exactly how the majority of the population regarded people with mental and physical handicaps in medieval and early modern Europe. Christianity, like Judaism, out of which it grew, taught compassion for the afflicted, and church as well as state law provided some protections for those who could not protect themselves. But there is also evidence, including many literary accounts, that the able-bodied often ridiculed, took advantage of, and abused those weaker than they were. Nevertheless it seems that in various ways society found places for those with mental and physical disabilities. The village idiot, court dwarfs, fools, beggars, and cripples were all familiar characters. They showed that, although life might not always be fair or good to those with handicaps, at least everyone recognized their existence and assumed that they, like the poor, were a permanent part of society.

By the nineteenth century the assumption that the handicapped would always be present had begun to change, at least for many people in Europe and elsewhere. Scientific and medical advances together with Social Darwinist notions led to the idea that society could be engineered so that only the supposedly healthiest elements would reproduce. This way of thinking, and the pseudo-science that grew up around it, is often referred to as eugenics.

Eugenics became popular all over Europe and North America in the early twentieth century. Many places introduced programs to sterilize people considered undesirable. Even though the proponents of such plans claimed to be objective and scientific, they tended to identify people already viewed as outsiders as the least desirable "breeding stock" and to label them "feebleminded" or "degenerate." For example, eugenics programs in some parts of the United States disproportionately targeted African Americans; elsewhere in North America native people were prime subjects. Europeans often focused on Gypsies and other itinerant people, and everywhere poor people came in for the closest scrutiny. In the wake of the First World War, many political leaders, interested in boosting the size and health of their populations—and their armies—promoted eugenics programs. Meanwhile, perennial problems such as crime seemed solvable to people who believed that criminal tendencies were inherited and that their carriers could be identified by physical characteristics.

Even many scientists, medical experts, and social workers who considered themselves progressive reformers supported programs to attempt to "raise" the quality of the population by "selective breeding," with or without the consent of those involved. For example, in the 1910s and 1920s the British sex reformer Marie Stopes helped thousands of men and women learn about birth control and gain access to necessary technologies and supplies. One of Stopes's arguments in support of legalizing birth control was the assumed need to curb the reproduction of people considered burdens on society. When a deaf man wrote to ask Dr. Stopes a question about reproductive rights she fired back an angry letter demanding to know why someone like him would even consider having children. Of course such efforts to "improve" humanity, even at the expense of those considered inferior, were different from attempts to build a Nazi-style "master race" that would rule the world. Still, by the 1920s, as notions about building a "better race" became mainstream, they served to legitimate more extreme schemes of exclusion, manipulation, and domination.

A look at one influential publication illustrates the radicalization of eugenic ideas after World War I. In 1920 Karl Binding, former president of Germany's highest court, and Alfred Hoche, a German professor of psychiatry, wrote *Permission for the Destruction of Worthless Life, Its Extent and Form*. Binding and Hoche believed that World War I (1914–1918) had produced a marked increase in the number of "mental defectives." As a result, they said, Germany was weighed down with people they called "living burdens." They expressed shock at the tremendous care that was devoted to inmates of mental hospitals at a time when the country had lost so many young men in war. In their view the mentally ill were "completely worthless creatures."

Binding and Hoche did not explicitly say that people who wanted to live should be killed, but their ideas still had radical implications. According to them, every human being's worth could be measured in terms of contribution to the community and the nation. Some people, they suggested, did not really have any value. Although Binding and Hoche's book was controversial, the mentality it expressed was widely shared in Europe and North America in the decades before World War II. Given this background, it is perhaps no surprise that Hitler's regime would begin its program of mass murder with attacks on people deemed mentally or physically handicapped.

PREJUDICES TOWARD ROMA (GYPSIES)

Hitler and his followers intended to wipe out the Gypsies of Europe, whom they associated with criminality and degeneracy. The Jews, people deemed handicapped, and the Gypsies were the groups toward which the Nazis most consistently followed a policy of annihilation that included murdering even babies and old people. Anti-Gypsyism, like antisemitism, was an old, familiar hatred in Europe, so with regard to the Gypsies too, Nazi Germany could draw on long-standing prejudices.

The origins of the European Roma remain somewhat contested, but many scholars agree that they moved into Europe from India during the Middle Ages. The English word "Gypsy," often applied as a pejorative term of insult, developed from the mistaken idea that the people in question originated in Egypt. The German term for Gypsies is "Zigeuner," but it too has taken on negative connotations, so that many people now try to avoid using that label. Instead they prefer to speak of "Roma," "Rom people," or "Roma and Sinti." The Sinti are a group of Gypsies primarily based in German-speaking Europe. It is hard to pin down whether Roma/Gypsies are a racial, ethnic, or social group, that is, whether they are defined by family relationships with one another, language and traditions, or lifestyle. Perhaps that difficulty itself is a useful reminder of how arbitrary such categories are. It is probably most useful to think of Gypsies as a group that includes elements of all those criteria.

When Gypsies first arrived in medieval Europe, they encountered hospitality from some European courts. Soon, however, they became targets of hostility from Europeans who were suspicious of these newcomers. Whether from habit or because of coercion, many Gypsies were itinerant, and their mobile lifestyle further roused the antagonism of others. The rest of European society labeled them thieves and tricksters who used their musical abilities and physical charms to lure the unsuspecting to their ruin.

A number of common attitudes toward Roma in the medieval period echoed anti-Jewish notions. Non-Jewish Europeans falsely accused Jews of stealing Christian children in order to use their blood; likewise non-Gypsies charged Gypsies with kidnapping children for evil purposes. Like Jews, Gypsies were easy scapegoats in times of disaster, such as plague or earthquakes. Their opponents claimed that they poisoned the wells, practiced magic, and consorted with the devil. European folklore did not accuse Gypsies of killing Jesus, but because the Roma were known for their skills as metalworkers, it charged them with forging the nails that pierced his flesh.

According to European myths, Gypsies, like Jews, had been condemned by God to wander the earth without ever finding a homeland. One popular version of events held that while still in Egypt, the Gypsies had tried to prevent Joseph, Mary, and the baby Jesus from gaining refuge from King Herod, and God punished them with eternal homelessness. Probably by the twentieth century few Europeans would have accepted such myths as the literal truth. Nor would most non-Gypsies have realized that in some parts of southeastern Europe, Roma had been enslaved until the mid–nineteenth century. Nevertheless what remained was a widespread sense that Roma were somehow evil outsiders who did not merit the respect or protection awarded to other members of society.

Nineteenth- and twentieth-century notions about heredity and criminality also contributed to attacks on the Roma in Europe. If criminality was inherited and Gypsies were criminals, "experts" reasoned, then one could fight crime by preventing Gypsies from having children. Social scientists, medical specialists, and criminologists tended to regard Roma as if they were some kind of disease, as evident in references to the "Gypsy plague." Public authorities introduced all kinds of restrictions on where Gypsies could reside and what activities were permitted them, and police all over Europe were especially diligent when it came to enforcing such laws and "controlling" Gypsies. Years before Hitler came to power in Germany, Roma in that country were required to carry photo identification cards and to register themselves with local police. France, Hungary, Romania, and other European countries had anti-Gypsy measures of their own.

It is even harder to make meaningful generalizations about the lives of people considered disabled and the Gypsies in Europe prior to World War II than it is about Jews. There is certainly much less published about members of these two outsider groups. Many handicapped people were not in a position to leave written records. For that matter, many probably did not think of themselves as members of a special group whose particular experiences should be preserved. Romany tradition, it seems, has always been more connected to the present than the past, more oral than written, and centuries of persecution produced a tendency to be secretive with people outside the immediate group.

Even something that seems as obvious as the numbers of people in these categories cannot be pinned down with any precision. Who was considered handicapped, mentally or physically, could vary enormously from place to place and time to time. For their part, Gypsies were skilled at evading such formalities as government censuses. Experience with various bureaucracies had taught them that they had little to gain and much to lose by being counted.

The European officials who introduced restrictions on Gypsies and the police who enforced them were often unclear about who exactly was a Gypsy. Non-Gypsies tended to assume they could recognize Gypsies by their appearance: many Roma had darker hair, skin, and eyes than most people in northern, western, and eastern Europe, but by no means were there always physical

A man cares for the family mule beside wagons in a Gypsy encampment in the Dutch city of Haarlem. This photograph was taken in late 1940 as part of the German occupation authorities' efforts to register the Roma in Holland.

markers. In some areas Gypsies were associated with certain trades, such as working with metal or leather. Most Europeans thought all Gypsies were wanderers who made a living from fortune-telling, music, dancing, and theft. In fact, not all Roma were itinerant, and many held regular jobs, for example, as civil servants. Nor were all wandering people in Europe Gypsies in any sense of the word. Sometimes, however, police and other authorities treated people who were not ethnic Roma at all as if they were Gypsies, because they fit the stereotype of homeless, petty thieves.

Just as Nazi ideologues invented the category of "the Jew," as if all Jews were somehow the same, they created the stereotypical, deformed "life unworthy of living" and the monolithic "Gypsy." In actuality people deemed handicapped represented the full range of European society: they were Christians, Jews, Gypsies, women, men, children, rich, poor, beautiful, dependent, self-reliant, and anything else you might add. As for Roma, they too varied considerably from one another in terms of religion, lifestyle, language, appearance, name, and occupation. Many were Christians; some intermarried with non-Gypsies. Some spoke a language known as Romani, which linguists believe is linked to languages on the Indian subcontinent; others spoke the languages of the people around them. As would be the case with European Jews, the shared experience of Nazi persecution created a degree of commonality among Gypsies that would not have existed otherwise.

IMPERIALISM AND RACISM

European imperialism, especially its nineteenth-century forms, was also indirectly part of the preconditions to the Holocaust. Through the experience of ruling over subject peoples in their overseas colonies, Europeans gained habits of behavior and thought that lent themselves to developing hierarchies among peoples within Europe. For example, from their experiences in Africa, Asia, and elsewhere, Europeans learned methods and technologies for oppressing and enslaving large groups of people. Ways of thinking about subject peoples whom Europeans considered inferior to themselves were also transferred onto targets of abuse within Europe, such as Jews. The notion that humanity was divided into races that struggled with one another for survival and dominance was in large part a product of the colonial experience.

Over the course of the nineteenth century, Europeans divided almost the entire continent of Africa among themselves. The British and French had large colonial holdings in Africa, as did the Portuguese, Belgians, and Germans.

These and other European powers already dominated vast territories around the world. In Asia, the British controlled India, for example, and the Russians, Central Asia. The Dutch held Indonesia, and various Europeans had colonies in the Pacific, the Caribbean, and the Americas. The rule of law and protections of citizens' rights that had been introduced in many European jurisdictions by the late 1800s usually did not apply in the colonies, so missionaries, entrepreneurs, administrators, and military men often had very few limits on their behavior once they were overseas. They could and did use flogging, torture, and even death for offenses committed by native peoples that could never have been punished so severely at home. In the Belgian Congo, for example, European rubber magnates sometimes ordered that the hands be cut off of Africans whose production did not meet certain quotas.

Europeans' technological and military advantage enabled them to carry out such acts more or less with impunity. A massacre known as the Battle of Omdurman provides a graphic illustration. In 1898, a small group of British military on an expedition south of Egypt encountered resistance from local Sudanese tribesmen. The British, armed with machine guns, opened fire. The Sudanese, mounted on horseback and equipped with swords and other weapons for hand-to-hand combat, rode wave after wave into the barrage. The British killed an estimated eleven thousand Sudanese and lost only twenty-eight of their own men. Such events must have contributed to a sense among many Europeans that human life—at least the lives of people they considered inferior—was extremely cheap. Notions of racial superiority were by no means unique to Germany.

Nevertheless, Germans did engage in their own atrocities overseas during the imperial era. Since 1883, Germany had a protectorate over Southwest Africa, the modern-day country of Namibia. By 1904 white pressure on native lands led to a revolt of the largest tribe in the area, the cattle-herding Herero. A smaller group called the Nama joined the rebellion. It took some fourteen thousand German soldiers three years to crush these uprisings. By 1907, fifteen hundred German men had died in the Southwest African conflict, half of them from illness.

But the Herero and Nama suffered far more. In what developed into an act of genocide, the Germans slaughtered more than fifty thousand Herero and ten thousand Nama. They shot many, especially adult men; hunted women, children, and old people into the desert, where they died of thirst and starvation; and forced others into concentration camps, where disease, inadequate food, and horrendous conditions took a terrible toll. In the end, between 75 and 80 percent of all Hereros died; among the Nama the death rate was over 45 percent. This carnage was not ordered by German authorities in Berlin but evolved out of specific military goals: a demand for "total victory" and a drive to annihilate the enemy in order to prevent any possibility of resurgence. Such practices left a brutal legacy that would be evident in both the First and the Second World War.

Anti-Black Racism in Germany before the Nazis

Many Nazi ideas about what a race was grew out of ways of thinking about people of color that were common among white Europeans—and Americans—in the early twentieth century. An obvious illustration of some of these ideas comes from Germany in the 1920s. After World War I, the French occupied the Rhineland, an area in the western part of defeated Germany. The occupation forces included some indigenous troops drawn from France's overseas territories in Africa and Asia. Many Germans were horrified at the presence of these men of color on German soil.

Stereotypes about African men as sexual predators on white women were widespread in Europe, and German racists and nationalists played on such fears and fantasies to stir up resentments against the French occupation. Judging from the hysteria in the German press in the early 1920s, one might have thought that hordes of Africans were raping and pillaging all over Germany. In fact there were at most about five thousand black men stationed in the Rhineland at any given time between 1919 and 1923 and perhaps another twenty thousand nonwhite forces. Among these men of color were Senegalese and a small number of Sudanese; Frenchmen, Arabs, and Berbers from Morocco; Malagasies from Madagascar; Annamese from Indochina; and others. They seem to have gotten into no more trouble than any other French units. Nevertheless, Nazi propagandists would return to this topic in the 1930s in their own efforts to whip up German anxieties about supposed racial defilement.

Some of the French African troops in Germany in the 1920s became involved with German women, and in some cases those liaisons produced children. These few biracial individuals—who in 1924 may have numbered only seventy-eight—also attracted a great deal of attention. Fanatical German nationalists and racists of various kinds referred to these people as the "Rhineland bastards." Throughout the 1920s some Germans claimed that the existence of those biracial individuals proved there was a vast conspiracy—controlled by the French, the Jews, or simply by the unnamed enemies of Germany—to befoul German blood and weaken the German nation. It is no surprise that once in power, Hitler and his Nazi regime would take steps against Germans of African background, too.

ANTI-SLAVIC ATTITUDES

Hindsight, they say, is twenty-twenty. Looking back on European history more than half a century after World War II, it is clear that certain widespread German attitudes toward eastern Europeans, especially the Slavic peoples— Poles, Russians, Ukrainians, Czechs, Serbs, and others—were also a precondition for the atrocities of the Second World War.

The origins of these negative ideas are hard to identify. Certainly nineteenth-century German nationalists commonly contrasted what they considered their culture's unique achievements with the supposed primitivism and barbarism of their neighbors to the east. Even the German language included slurs against Slavs. For example, a common German expression for a chaotic situation was a "Polish economy." In general many twentieth-century Germans considered Slavic people to be backward, uneducated, slovenly, brutish, and childlike. The fact that eastern European industrialization lagged behind that of the west seemed to confirm those stereotypes for many Germans who conveniently ignored the artistic, cultural, and scientific achievements of their eastern neighbors.

Developments in the early twentieth century added new dimensions to German notions of superiority over the Slavs. After World War I, for the first time since the late 1700s, an independent Polish nation was established. Until the war, territories in which many Polish people lived had been ruled by the German, Austro-Hungarian, and Russian empires. With the defeat of Germany and the collapse of the old Habsburg empire in Austria-Hungary in 1918, the way was cleared for creation of an independent Polish state. Many Germans resented this new neighbor and the loss of territories formerly under German control to Polish rule.

Instead of disbanding at the end of World War I, some German soldiers reformed themselves into units called the Freikorps (Free Corps) to fight Communists and others they considered Germany's enemies. Freikorps activities included attacks on Poles both inside Germany and across the border in Poland. During the decades before Hitler came to power, Germans inside Germany also encouraged the ethnic Germans who lived in Poland to provoke clashes with Polish authorities.

A similar situation existed with the German minority who lived in Czechoslovakia. Like Poland, Czechoslovakia was a newly created state after World War I. Politically and economically weak, it was no match for its powerful German neighbor. Some members of Czechoslovakia's German-speaking population were happy enough to live in a country where they were far fewer in number than Czechs and Slovaks, but others resented their minority status. Here too Nazi agitators in the 1930s would find fertile ground for their notions of German superiority and their plans to rearrange the borders of Europe in Germany's favor.

Developments in Russia also added a new dimension to German suspicion of Slavs. Germany won some of its most dramatic victories during World War I against Russia. In fact, the Russian military effort collapsed in 1917, and as soon as Lenin and the Bolsheviks had claimed control of the country, they sued for peace with Germany. It was all the more humiliating for the Germans a few months later in 1918, when, still flushed with their successes in the east, they had to concede defeat in the west and abandon all claims to the territories they had won from Russia.

The Russian Revolution of 1917 and the civil war that followed were extremely violent. Accounts of the bloodshed reached Germany and, at least for some, seemed to add more reasons to fear and hate Russians. After World War I, many Germans believed they were surrounded by enemies who conspired for Germany's destruction. The fact that Communist ideology called for world revolution and the existence of a very visible Communist party in Germany itself after 1918 seemed proof that such a conspiracy was indeed under way.

Antisemitic Germans often linked their fear of the Soviet Union with their hatred of Jews. They pointed to some prominent Communists who were Jews or had Jewish names as evidence that Jews were somehow responsible for the Russian Revolution. Of course there were some Jewish Communists, but there were also many non-Jewish Communists as well as many anti-Communist Jews. Sometimes antisemites imagined or invented Jewish identities for powerful individuals, such as Lenin, who was often described as Jewish but in fact came from a Russian Orthodox family. This tangled web of prejudices toward Slavs, Communists, and Jews would emerge in a more massive and violent but still recognizable form in Hitler's Germany.

COMMON PREJUDICES TOWARD HOMOSEXUALS, JEHOVAH'S WITNESSES, FREEMASONS, AND SO-CALLED ASOCIALS

Historians often fail to mention some of the additional groups persecuted by the Nazi regime. In some cases, such as the Jehovah's Witnesses and Freemasons, their relatively small numbers make them easy for outsiders to forget or

A 1941 poster titled "The Jewish Conspiracy." It presented both Josef Stalin and Winston Churchill as Jews, although neither man was Jewish, and falsely claimed that 406 out of 503 members of the Soviet government were Jews and that the British House of Commons held 19 "full Jews" and ninety "half Jews." The text calls on Germans to destroy Bolshevism and crush the Jewish conspiracy.

ignore. In other cases, such as homosexuals, the persistence of prejudices against them long after collapse of the Third Reich may have blocked recognition of their suffering at Nazi hands. As for people who came under the vague label of "asocial," they have been criticized and attacked so often that their victimization is sometimes almost taken for granted. Study of the Nazi era, however, demonstrates that assaults on such people also grew out of a particular ideology.

Nazi officials created a category called "asocials" into which they put all kinds of people they considered problematic: Gypsies, the homeless, criminals deemed incurable, people with certain mental disorders, or those accused of sexual perversions. One did not have to be a Nazi in twentieth-century Europe to be afraid of "asocials." Explosive population growth in the nineteenth century and rapid urbanization in many parts of Europe in the twentieth century contributed to a perception among many people that the world was becoming a more dangerous place, full of bizarre and threatening people. In the decade before Hitler came to power in 1933, the Nazi Party in Germany played on such anxieties to present itself as the force that would "clean up" a society supposedly degenerating into lunacy.

Attitudes toward Homosexuals

Pre–World War II prejudices against homosexuals are hard to summarize, because scholars disagree as to when the category of "homosexual" even became recognizable in Europe. It seems evident that in the ancient world certain forms of intimacy between people of the same sex did not carry any stigma or preclude sexual relations with members of the opposite sex. By the modern era, it seems, much of this flexibility was gone, although even the supposedly prudish society of Victorian England showed considerable tolerance for at least some kinds of same-sex intimacies. For example, many people considered sexual experimentation among boys in boarding schools to be a normal part of development; loving relationships between women who often became lifelong companions were not uncommon either.

Nevertheless, by the late nineteenth century many parts of Europe had introduced laws against homosexuality. The German criminal code of 1871 explicitly forbade sexual relations between men. The state prosecuted some cases, and public interest in such "scandals" ran high. For example, it was an enormous sensation when Prince Eulenburg, a member of the inner circle of the German Kaiser Wilhelm II (1888–1918), was charged with homosexual activities and forced from public life. Somewhat paradoxically, an increased openness around the subject of human sexuality in the decades after World War I served to make homosexual men and women more visible in Europe and to increase the panic some heterosexuals felt about them.

Political changes in Germany after World War I made it possible for the first time for Berlin to develop a gay scene that included clubs, restaurants, and bathhouses frequented by homosexual men. Lesbians, it seems, tended to attract less public attention, although there were also some clubs popular with homosexual women. Laws against sex between men were still on the books in Germany's first democracy, the Weimar Republic, but enforcement was slacker than it had been before World War I, especially in the major cities. Many heterosexual Germans, however, disapproved of what they considered their overly permissive society.

Magnus Hirschfeld (1868–1935), a sex reformer and homosexual rights leader in Berlin, made an international reputation for his research in sexology, the new field of studies of sex and sexuality. Hirschfeld regarded homosexuality as the "third sex," a natural and legitimate variant between masculine and feminine. Homosexuals, he pointed out, looked and behaved normally and should be treated accordingly. For many people the work of researchers and activists such as Hirschfeld offered new possibilities for human freedom. For others it seemed to represent the decadence of a society that had abandoned its traditional values. Hitler's Nazis capitalized on such fears as well; they forced Hirschfeld out of Germany, and his research institute was one of the first casualties of their new regime.

A scene from around 1929 in the Eldorado, a nightclub frequented by the Berlin homosexual community. The balloon displays the nightclub's name and its address (15 Motzstrasse).

Attitudes toward Jehovah's Witnesses

As European outsiders, the Jehovah's Witnesses were relative newcomers. Founded in the United States in the late 1870s, the Jehovah's Witnesses, or International Bible Students, as they were initially called, were not a large group. By the early 1930s they had about twenty thousand members in Germany.

A number of beliefs and activities important to Jehovah's Witnesses made them stand out in European society. Because Jehovah's Witnesses considered themselves citizens of Jehovah's Kingdom, as a principle they did not swear allegiance to any earthly government, nor did they serve in any nation's military. The world, they believed, would soon enter a peaceful, thousand-year heavenly rule, but not until it had gone through the battle of Armageddon. In order to teach others, Jehovah's Witnesses emphasized door-to-door preaching and distribution of literature.

Jehovah's Witnesses were not popular with mainstream European society in the early decades of the twentieth century. Members of the established Protestant and Catholic churches labeled the Jehovah's Witnesses a "sect" or a "cult" and discounted their interpretations of Christian scripture. Some critics considered the Jehovah's Witnesses' emphasis on the Old Testament suspect and intimated that they might be somehow connected with Judaism. Many people found their proselytizing efforts and handing out of tracts to win converts annoying or offensive. Public officials were suspicious because most Jehovah's Witnesses refused to serve in the military or acknowledge state authority if it clashed with their understanding of God's commands. The group's international ties and connections to the United States were also suspect to some ardent nationalists in Germany and elsewhere. Jehovah's Witnesses would be easy targets for the Nazis, who made them the first religious group to be outlawed in 1933.

Attitudes toward Freemasons

Nazi authorities were also hostile to members of the Freemasons, a European association dating back to the eighteenth century and devoted to the ideals of the Enlightenment: progress, freedom, and tolerance. Many well-known Europeans in the age of the French Revolution and afterward belonged to the Freemasons. Mozart was an enthusiast, for example, and he incorporated some of the ideas and rituals of the Masons into his opera *The Magic Flute*.

Over the years the Freemasons had developed some secret rites, and the air of secrecy that surrounded the group made it seem all the more threatening in the eyes of its critics. Especially in central and eastern Europe, conservatives and nationalists regarded the Freemasons with suspicion, accusing them of spreading atheism, liberalism, and disobedience to authority. Not surprisingly, opponents of the Freemasons also often hinted that the organization was run by Jews as part of some supposed international Jewish conspiracy. When they attacked the Freemasons too, the Nazis chose a familiar target.

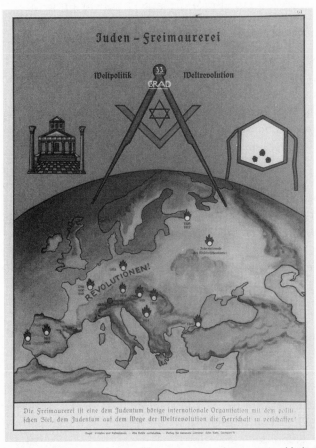

A 1933 poster depicting the Nazi view of Freemasonry and its purported links to a Jewish conspiracy. The temple, apron, square, and compass are all Masonic symbols. The text reads: "Jews—Freemasonry. World Politics—World Revolution. Freemasonry is an international organization beholden to Jewry with the political goal of establishing Jewish domination through worldwide revolution."

In fact, the number of Freemasons in twentieth-century Germany was always very small, and the organization neither wielded any significant power nor posed a threat to the state. Nevertheless, after 1933, under Nazi rule, men who belonged to the association would face a whole range of discriminatory measures. Some lost their jobs; others ended up in prisons and concentration camps.

WORLD WAR I AND THE
CHEAPENING OF HUMAN LIFE

It is important to conclude this survey of some common attitudes in Europe with reflections on the influence of the First World War (1914–1918). This cataclysmic event had a profound impact on Europe and on the world as a whole. In significant ways it too formed part of the preconditions that set the stage for the Nazi era, World War II, and the Holocaust.

The connections between the First World War and the horrors of the Nazi era, however, are rather different than is often claimed. You may have read that the victorious French and their allies imposed such a humiliating peace on the defeated Germans after 1918 that the Germans had no choice but to seek the restoration of national honor at any price. You may also have read that the victors in World War I, in particular the French, forced the Germans to pay crushing reparations, thereby sparking hyperinflation in the 1920s and destroying the German economy. According to this line of argument, the desperate Germans turned to Hitler to rescue them and turned on the Jews as a scapegoat for their suffering.

Both of these common sets of assumptions are deeply flawed. The Germans did lose the war—in fact, it was their military leaders Generals Paul von Hindenburg and Erich Ludendorff in October 1918 who convinced the civilian government that it was necessary to sue for peace. And the Germans did have to accept the terms of the Treaty of Versailles in 1919, without having been part of the negotiations that drew up that accord. Still, the treaty was not exceptionally harsh. In fact, if you compare it to the Treaty of Brest Litovsk, which the Germans had imposed on the defeated Russians just a year earlier, you might almost call it generous.

In March 1918 the Germans had demanded that the Russians cede about 30 percent of their territory, including much of their agricultural, industrial, and mineral wealth. Under the terms of the Treaty of Versailles the Germans lost about 10 percent of their territory, much of it fairly recently acquired:

Alsace and Lorraine, for example, taken in 1870 from France. Contrary to what is often said, the Treaty of Versailles did not blame the Germans for the war itself. Article 231, often referred to as the "war guilt clause," was in fact not a moral judgment but a general, legal statement stipulating that Germany was responsible for paying for damages in the places outside Germany where most of the fighting had occurred. A similar clause appeared in the treaties with Germany's former allies Austria, Hungary, and Turkey.

As for reparations, the Germans paid only a very small amount of the bill originally presented to them, which was repeatedly adjusted downward. The victorious nations, above all the British and the French, had neither the ability to make Germany pay nor the will to risk another war after all the suffering and loss they had experienced between 1914 and 1918. Certainly the payments that were made imposed hardships on the Germans, and especially in the aftermath of a devastating war, the notion of reparations itself was psychologically harsh. All of Europe, however, faced terrible economic problems after what had been an extremely costly war, and the Germans were by no means alone in their difficulties, although admittedly the knowledge of widespread hardship probably provided little comfort to anyone.

The First World War did not cause Nazism or the Second World War in such direct ways. Its impact was both less obvious and more insidious. Although the Germans ended World War I in better shape economically than many of the actual victors, they cultivated a politics of resentment that promoted a bitter sense of humiliation and poisoned the chances for the new German democracy formed in 1918. Refusal to accept the reality of defeat led many Germans to search for people to blame for what they perceived as a betrayal. That climate of scapegoating, in turn, created a kind of open season on many familiar outsiders. For example, old accusations that Jews had crucified Jesus dovetailed with the popular stab-in-the-back myth that blamed treacherous Jews for Germany's loss of the war. Communists, homosexuals, and hostile neighbors were blamed too, especially by German military leaders who falsely claimed that their forces had been undefeated in the field.

World War I brought tremendous bloodshed and disastrous implications that extended far beyond Germany. An estimated 20 million Europeans died in the war; it wiped out almost an entire generation of young men. Those who made it home again included many wounded, crippled, and shell shocked. In addition to combat, blockades, food shortages, and disease took their own tolls. From the Russian steppes to Belgium, from England to Serbia, by 1918 there would be scarcely a European family without casualties.

In many cases, soldiers, their families, and their political leaders emerged from four years of carnage with a deep fear of ever risking another war. In other cases, however, they took away different, and more dangerous, lessons: the notion that only in warfare could a man prove himself a real man; the conviction that the sense of camaraderie between fighting men was the most perfect form of human communion possible; the belief that sheer force was in the end the strongest thing in the world.

Perhaps most importantly, the Great War, as it was called at the time, seemed to many Europeans to prove that human life was cheap and expendable. It sparked a cult of violence that flourished in the brutality of the revolution and civil war in Russia, in the paramilitary groups that sprang up around Europe in its wake, and in the nihilistic pessimism of so many Europeans in the 1920s and 1930s. World War I did not lead inevitably to either the rise of Nazism, the outbreak of World War II, or the Holocaust. However, the massive legacy of death and suffering it left behind did constitute one of the preconditions that made possible an unprecedented explosion of violence just two decades later.

2

LEADERSHIP AND WILL: ADOLF HITLER, THE NATIONAL SOCIALIST GERMAN WORKERS' PARTY, AND NAZI IDEOLOGY

The previous chapter described some preconditions for developments in the Nazi era: historical antisemitism, eugenics, racism, negative German attitudes toward Slavs, and the cheapening of human life after World War I. If historical prejudices made the timber of European and German society combustible, Hitler lit the match that set the house on fire. This chapter examines the leadership provided by Adolf Hitler and the National Socialist German Workers' Party. Who was Hitler, and what was his view of the world? How did he come to power in Germany?

ADOLF HITLER

Any discussion of Adolf Hitler (1889–1945) raises both general and specific questions about the role of the individual in making history. Do personalities shape events? Would the Nazi era, or World War II, or the Holocaust have occurred without Hitler? Certainly common wisdom assumes that Hitler was central to the shaping of those sets of events. There is no denying that Hitler has caught the popular imagination like no other tyrant—walk into any video store and you will see the evidence. Fascination with Hitler seems to cut across all kinds of lines: nationality, age, gender, level of education.

Is so much interest in Hitler justified? Scholars in fact disagree about just how crucial Hitler was. One group, often referred to as intentionalists because they emphasize Hitler's intentions and consider the Holocaust the result of long-term planning, describes Hitler as the mastermind of mass murder. These scholars point to the consistency of Hitler's views from the early 1920s right down to his final testament in 1945. They emphasize the direct, hands-on way he made the major decisions in Nazi Germany.

Others, sometimes called functionalists because they describe the Holocaust as a function of other developments, especially during the war— something that evolved over time in an improvised way—downplay the role of Hitler. Some functionalists argue that Hitler was actually a weak dictator, more a pawn swept along by forces outside his control than the orchestrator of colossal events.

Scholars influenced by Marxism have also tended to pay little attention to Hitler. In their interpretations, Nazism was an extreme form of capitalism that had much more to do with broad, economic structures than with the ideas or actions of any one individual.

These debates about Hitler have moral as well as historical implications. Some people criticize the intentionalist stance because they think it focuses too much on Hitler and lets everyone else off the hook. Others attack the functionalist and Marxist positions for depersonalizing the past. They say that functionalists, who describe the Holocaust and other crimes of Nazism as the result of developments or events, draw attention away from the people who in fact made the decisions and took the actions involved in genocide. Still other people reject both the intentionalist and the functionalist positions and argue that we should pay less attention to the perpetrators altogether and concentrate instead on the victims of Nazi crimes.

In this book I proceed on the assumption that in order to understand the causes of Nazi crimes we need to study those who initiated and carried them out. With regard to Hitler I take what might be called a modified intentionalist position. Hitler was an essential factor in Nazism and the genocide it produced. He did not have complete power—even dictators depend on popular support—and a program as massive as the crimes of Nazism required many accomplices. Nonetheless, Hitler's leadership was essential in setting the agenda. Hitler was no mere opportunist; he operated from a consistent view of the world. He could be flexible, pragmatic, and responsive to the situation "on the ground," but he took the initiative and provided much of the drive and the will that proved crucial in setting Germany on the path to war and genocide.

Without Hitler, Nazism, World War II, and the Holocaust would have taken very different forms, if they had occurred at all.

A Brief Biography

Adolf Hitler was born in 1889 in the small Austrian border town of Braunau am Inn. Not much is known with certainty about Hitler's childhood, because the most detailed source—his autobiographical book *Mein Kampf* ("My Struggle")—was a work of propaganda intended to depict him as someone who had been marked from his earliest days for greatness. In fact, Hitler's early life seems to have been fairly typical for a middle-class boy in late-nineteenth-century central Europe.

Adolf was the fourth child of an Austrian customs official and his third wife, but the first to live past infancy. The family was comfortable although not wealthy and did well enough to afford a cook and a maid. Adolf's father, Alois, was a strict, authoritarian man with a bad temper, who seems to have

Adolf Hitler and Heinrich Himmler review SS troops during Reich Party Day ceremonies in September 1938. Hitler demanded loyalty from his subordinates but allowed his favorites wide latitude in their own spheres of activity.

taken little interest in his family. For reasons now unknown, Alois changed his last name from Schicklgruber to Hitler, more than a decade before the birth of the son who would make the new name notorious. Alois Hitler died in 1903, when Adolf was still an adolescent.

Adolf's mother, Klara, was much younger than her husband, whom she met when she worked as a maid in his household. According to the account of her doctor, Klara Hitler was a gentle, pious woman devoted to her children, especially her one surviving son. Adolf returned the affection and later wrote in *Mein Kampf,* "I had honored my father, but loved my mother." Other than his mother, Hitler does not seem to have been close to anyone in his family.

Even decades after his death the rumor persists that Hitler had "Jewish blood." That claim is false. It is true that Hitler did not know the identity of his paternal grandfather, because his father, Alois, was born to an unmarried woman. Alois was baptized into the Roman Catholic Church, as his son Adolf would be, too. In the 1920s and later, rumors circulated that Adolf Hitler's grandmother had been a maid in a Jewish household and had become pregnant by one of her employers' sons. Those allegations were unfounded. In fact there were no Jews in the town where Hitler's grandmother lived, because Jews were prohibited from living in that part of Austria at the time.

What is the significance of this rumor? First of all it shows the extent to which people in Hitler's time became obsessed with issues of blood and race. In Nazi Germany, accusations of so-called Jewish blood were a sure way to discredit someone. It is no surprise that similar rumors circulated about many top Nazis and about other people, too.

The persistence of such a rumor may also tell us something about our own society. What would it actually explain even if the rumor of Hitler's "Jewish blood" were true? Obviously nothing, just as it would explain nothing if there were any truth to the claims that Hitler was secretly homosexual or that he had only one testicle. (Both of those common allegations, to the best of anyone's knowledge, are false as well.) Such claims reflect a desire to find easy explanations for historical processes that in fact have many complicated causes. Rumors of that kind also reflect a widespread tendency to blame the victims for their misfortunes, as if someone who was "part Jewish," or "secretly homosexual," or in some way physically deformed might somehow be expected to initiate programs to murder Jews, persecute gay men, or kill people deemed handicapped. An honest understanding of history requires a critical—and self-critical—response to such simplistic notions.

As a child Hitler was a mediocre student. Later, in *Mein Kampf,* he would claim that he led his class in geography and history. That was not the case, although he did better in those subjects than in some others, where he received failing grades. When he was sixteen he dropped out of school. Young Hitler spent the next two and a half years in the Austrian city of Linz, idling, dreaming, drawing, and redesigning the city on paper. He always had a penchant for grandiose plans.

In 1907 Hitler relocated to Vienna, where he planned to study art. He failed to get into art school, however, a fact he concealed from members of his family and even close friends for as long as possible. Hitler's many drawings, paintings, and architectural sketches showed some technical ability but little creativity. It is not surprising that years after his death an ambitious forger would have no trouble cranking out many convincing fakes. Hitler later made much of his dire poverty during his years in Vienna, and he did face some hard times when he could not afford lodgings and had to live in a men's shelter. His means of support included selling cards on which he painted local scenes. During most of his young adult years in Vienna, however, Hitler received funds from his family that enabled him to live quite comfortably without ever being employed. For example, he could afford to see Richard Wagner's opera *Lohengrin* and other favorites over and over again.

While in Vienna Hitler picked up on many ideas and currents around him. He was interested in Pan-Germanism—the conviction that Germans should be unified in one state instead of dispersed throughout central and eastern Europe—as well as in ultranationalism and antisemitism. He admired Karl Lueger, mayor of Vienna from 1895 to 1910 and a member of the antisemitic Christian Social Party. Lueger's use of propaganda particularly impressed Hitler.

In Vienna Hitler began to fuse his ideas into a worldview and to get acquainted with political extremists of various kinds. He became enthusiastic about Social Darwinist theories that described life as a struggle between races. His reading consisted mostly of popular tracts about mythology, biology, and even the occult. Hitler preferred to read summaries and pamphlets rather than the actual writings of people such as the philosopher Friedrich Nietzsche. Enthusiasm for the operas of Wagner encouraged Hitler's tendencies toward a grandiose style. If you have seen or heard any of Wagner's operas you know something about their huge casts, imposing music, exaggerated passions, and powerful depictions of Germanic myth; all of those elements inspired Hitler as he developed his own vision of politics and power.

In 1913 Hitler left Vienna for Munich. He crossed the border from Austria to Germany in violation of Austrian law, which required him as an able-bodied young man to perform military service for his homeland. Hitler's motivations for moving are not known for certain, but he had never made a secret of his contempt for the Austrian government and his conviction that the future lay with Germany.

In Munich Hitler's self-education was interrupted by the outbreak of war in 1914. He volunteered for the German army, where he reached the rank of corporal. Wounded in action during World War I, he served with distinction as a runner who relayed messages from the rear to the front. It was a dangerous job, although not exactly the combat role Hitler would later imply he had played, and he received an Iron Cross for his bravery. Nevertheless, a report by one of his superiors—in hindsight tinged in irony—commented that Hitler lacked leadership qualities.

It is not completely clear when and how Hitler developed his fanatical antisemitism. He certainly came into frequent contact with antisemites in Vienna, although he also had acquaintances, associates, and even what might be called friends who were Jewish. In any case, Hitler's experience of Germany's defeat in World War I deepened and hardened his hatred of Jews, or at least he would later claim that his conversion to antisemitism came in 1918. To his mind, the Jews were somehow to blame. That reaction was completely unfounded; German and Austro-Hungarian Jews had fought and died loyally alongside fellow citizens in their countries' armies. But as he would do with every disappointment he faced throughout his life, whether it was failing to get into art school or losing a war, Hitler considered the Jews at fault.

In 1919, a year after the war ended, Hitler got involved in a political organization called the German Workers' Party. It would soon change its name to the National Socialist German Workers' Party. The German acronym was NSDAP. English-speakers commonly use the abbreviation "Nazi," taken from the first two syllables of the German pronunciation of "National." Within a year Hitler had become a full-time agitator and extremely popular speaker for the group.

On 9 November 1923, Hitler and a group of coconspirators that included the war hero Erich Ludendorff launched what became known as the Beer Hall Putsch in Munich. They intended to overthrow the government of Bavaria in order to install a regime that would be the beginning of a national revival in Germany. Poorly planned and disorganized, the Putsch failed; Hitler was captured and sentenced to five years in prison for high treason. He served only thirteen months in Landsberg Prison, where he was treated like a celebrity by most of the staff and many of his fellow inmates. So many admirers flocked to visit him that he eventually stopped receiving them in order to have time to write the book he had begun. By the time Hitler was released in 1925, he had written and published *Mein Kampf,* a combination memoir and propaganda tract. The book did not become a best-seller until Hitler became chancellor of Germany in 1933.

In this earlier phase of his career, Hitler was still relatively obscure, part of the fringe elements that proliferated in German society after the First World War. Most Germans outside Bavaria knew little about him and did not take him seriously. His modest background, his relatively unremarkable military career, and his lack of education and experience with the wider world all made him seem almost laughable to some of the people he encountered. For example, one German aristocrat, a Bavarian baron called Fritz Percy Reck-Malleczewen, described his early impressions of Hitler with contempt. He once saw Hitler in a deserted restaurant in the early 1930s, Reck-Malleczewen recorded in his diary, later published as *Diary of a Man in Despair.* Reck-Malleczewen had a pistol in his pocket and could easily have killed the future dictator. "But I mistook him for a cartoon character," the baron said, looking back on the event, "and I did not shoot."

Because of the tremendous fascination with Hitler, the person, we know quite a bit about some details of his daily life. He was a vegetarian who loved animals and hated cigarette smoke. He liked to watch movies, especially comedies, and enjoyed reading Westerns, like those by the popular German writer Karl May. May, like Hitler, never set foot in the Americas. Hitler's most intense emotional attachment after the death of his mother seems to have been his relationship with his niece Geli Raubal, the daughter of his half-sister Angela. Hitler had invited Angela to live with him to supervise his household in Munich.

Evidence points toward some kind of affair between Hitler and his much younger niece. Proud of the vivacious young woman and possessive of her time and attention, Hitler was often seen with her in public. Geli seems to have chafed under the control of her domineering uncle, and some observers later claimed she was trying to get away from him. In 1931 Geli died under suspicious circumstances. The official verdict was suicide, but rumors of foul play persisted for years. The young woman was found in her uncle's Munich apartment, shot with his pistol. Stories circulated—Geli was pregnant, people whispered; she had a Jewish lover, some hinted; her jealous uncle had her killed, people speculated. Given the few documents and witnesses available and the years that have since passed, it is unlikely that we will ever get to the bottom of events surrounding Geli Raubal. Scandalous and intriguing as the whole affair is, it does not seem to have played a major role in shaping Hitler or his view of the world.

Indeed, none of the details of Hitler's life that can be found have managed to provide the clue needed to explain the strengths of his obsessions or his ability to realize his convictions. The magnitude of the crimes he initiated remains oddly out of proportion to the banality of his person and his life.

Hitler's Worldview

It is impossible to talk about Nazi ideas without borrowing Nazi terminology, most of which, even translated into English, is offensive, nonsensical, or both. Words like "Aryan," "race," and "blood" had particular meanings within the Nazi system of thought, but those terms do not describe objective realities. However, once Nazi ideology became enshrined in laws and regulations and implemented in practice, such labels would take on very real implications of life and death.

The main elements of Hitler's ideology developed during his years in Vienna, his time in Munich, and his years with the German army during and immediately after World War I. Those ideas remained remarkably constant from the beginning of his political career in the early 1920s to his death in 1945.

Hitler's core ideas can be summed up in the phrase "race and space." Hitler was obsessed with two notions: that humanity was engaged in a gigantic struggle between "races," or communities of "blood"; and that "pure Germans," members of the so-called Aryan race, needed space to expand, living space that Hitler called by the German term "Lebensraum." For Hitler, these two notions of race and space were intertwined. Any race that was not expanding, he believed, was doomed to disappear. Without living space—land to produce food and raise new generations of soldiers and mothers—a race could not grow. Hitler saw the potential living space for German "Aryans" to Germany's east, in the territories of Poland and the Soviet Union. The "races" that he considered prime threats to the survival and dominance of his "Aryans" were the Slavs who occupied that land and the Jews, who, in his theory, sought to infiltrate, weaken, and destroy German strength.

What was an "Aryan"? Like all races the category "Aryan" was an invention, a social construction rather than a physical fact. Hitler did not coin the term "Aryan" but borrowed it from eighteenth- and nineteenth-century European racial theorists who used various labels for the categories into which they divided humanity. The word "Aryan" originally referred to a group of people in ancient India. Hitler drew on vague theories that these people, supposedly taller and lighter-skinned than their neighbors, were a superior group who somehow ended up in Europe, where they continued to be the bearers of all cultural creativity. Hitler and other Nazi writers tended to be rather vague when it came to the details of their theories, and they were not troubled by internal contradictions. Thus Hitler considered the ancient Greeks to have been Aryans; so, at least in his mind, were the best elements in ancient Rome as well as the Germanic tribes that finally destroyed Roman power.

Using the term "Aryan" to describe his supposed master race gave Hitler a degree of flexibility that proved very useful. Had he simply preached the "German" master race he would have had to find some way to exclude German Jews, many of whom were certainly as German as their fellow citizens in terms of language and ethnicity. Had he drawn exclusively on terms like "Nordic," which tended to describe physical appearance rather than less visible qualities of blood and character, he might have had some explaining to do with regard to the inclusion of many loyal Nazis in the privileged category. As it was, Germans would tell jokes during the Nazi years about the less-than-perfect specimens who were their leaders: "What does the ideal Aryan look like? As tall as Goebbels, as slim as Göring, as blond as Hitler." In fact, propaganda minister Joseph Goebbels was short and had a clubfoot. Hermann Göring, commander of the German air force, was a fat man, and Hitler had dark hair.

In general the label "Aryan" combined the ring of scientific authority with the vague, elastic quality of a new invention. It could be and was redefined as needed to fit the imperatives of race and space. The only reliable constant was the claim that "Aryan" was the opposite of "Jew."

By the early 1920s, hatred of Jews was a fixed point in Hitler's ideology. No mere opportunist, he maintained until his death a fanatical antipathy to anything he considered Jewish. Hitler's antisemitism incorporated all of the strands of previous generations. It had religious and metaphysical dimensions: he regularly spoke of Jews as evil enemies of virtue and honor. It was political, too: his theory of a Jewish conspiracy extended in every direction. At various times Hitler described Communism, capitalism, liberalism, anarchism, atheism, Christianity, Great Britain, the United States, and France as parts of some international Jewish plot. There were cultural elements to Hitler's antisemitism: he considered jazz, abstract art, and many other forms of modernism somehow degenerate and "Jewish," because, in his view, they distorted reality and lured people away from racial purity. Of course, Hitler's hostility included familiar social and economic resentments. He shared all the stereotypes of Jews as greedy bankers, legalistic pedants, lecherous males, and seductive, destructive females. "Jewish" to him meant everything he considered negative, the antithesis of the supposedly perfect Aryan. Hitler regarded Jewishness as a race, a biological fact that could not be altered by any change of religion, name, or habits. The sheer multidimensionality of Hitler's antisemitism gave it a kind of mass appeal. Many Germans could find something in it they shared, even if they did not buy the whole package.

Hitler drew on old forms of antisemitism, but he combined them in ways that produced something new. The historian Saul Friedländer has labeled Hitler's particular strain of hatred "redemptive antisemitism." By this phrase Friedländer means that Hitler combined a murderous rage with an idealistic goal. Hitler, and the hard-core Nazis who accepted his views, had a religious fervor, a fanatical conviction that attacks on Jews were necessary to save the world for Aryan Germany. Hitler stated his faith at the end of the second chapter of *Mein Kampf:* "Today I believe that I am acting in accordance with the will of the Almighty Creator: by defending myself against the Jew, I am fighting for the work of the Lord."

Hitler's view of "the Jew" was full of internal contradictions. He called Jewish men effeminate and weak yet also characterized them as sexual predators. He denounced Jews as inferior idiots yet believed they had a cunning intelligence, which made them a diabolical threat to the supposedly superior "Aryans." Certain images enabled him to reconcile these contradictory accusations, at least rhetorically. One of his favorites was that of the germ. A germ or a parasite, Hitler was fond of pointing out, was very small, even invisible, and yet it had an incredible, superhuman ability to kill. He claimed that Jews were similar: they might seem few and weak, but according to Hitler's paranoid view, they had enormous powers of destruction.

Another important feature of Hitler's ideology was its sense of urgency. According to Hitler, time was running out: it was five to midnight for the Aryan race, he warned, and the clock was ticking. The race was already dangerously polluted, he insisted; if it were not saved immediately it would perish. That notion of impending doom added an apocalyptic dimension to Hitler's thought. His belief in the necessity—and desirability—of war gave that mythical struggle concrete form. Only war would redeem the Aryan race, Hitler maintained: war in the name of racial purity and in the quest for living space.

Other traits of Hitler's worldview were also connected to his key notions of race and space. Hitler was passionately anti-Communist, although once in power he would show himself willing to make at least temporary concessions toward Communism in favor of his more central goals. Hitler blamed German Communists as well as Jews for the loss of World War I. By the late 1920s he regularly linked Communism and Bolshevism with Jews, and he accused Jews of creating Communism as part of a plot to destroy Germany. During World

War II, Hitler would return repeatedly to the idea of some diabolical Jewish–Communist plot in order to rally Germany against the Soviet Union. One of Hitler's typical terms of derision was "Bolshevik Jewish internationalists."

Hitler's ideas about women and men also fit into his worldview. He claimed that he would restore women to what he called their rightful place in the home. He regarded women's bodies as important to the state, because they produced new generations of soldiers and breeders. But women's bodies in Hitler's view could also be the floodgates to racial impurity, the means through which supposed pollutants entered the Aryan bloodstream. Some German women found such theories appealing, because they seemed to offer women a powerful position as mothers and guardians of the master race. Others recognized the misogyny inherent in Nazi ideas.

Hitler's sexism and antisemitism were mutually reinforcing. He used anti-woman images and vocabulary to belittle Jews and other so-called enemies. At the same time, he equated feminists with Jews and derided Jewish men as defilers of Aryan womanhood and champions of homosexuality and other supposed perversions. Such sexual images caught the attention of Hitler's audiences and played on many of their own anxieties.

Hitler endorsed a position that he and other National Socialists referred to as the "führer principle." The German term "der Führer" means "the leader" in English. Hitler would later take that title for himself. The führer principle meant commitment to uncontested leadership. When individuals in the Nazi organization grew powerful enough to pose a potential threat to Hitler's position, he found ways to clip their wings, even if it meant temporarily weakening the Nazi Party's base of support. Hitler believed power had to be focused in order to be effective; the crucial focal point, in his view, was himself.

As führer, Hitler demanded total loyalty from his followers. One of his most devoted associates turned out to be Joseph Goebbels, later minister of propaganda, who wrote in his diary: "I love you, AH." Hitler rewarded faithful subordinates with privileges, powers and, in special cases, access to him and his inner circle. Admittedly, spending time with the führer had disadvantages even for the most dedicated Nazis: his impromptu speeches, lectures, and dinner diatribes could last for hours and often put his listeners to sleep. Nevertheless, the Nazi focus on Hitler as leader gave the movement and subsequently the entire system a powerful dynamic that the historian Ian Kershaw calls "working toward the führer." Once his position and power were assured, Hitler did not need to issue specific orders in most cases. It was enough to let his wishes be known in general terms and his underlings would rush to fulfill and even anticipate them, in the hope of winning his favor and advancing their own careers. In the words of one Nazi functionary: "It is the duty of every single person to attempt, in the spirit of the Führer, to work towards him."

The führer principle was also linked to the goals of race and space. Hitler was convinced that he needed unquestioned power to complete his historical mission. Democracy, he claimed, was a product of Jewish-Bolshevik-liberal-internationalism; in his opinion, democratic institutions obstructed the work of "great individuals." Hitler's führer principle was both a means to achieve his policies of race and space and an end in itself.

Adolf Hitler was not a brilliant, original thinker. There was nothing really new about his ideas nor even about the way he combined them. His ideology was a mix of nineteenth-century racial theories, Social Darwinism, post–World War I resentments, antisemitism, antimodernism, and sexism dressed up in familiar symbols drawn from nationalism, mythology, and even Christianity, although Hitler and many of his closest associates actually detested Christianity, which they considered a religion for the weak. What was different was the intensity with which he held his views and his ability to captivate large audiences in such a way that many who heard him speak felt he gave voice to their own feelings and beliefs. Above all, what differentiated Hitler from the many other demagogues and ideologues in Europe between the wars was the tremendous power he achieved after he became chancellor of Germany in 1933. From that position he was able to harness an entire government—its military, diplomacy, and bureaucracy—behind implementation of his notions of race and space.

Old Fighters and "True Believers"—The Inner Circle

Hitler neither rose to power alone nor developed his ideas in a vacuum. A rather motley crew of men formed his inner circle. Three individuals who stuck with Hitler throughout his political career were Hermann Göring, Joseph Goebbels, and Heinrich Himmler. All of them would play key roles in the Nazi regime.

Hermann Göring (1893–1946) was a hero of World War I who rose through the air force to become commander of the famous Richthofen Squadron. Somewhat at a loss after the war ended with Germany's defeat and massive demilitarization, he joined the Nazi Party in 1922. One of Hitler's oldest associates, Göring had the distinction of having been wounded at the Beer Hall Putsch in 1923. Nazi lingo reserved the label "old fighters" for those of the faithful who had been members before the failed Putsch.

Hitler often presented Göring as one of Nazism's more respectable fig-

Hermann Göring delivers a speech at the District Party Day rally in Weimar in April 1931. Notice Hitler standing beside the car.

ures. Göring's father had been a judge and consular official, and he had ties with conservative and nationalist circles. Göring senior had even served as resident minister plenipotentiary in German Southwest Africa, site of the German genocide of the Herero and Nama people in 1907. In fact there is a street named after him in Windhoek, the capital of Namibia. Throughout the 1930s Hitler showered appointments on Hermann Göring: when the Nazi Party became the largest party in the German parliament, Göring became president of the Reichstag (as the German parliament was called). Göring established the Gestapo, a political police force, and was named commander-in-chief of the Luftwaffe (air force). In 1936 Hitler chose Göring to head the Four-Year Plan to prepare Germany for war. A swaggering, flamboyant individual who relished luxury and excess, Göring was also an ambitious schemer and a vicious infighter.

Joseph Goebbels (1897–1945) was a rather different kind of Nazi. A journalist and writer, he had a Ph.D. and wrote a novel called *Michael*, although it remained unpublished until the Nazi Party press picked it up in 1929. Goebbels first came into contact with members of the Nazi Party in 1924; by 1928 Hitler had made him head of propaganda. In 1933 Goebbels became minister for popular enlightenment and propaganda. He kept that post throughout the entire Third Reich, although his ambitious, energetic nature meant that he was always trying to find ways to play even bigger roles.

Goebbels was a master propagandist who excelled in stirring up hatred and orchestrating gigantic extravaganzas, such as the annual Nazi Party rallies. He was the only one of Hitler's early associates who stayed with him right to the end. When Hitler committed suicide in 1945, Goebbels did so, too: he and his wife Magda had their children poisoned before he had her and himself shot. Goebbels's extensive diaries, large parts of which have been published, reveal him to have been a "true believer," committed to Hitler as a person and to realization of his ideas.

Heinrich Himmler (1900–1945) would become, next to Hitler, the most powerful man in the Third Reich. Head of the elite Nazi guard known as the Schutzstaffel (SS) from 1929 to 1945, by 1936 he had also become chief of all German police. In these positions he presided over a vast network of offices and agencies that implemented terror and mass murder all over German-occupied Europe.

Himmler was neither flashy like Göring nor educated like Goebbels. Awkward and homely as a young man, he read voraciously and had developed his own conspiratorial view of the world even before he met Hitler in 1926. Like Hitler, Himmler feared and hated Jews and believed in the superiority of the so-called Aryan race. Himmler too was convinced that Germany had to expand to the east. Dogged and capable of meticulous attention to detail, Himmler involved himself directly in projects that targeted homosexual men and Gypsies as well as Slavs and Jews. With justification the historian Richard Breitman and others have labeled Himmler the "architect of genocide."

There were no women in Hitler's inner circle, nor did any women wield direct political power. The closest was Gertrud Scholtz-Klink (b. 1902), national women's leader from 1934 until 1945. A true believer in Hitler's

By catching Goebbels off guard, renowned photographer Alfred Eisenstaedt
captured something of the propaganda minister's sinister character. Of this image
Eisenstaedt said, "This picture could be titled 'From Goebbels with Love.'"

worldview, Scholtz-Klink described herself as fighting for Hitler's cause with
the weapons of a woman. According to Scholtz-Klink, the crowning achievement of a Nazi woman was motherhood. Her own three marriages produced
eleven children.

Hitler referred to Scholtz-Klink and her Nazi women's organizations
when it suited him to do so, but he did not consult her or for that matter seem
to take her seriously. Like many women in the Third Reich, Scholtz-Klink
played the role of the enthusiastic supporter and beneficiary of Nazism.

*Hitler on vacation, shown with Helga, the daughter of Joseph and Magda Goebbels. Helga
Goebbels, together with her brothers and sisters, was killed at her parents' orders in April
1945 before Joseph and Magda committed suicide in the bunker with Hitler.*

THE NAZI RISE TO POWER

How did Hitler come to power in Germany? It is important first to outline
some of the common—and mistaken—answers to this question. Hitler's rise
to power was not inevitable. It was neither an automatic product of Germany's
defeat in World War I nor the unavoidable result of the Great Depression. Hitler was not swept to power by a stampede of German voters hypnotized by his
oratorical skills, nor did he seize power in an illegal coup d'etat. The road that
brought Adolf Hitler into the chancellor's seat by 1933 was both less direct and

more mundane than these standard interpretations suggest. Briefly put, it was a combination of difficult circumstances, political maneuvering, luck, treachery, and miscalculation on the part of many people that catapulted Hitler into power.

The Weimar Republic

What was the situation in Germany prior to Hitler's rule? In the wake of military defeat in 1918, Germans introduced a form of government new to them: a republic based on a democratic constitution. It was called the Weimar Republic, after the city of Weimar, which served as its temporary capital until the situation in Berlin was stable enough for the government to set up shop there.

In hindsight it is easy to dismiss the Weimar Republic as a failed experiment in German democracy, nothing more than a chaotic prelude to Nazism. In fact the Weimar Republic lasted two years longer than the Nazi regime Hitler and his followers promised would be a "Thousand-Year Reich." The Weimar Republic persisted in some form for fourteen years, from its proclamation in November 1918 to Adolf Hitler's appointment as chancellor in January 1933.

The Weimar Republic witnessed considerable achievements in the political and cultural spheres as well as in foreign policy and the economy. Antidemocratic Germans often complained that the victorious powers of World War I had forced democracy on a defeated Germany. The Weimar Republic, however, was able to build on liberal and democratic tendencies within Germany that predated the war. Under the Weimar Constitution of 1919, Germany became the first major European power to give women the vote. Weimar Germany produced the most modern, innovative film industry in the world at the time, and it returned Germany to international respectability with the country's incorporation into the League of Nations in 1926. In short, the existence of the Weimar Republic by no means made Hitler's rise inevitable.

It may come as a surprise that Weimar Germany had the strongest economy in continental Europe for most if not all of its history. Its postwar recovery was eased by the fact that very little of the fighting in World War I had taken place on German soil. As a result Germany's infrastructure and industry remained mostly intact. In contrast, Germany's neighbors to the west—France and Belgium—had been demolished by the war. They sought reparations, but the Germans managed to avoid paying most of the sums charged, by negotiating the amounts downward, by falling behind on payments, and eventually by ceasing payments altogether. To the east, the territories of Poland and the Soviet Union had been on the whole less industrialized than Germany already before 1914. The enormous costs and devastation of years of war put their struggling economies even further behind the Germans.

Of course Weimar Germany faced very real economic problems itself, the most dramatic of which was inflation. In 1923 inflationary tendencies spiraled into a hyperinflation that saw the value of the German Mark plummet to impossible levels. The situation got so bad that people needed enormous quantities of bills merely to buy a loaf of bread or a glass of beer. Images of desperate Germans demanding their pay hourly before it could become worthless and moving their petty cash in wheelbarrows have become standard features in histories of the Weimar years.

The hyperinflation of 1923, however, was not simply the result of crushing reparations payments, as is often assumed. Instead it was irresponsible fiscal policies on the part of the German government during the war and an attempt to thwart French and Belgian efforts to seize reparations directly from Germany afterward that destroyed the value of the German currency. Moreover, all of Europe experienced inflation after the war, although the months of massive inflation in Germany in 1923 were especially dramatic.

As in any inflation, some Germans lost a great deal. Those on fixed incomes, such as pensioners, and people who had loaned out money, were particularly hard hit. Yet there were also big winners in 1923, as is true of every inflationary situation: people with property in forms other than money, speculators, and above all debtors who can pay back what they owe in currency worth a fraction of its value when they borrowed it. Currency reform in 1923 halted the hyperinflation and began a period of economic stabilization in Germany that lasted until the end of the decade. By the time Hitler came to power, the hyperinflation of 1923 was ten years in the past.

Weimar Germany's situation in terms of national security was also much stronger than is often recognized. The old Habsburg Empire, once Germany's rival for power in central Europe, disappeared completely in the war, leaving a small, weak Austria as Germany's neighbor to the south. Before World War I, the Habsburg Empire had ruled large parts of central and eastern Europe, including territories that lie in modern-day Austria, Poland, Hungary, the Czech Republic, Slovakia, Croatia, and other countries. After the war, those lands were organized as much smaller, independent countries that often had reasons to focus their animosities on one another rather than competing with or challenging German power in Europe.

After World War I, Germany's former rival to the east, the once formidable Russian Empire, was gone too, replaced by Lenin's new Soviet Union. Racked by civil war until the early 1920s, the Soviet Union was in no position to threaten German interests. In any case, the postwar settlement in Europe meant that Germany no longer shared a border with Russia, because the creation of an independent Poland created a buffer between the two larger nations. After 1918, Germany's immediate neighbors included Poland in the east and Czechoslovakia in the southeast—tenuous, new nations engaged in their own struggles for stability.

In short, all of Europe faced enormous economic, political, and social challenges in the 1920s. Even Great Britain, with its massive empire, was weakened after years of war. The British retained wartime rationing of bread longer after hostilities ended in November 1918 than did the Germans. The Weimar Republic had as good a chance to survive as did most of its European counterparts. Being surrounded by neighbors poorer and weaker than itself gave it some significant advantages.

World War I and the Myth of a Stab in the Back

But what about the shame of defeat? Many textbooks argue that Germans who wished to return their nation to greatness naturally turned to Hitler to lead them out of humiliation. This view is oversimplified. Military defeat need not usher in tyranny and destruction. In fact it can generate reassessment and reform, as was the case with Russian defeat in the Crimean War of 1854–1856, which prompted the tsar to free the serfs. In Germany after 1918, however, such positive change was blocked by a widespread refusal to accept the reality of defeat.

In the fall of 1918 Germany's military leadership—Generals Paul von Hindenburg and Erich Ludendorff—had insisted on suing for peace. Germany simply did not have the resources to fight on, its top generals realized. Even before the armistice was concluded, however, they began to spin the account of events to save their own reputations. It was not the military but the German civilians who had lost their nerve, they claimed. It was the disloyal, revolutionary homefront, they accused, that had stabbed the fighting men in the back and betrayed them to their enemies.

The myth of a stab in the back spread quickly. Many Germans needed an explanation for defeat in a war that their military leadership had never let on it was losing. The fact that the war ended with almost no foreign troops on German soil lent credence to the idea of betrayal from within Germany. And the notion of an undefeated military fit with comforting myths about national greatness. In the eyes of many Germans, their new, democratic government symbolized the civilian weaklings who had supposedly betrayed Germany's fighting heroes. This perception in turn undercut the authority of the Weimar Republic.

Hitler would later capitalize on the stab-in-the-back myth. He was able to do so because, by the time he appeared on the national scene, the idea had been propagated within Germany for more than a decade: by military leaders who refused to take responsibility for defeat; by nationalist professors, schoolteachers, and clergy; and by antidemocratic politicians and publicists who found it easier to live in a glorified past than to face the challenges of the present. Defeat in World War I did not make Hitler's rise to power inevitable, but the way that many Germans chose to respond to the challenges of defeat weakened the base of support of their own government and prepared the way for even more extreme manipulation of public opinion.

The National Socialist German Workers' Party in the 1920s

From its beginnings, the Weimar Republic faced a crisis of legitimacy. Its critics on the left wanted a revolutionary, Communist regime instead of a liberal, democratic republic. Conservatives and those further to the right considered the whole idea of democracy to be weak, ineffective, and non-German. Beset by extremists of all kinds, Weimar authorities tended to crack down hard on the left but treat the right with leniency.

The new government in 1918 had not purged the judiciary or the civil service, so the republic's judges, lawyers, and bureaucrats were the same people who had served the German kaiser before World War I. Many of them were less than enthusiastic about the democratic constitution they supposedly upheld. When faced with illegal actions or revolutionary efforts by Communists, they dealt out long prison terms and imposed death sentences. Rightwing extremists charged with criminal acts or caught in plots to overthrow the government received much lighter penalties. Critics of the Weimar system often fault its liberal constitution for tolerating antidemocratic movements such as the National Socialists. But there were laws that might have curbed the growth of Nazism; they were simply not enforced.

Hitler's early career is a case in point. In 1923 he was arrested for his role in the Beer Hall Putsch and charged with high treason. Instead of being a setback, the trial gave Hitler a chance to gain national publicity. He was sentenced to five years—a rather light term for someone caught in the act of trying to overthrow the government—and served a total of only thirteen months. Communists in the Weimar Republic charged with similar offenses regularly received much harsher treatment: life terms and death sentences were not uncommon for them.

Hitler spent the decade after the failed Putsch building his party. He presided over a two-pronged approach. On the one hand was the paramilitary, street-fighting wing of the movement: the SA (Sturmabteilung), or Stormtroopers. On the other hand was the legal, political party, the National Socialist German Workers' Party (NSDAP). The brown-shirted Stormtroopers, modeled after Benito Mussolini's Fascist Black Shirts in Italy, brawled with Communists and Social Democrats, harassed and attacked Jews and homosexuals, and generally used terror tactics to intimidate the public. At the same time, the existence of the Nazi Party allowed for legal actions: collecting funds, organizing local support, putting forward candidates for election, and hosting rallies and other events.

Until 1928 the NSDAP was just one of many splinter political groups vying for the attention of voters. That year brought an electoral breakthrough: for the first time the party became a force in the Reichstag, the German parliament. This first evidence of national popularity preceded the Great Depression; it was not simply economic hardship that brought some Germans to support the NSDAP, although hard times certainly brought some new voters and activists. Indeed a general climate of political polarization meant that all parties at the extremes—Nazis and ultranationalists on the right, Communists on the left—gained at the expense of the moderate middle. Over the course of the 1920s, the NSDAP became a genuine mass party with voters in all social classes: workers, members of the lower middle class, students, academics, clergy, the wealthy, women as well as men.

The 1930s and the End of Democracy in Germany

The U.S. stock market crash of 1929 was felt all over the world, not just in Germany. It is with good reason that the depression associated with that event has been called a world depression. Germany faced growing unemployment as did much of the industrialized world. Economic hardship did not make the rise of a Nazi dictator inevitable, but it did add to the challenges of the Weimar Republic.

By early 1930 economic difficulties had brought Germany into a political crisis. High taxes, increased tariffs, cuts in government spending, and deflationary policies did nothing to ease the situation. In the midst of that misery and strife, few people even noticed the evacuation of the last French troops from German soil in June 1930.

The chancellor, Heinrich Brüning, was unable to get the backing of the Reichstag for his measures. So he convinced the German president, the old war hero Paul von Hindenburg, to invoke Article 48 of the constitution. Article 48 allowed the president to govern by decree in a state of emergency. Brüning had no problem convincing Hindenburg. Never a fan of democracy, Hindenburg had long believed that parliamentary government was too chaotic. By 1930 he was an old man—some say he was senile. A joke made the rounds: one aide to another, "Don't put your sandwich paper down in front of the president. He might sign it!"

From 1930 until the end of 1932, Hindenburg and his various chancellors ruled by decree rather than relying on the democratically elected Reichstag. Democracy was essentially dead in Germany, but there were still alternatives to Hitler: some people awaited a military coup; others expected some kind of conservative, authoritarian rule.

In that climate Hitler and the Nazi Party ran in a number of important elections. In one, the presidential election of 1932, Hitler lost his bid for the presidency to the aged Hindenburg. In another, in July 1932, the Nazi Party won 37 percent of the votes cast, its highest return ever. Although some Germans later would claim that no one could resist the magnetic force of Hitler's oratory, more than 60 percent of German voters had no trouble doing so in 1932. Some of them are on record as having found his style braying, annoying, low-class, and offensive. Nevertheless, the July election brought the Nazis more seats than any other party in the Reichstag.

In the third election, in November 1932, support for the Nazis dropped, and the party lost 2 million votes. With 196 seats, it was still the strongest party in the Reichstag, but the Communists, with 100 seats, were not far behind. Some observers thought the Nazis had peaked. In his disappointment Hitler contemplated suicide and wondered whether he had missed his opportunity.

Hitler was saved, not by his own ingenuity but by the miscalculation of his rivals. Former chancellor Franz von Papen, a conservative and nationalist, convinced Hindenburg to name Hitler chancellor. Papen reckoned that giving Hitler the post would buy popular support for his own cause—he planned to make sure it did so by getting himself named Hitler's vice chancellor. From that position, he told Hindenburg, he and others loyal to the president would be able to control the Nazi upstart.

Other conservatives and some industrialists backed Hitler as well. They hoped to defuse discontent among workers and prevent any increase of Communist strength. Hitler could not do much harm, they told President Hindenburg, as long as he was surrounded with members of the cabinet who were not Nazis. Hitler for his part said he would accept the chancellorship only if he could name two of the Nazi Party members of the Reichstag as government ministers. Hindenburg agreed, and on 30 January 1933 Hitler became chancellor of Germany. Like all the members of his cabinet he swore an oath to the constitution. A photograph widely distributed in the German press showed him shaking hands with President Hindenburg. The Bavarian aristocrat Reck-Malleczewen described the look on Hitler's face as that of "a headwaiter as he closes his hand around the tip." Hitler did not need to seize power. It was handed to him.

3

FROM REVOLUTION TO ROUTINE: NAZI GERMANY, 1933–1938

L ooking back it is easy to forget that half of the Nazi era occurred before World War II began. Those first six years proved crucial. Between 1933, when Hitler became chancellor, and 1939, when German forces invaded Poland, Nazi rule revolutionized Germany. During those same years, the "Third Reich" or third empire, as Hitler and his followers called their new Germany, became routine for many Germans. This chapter examines those two phases of Hitler's rule: first, the Nazi revolution, and second, the routinization of Nazism that followed. How did Hitler begin to implement his ideas of race and space during the peacetime years of Nazi rule? How did the German public respond, and what was life like for Germans under the Nazi system?

The previous chapter outlined Hitler's worldview and described how he came to be chancellor of Germany. Throughout that discussion you might have noticed an imbalance between the ordinary aspects of Hitler's life and the extraordinary impact he had. There was nothing so unusual in Hitler's background, nor were his ideas original. Even the factors that brought him to power—misfortune, opportunism, miscalculation—were unsensational. And yet the destructive role that Hitler would play was far from ordinary. Even today, when asked to name one individual who has dominated the past millennium, many people say "Adolf Hitler."

That same dichotomy or gap between the extraordinary and the ordinary is evident throughout the entire Nazi period. On the one hand, Hitler revolutionized Germany, but on the other hand, the ways in which he did so seemed undramatic to many participants and observers at the time. Between 1933 and

1938, Nazism became everyday and ordinary for many Germans, but that routine normalized terror and legalized extraordinary persecution.

PHASE I: THE NAZI REVOLUTION, 1933–1934

Hitler's appointment as chancellor in January 1933 was in itself unspectacular. Since 1918, Germany had seen many chancellors from a range of political parties, and many of their governments had been short lived. Yet that seemingly unremarkable event on 30 January 1933 marked the beginning of a revolution that would transform German politics and society. The new chancellor lost no time in attacking the elements of the population he despised, but he did so in ways that expanded his own power even as he isolated his enemies.

Political Revolution

Hitler's political position in early 1933 was not that strong. His party's support had dropped from its July 1932 peak, and even then it had received only 37 percent of the votes cast. The Nazi Party faithful themselves were divided into factions with very different visions for Germany's future. Meanwhile, Hitler's cabinet included only two members of the Nazi Party besides himself: Hermann Göring and another longtime associate, Wilhelm Frick, as minister of the interior. The rest of the cabinet posts were assigned to conservatives and nationalists, members of the Catholic Center Party, and military men who thought they could control their inexperienced new chancellor. Instead he proved skilled at manipulating them.

Hitler made his first major move in early 1933 against the Communists, a target he chose with care. Communism could have posed a real threat to Nazi power. Like the Nazi Party, the Communist Party had local cells throughout Germany. It was well represented both in the Reichstag and in the streets, where its men had fought the Nazi Stormtroopers for more than a decade. The Communists, however, were an ideal first target for another reason as well; Hitler was guaranteed to have allies against them. Precisely those elements in German society that had helped Hitler into the chancellor's seat— conservatives, nationalists, industrialists, and military men—hated and feared Communism. They were unlikely to protest any anti-Communist measures, no matter how unconstitutional or harsh.

On 27 February 1933 the Reichstag—the German parliament building— burned down. The Reichstag fire gave Hitler the opportunity he wanted. His spokespeople insisted that Communists had torched the building, and the German press, relying on information from Nazi sources and reluctant to speak against the new regime, echoed those accusations. At the time some non-Nazi Germans assumed that Hitler's own people had started the fire, but they could do little except grumble in private, unless they were willing to risk being accused of sympathizing with the Communists. The most up-to-date research seems to indicate that the blaze was, in fact, the work of a lone, Dutch arsonist named Marinus van der Lubbe, who was linked to neither the Communist nor the Nazi Parties.

Hitler ordered massive reprisals against the German Communists in response to the fire. He had thousands arrested, tortured, and beaten; hundreds were "shot while trying to escape." That phrase was a euphemism or indirect way of saying that police or soldiers had shot them in the back. Thousands more fled into exile. Shortly after the Reichstag fire, in March 1933, German newspapers announced the opening of the first official concentration camp—at Dachau, near Munich. Among the first prisoners sent there were many Communist men.

With the actions of late February 1933, Hitler crippled Communist power in Germany. That assault was only the beginning: by the end of the Nazi regime, about 150,000 German Communists would be arrested, and many of them would be killed by 1945.

The Reichstag fire gave Hitler a pretext to dismantle what was left of Germany's democratic institutions. Pointing to the supposed risk of disorder and to his now proven ability to act decisively, he convinced the members of the Reichstag to pass the Enabling Law of 23 March 1933. The Enabling Law allowed Hitler to put through any measure without approval from the Reichstag. He no longer even needed to have the president declare a state of emergency or sign a decree. Social Democratic representatives opposed the Enabling Law, but they were the only mainstream party to do so. In effect the Reichstag was now defunct; its own members had voted it out of existence. Their reasons for doing so varied: quite a few welcomed the new regime they thought would replace the cumbersome parliamentary system they hated with authoritarian order; others felt intimidated by Nazi attacks on Communists and Social Democrats; some hoped to curry favor with Hitler and his people by proving how willing they were to cooperate.

By the end of the summer of 1933, Hitler had used his authority to dissolve or outlaw all political parties except the NSDAP—the National Socialist German Workers' Party, or the Nazi Party. Even the facade of German democracy was gone. Hitler's political revolution was not without violence, but he

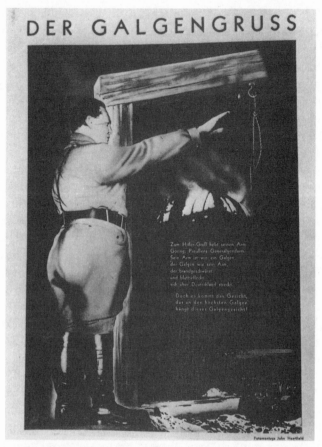

The German artist John Heartfield created this photomontage in response to the Reichstag fire in February 1933. The text, titled "The Gallows Greeting," reads: "He raises his arm for the 'Heil Hitler,' Göring, Prussia's General Policeman. His arm is like a gallows, the gallows like his arm, which blackened by fire and flecked with blood, stretches itself across Germany. But the judgment is coming that will hang this gallows-face on the highest gallows."

established his dictatorship through means that were, at least in a narrow sense of the word, legal.

Social Revolution—Testing the Waters

The Nazi revolution had immediate effects on those groups Hitler had described as enemies for years. It was not only political opponents like the

Communists who felt early blows; homosexuals, Jehovah's Witnesses, German Jews, people considered physically or mentally handicapped, and Afro-Germans all experienced attacks within the first year of Nazi rule.

Hitler and his associates in the new German leadership struck in dramatic, decisive ways, but they always tested the public response to each move before proceeding further. This mixture of boldness and caution would be typical of Nazi tactics throughout the Third Reich, from its inception in 1933 to its collapse in 1945. Public opinion was very important to Hitler. A firm believer in the stab-in-the-back myth, he was convinced that a disgruntled German public had lost Germany the First World War. He was determined to avoid a repeat of that situation under his rule.

In *Mein Kampf* Hitler had made it clear that he planned to "deal with" the Jews. He started his social revolution, however, with attacks on a group that was even less likely to receive public support: homosexual men. In the 1920s and early 1930s, Berlin and other major German cities had become centers of a small but vibrant gay culture. Even before the Nazis came to power, police had sometimes harassed men known or suspected to be homosexual; many Germans regarded homosexuality as deviant and decadent and urged their government to crack down by imposing what they considered moral and sexual order.

Since 1871, Paragraph 175 of the German criminal code had outlawed sexual relations between men: "A male who indulges in criminally indecent activities with another male or who allows himself to participate in such activities will be punished with jail." The prohibition did not mention sexual acts between women. Hitler built on this law in early 1933 to ban homosexual rights organizations in Germany. According to National Socialist teachings, homosexuals were an abomination because they opted out of the reproduction of the so-called Aryan master race. Moreover, according to Himmler and others, homosexual men in public positions of any kind were dangerous because they were always vulnerable to blackmail. Antagonistic Nazis focused on gay men; they seemed for the most part not to see lesbians or bisexual women as posing a particular threat, because women did not exercise public power by serving in the military or at high ranks of the bureaucracy. In any case women, some Nazi activists presumed, could always be forced to bear children for the German Volk, regardless of their own sexual orientation. Nevertheless, in some individual cases lesbians were persecuted as so-called asocial elements.

Leadership from above prompted initiatives by people acting out their own hostilities. In 1933, Nazi Stormtroopers and other thugs raided gay bars and clubs in German cities and forced many of them to close. A few managed to remain open longer—some intermittently until the end of World War II—but under constant threat of raids and violence. In May 1933, a group of Nazi students stormed and destroyed the Institute for Sexual Research in Berlin. Its director was the gay rights activist Magnus Hirschfeld. For the most part the German public was indifferent or cheered such offensives.

There was likewise no protest within Germany in the spring of 1933, when Nazi regulations banned the Jehovah's Witnesses. In fact, leaders of the official German Protestant and Catholic churches actively encouraged state measures against a religious group they considered a dangerous cult. Many mainstream Christians in Germany disliked Jehovah's Witnesses for their efforts to win converts; German nationalists inside and outside the churches found Jehovah's Witnesses suspect because they neither swore allegiance to the state nor in many cases served in the military.

Most Germans were just as unlikely to complain when the new regime used existing laws and conventions to bear down hard on Gypsies. Stereotyped as shiftless wanderers, Roma and Sinti had suffered police harassment and public prejudice for decades, even before Hitler came to power. Nazi persecution in its early stages hardly seemed new.

Germans of African descent were easy targets as well. They were few in number—probably only hundreds in the early 1930s—and vulnerable in their visibility; those with dark complexions stood out in a nation of white people. Some had come from Germany's former colonies in Africa—territories in modern-day Cameroon, Namibia, Burundi, and Tanzania—or were children of colonials. Some were the offspring of African soldiers or other men of color stationed in the Rhine area after 1918 as part of the French occupation forces. Many Germans had responded with panic to the appearance of black troops in their midst, and the children some of them left behind seemed to many racist Germans to be living examples of Germany's humiliation. Even before he came to power Hitler had spoken of his desire to see all Germans of African descent—people he, like others, called the "Rhineland bastards"—sterilized. The early months of Nazi rule brought attacks, official as well as spontaneous, on these people as well. Compulsory registration of all Germans deemed "half-breeds" revealed 385 such individuals, 370 of whose fathers had been part of the French occupation. In 1937 most of those 385 people were sterilized.

One German woman named Doris Reiprich recalls how her landlord evicted her and her African father, white German mother, and sister from their apartment after Hitler came to power. She lost her job, and fellow students tormented her sister, Erika, in school. Teachers were no better; they forced

Baſtarde zwiſchen Hottentotten und Weißen
(links oben Hottentottin)
Aus „Siemens, Vererbungslehre"

Schulß, Lichtbilder=Vorträge.   Vortrag II, Karte 5.

These portraits of the offspring of a union between an African woman (upper left) and a white man (not pictured) come from a set of slides illustrating a 1934 lecture on race and heredity by a researcher at the SS Race and Settlement office. The heading reads, "Bastards between Hottentots and Whites."

Erika to take part in a course on "race" and listen to such statements as "God made all whites and blacks; half-breeds come from the Devil." The authorities tried to convince the girls' mother to divorce their father, but she refused.

Both Afro-German sisters would make it through the war by acting in movies. They recount their experiences in the book *Showing Our Colors: Afro-German Women Speak Out*. German filmmakers needed a few people of color to make movies promoting German colonialism in Africa. Throughout the Nazi years most Afro-Germans had no such protective positions. Like Doris

Reiprich and her sister, they suffered a whole range of indignities and abuses, and many of them experienced even harsher treatment—sterilization, incarceration, and death.

The Nazi Revolution and the Jews

Of course the Nazi revolution also meant assault on German Jews. In 1933 Germany's Jewish population was small: about half a million people, less than 1 percent of the total population. New regulations in April banned Jews from the German civil service. That same month the Nazi Party organized a boycott of Jewish businesses throughout Germany, although the boycott was not the success its planners had anticipated.

Hitler's Nazis used a combination of intimidation and legislation to create a mood of hostility toward Germany's Jews, a kind of open season for abuse. During the boycott Stormtroopers stood outside Jewish businesses to frighten potential customers. Some Jewish children experienced vicious harassment in school from teachers as well as fellow students. Nazi activists staged public humiliations of Jews and friends of Jews. In one case, for example, they forced a gentile woman and her Jewish boyfriend to stand in the street wearing sandwich boards. Hers read, "I am the biggest pig in the place and go around only with Jews." His said, "As a Jewish boy I only take German girls to my room."

The civil service ban and the boycott were less successful for Hitler's new regime than Nazi activists had hoped. For one thing, there was no concrete definition of who exactly counted as a Jew. So it was not always clear to whom the ban applied. Given Hitler's sensitivity to public opinion, it was important not to antagonize potential "Aryan" supporters by mistaking them for Jews. Moreover, by April 1933, German Jews had not yet been isolated from the rest of population. The Nazi government did not dare impose measures against Jewish veterans of World War I, for example, or against Christian spouses of Jews. Outraged German Jews who did not yet know how far the regime would go in attacks on them deluged authorities with petitions and requests for exceptions, and sometimes non-Jews supported their efforts.

Some non-Jews, however, went even further than the civil service law to introduce anti-Jewish measures on their own. Some gentile spouses quietly divorced "undesirable" Jewish mates. In many universities, gentile administrators fired scholars who were not in fact targeted by the law, for example, Christian men with Jewish wives or people whose parents had converted from Judaism to Christianity. Removing such individuals made those supervisors look especially eager to cooperate with the new government. Students and the

This snapshot shows a woman emerging from a Jewish-owned business in violation of the April 1933 boycott. Such photos were used to denounce individuals and intimidate members of the German public into compliance with anti-Jewish measures.

other professors were not too likely to complain, because they hoped to benefit from the situation. After all, professorial positions were in high demand in German society, with its many educated people, high level of unemployment, and great respect for academics.

In the Protestant church, pro-Nazi clergy who belonged to a group called the German Christian Movement tried to expel from the pulpits any pastors who had converted from Judaism to Christianity or who were the children or grandchildren of such converts. Only a handful of clergy actually fell into those categories. Uneasy as to how Protestant church people inside Germany and abroad would respond, Nazi government authorities decided in 1933 not to back that scheme. Public opinion was still more important to Hitler than complete thoroughness. There would be time to widen the net later.

As for the anti-Jewish boycott of April 1933, it did not really catch on. Some German gentiles complained that the ban on Jewish businesses disrupted their lives and created public disorder. Many continued to frequent Jewish shops out of habit or convenience. Outside Germany there was considerable negative publicity around the anti-Jewish measures. In the United States, Britain, and elsewhere, Jews and people who generally opposed abuses of human rights threatened to organize a counterboycott of German goods to pressure the German government into curbing antisemitic behavior. Aware that the anti-Jewish boycott was damaging his public image at home and abroad, Hitler ended it.

Nazi leaders learned some lessons from these early anti-Jewish experiments. First, they realized that it was easiest to attack people who were already marginalized. Second, they learned that members of the general public were more likely to participate in or at least tolerate attacks on minorities if they stood to gain rather than to lose from such initiatives. In any case, leading Nazis found out that unanimous approval was not required. Indifference of the majority was all that was needed to carry out many plans.

German Jewish Responses

How did German Jews respond to Nazi attacks? Like Communists and homosexuals, some left the country. Departure, however, was not a simple proposition, especially for people with families and deep roots in Germany. There had been Jews in German territory for some sixteen hundred years; many Jews were at home in German society in ways that made leaving almost unfathomable. Moreover, some of the people who antisemites considered Jews did not regard themselves as Jewish at all. Over the centuries Jews had intermarried with Christians and some had converted to Christianity, but because Nazi ideology was based on the notion of blood, its adherents claimed all such people were still Jews.

Unlike Communists, who could (mistakenly) expect a haven in the Soviet Union, there was no obvious place for Jews to go. No State of Israel existed yet in the 1930s, and the traditional countries of immigrants—the United States, Canada, Australia—all had very restrictive immigration policies. Economic problems linked to the Great Depression and a climate of nativism made governments and public alike hostile to immigrants, especially those who were not Christian or did not come from western Europe.

Many German Jews tried to find new ways to pull together within Germany. They organized self-help efforts and sought to combat social isolation by providing educational and cultural opportunities for themselves. To these ends, in September 1933 a group of Jewish leaders created the Reich Representation of the German Jews to unify attempts to preserve Jewish religious life and offer practical assistance to Jews from all over Germany. The group's president, Berlin Rabbi Leo Baeck (1873–1956), would steadfastly refuse to leave even when he had opportunities to do so. As long as any Jews remained in Germany, Rabbi Baeck believed, he belonged with them.

Once German officials began deporting German Jews to the killing centers in late 1941, the Reich Representation of the German Jews lost its already very limited ability to do anything to help its members. Its leaders too were sent to camps and killing centers. In 1943 German police sent Rabbi Baeck to the ghetto and transit camp at Theresienstadt, also known as Terezin, near Prague. Rabbi Baeck survived the war and moved to London.

In 1933 some German Jews joined Zionist associations. The Zionist movement had emerged in the late nineteenth century. Its members believed that Jews were not only a religious group but a distinct people who deserved a country of their own. Zionists took their name from the biblical name "Zion," the hill in Jerusalem on which the Jewish temple had stood. They worked to establish a Jewish national homeland, and some even moved to Palestine. Before the 1930s Zionism had been rather unpopular among German Jews, but Nazi measures made many Jews in Germany think it was their only alternative. Others continued to wait and hope that somehow the storm would pass.

The Nazi Revolution and the Handicapped

The Nazi revolution advanced on all fronts in its drive for so-called racial purity. In May 1933 Hitler introduced a law to legalize eugenic sterilization, that is, sterilization to prevent reproduction by people deemed unworthy on the basis of mental or physical conditions. More radical legislation followed just two months later.

In July 1933 Hitler proclaimed the Law for Prevention of Hereditarily Diseased Offspring. It ordered sterilization of people with certain physical and psychiatric conditions. The list included people characterized as severe alcoholics, epileptics, schizophrenics, and a number of other loosely defined categories such as the "feeble-minded." Roma and Sinti were targeted too, as "asocials." Nazi minister of the interior Wilhelm Frick went so far as to suggest that 20 percent of the population should be sterilized. Ultimately the number of Germans sterilized under this law would come to less than .5 percent of the German population, but that still meant destroying the reproductive capabilities of some quarter of a million people without their consent and in many cases against their wills.

There was some criticism of the sterilization law, especially from Catholic clergy. Nevertheless proponents of the measure also found a few Catholic

This 1936 image comes from a filmstrip of the Reich Propaganda office titled "The Terrible Legacy of an Alcoholic Woman." It claims that in eighty-three years, one such woman produced 894 descendants, 50 percent of whom were "asocial," including 40 paupers, 67 habitual criminals, 7 murderers, 181 prostitutes, and 142 beggars. Taken together, these "deviants" allegedly cost the state 5 million Reich Marks.

theologians who were willing to endorse it. Meanwhile enforcement required the participation of many people: lawyers who drafted the legislation; medical and social workers who reported people to be sterilized to the authorities; bureaucrats who handled the paperwork; doctors, nurses, and aides who performed the procedures. As the Nazi regime established and reinforced its power, it involved ever larger numbers of people, who in turn developed a stake in its continuation. Through this dynamic, Nazi ideas gained acceptance, even among people who might earlier have opposed them.

The Policy of Coordination

The Nazi revolution brought rewards for those who cooperated as well as attacks on those deemed undesirable. Many Germans of all ages enjoyed participating in an exciting, dynamic movement that welcomed them as long as they were "the right kinds of people."

In 1933 Hitler and his accomplices introduced a process called Gleich-schaltung, which means "coordination," literally "shifting into the same gear." In the name of national unity, new Nazi organizations swallowed up other, independent groups and clubs. For example, the Nazi-run German Labor Front replaced the old trade unions. Nazi organizations of farmers, women, boys, girls, writers, and artists absorbed associations of people in those categories. These new groups had monopolies over their clienteles and did not tolerate competing organizations.

Local cooperation and leadership were essential to the success of "coordination." So was a bombardment of propaganda from party-controlled newspapers and publicists enthusiastic about the "national awakening." For at least some Germans the surge of group activities provided an exciting sense of belonging. Melitta Maschmann, a teenager in 1933, later described how she loved being part of the Nazi League of German Girls. It gave her a chance to assert independence from her parents, she said, and to feel like someone important, part of dramatic new developments.

Members of the League of German Girls (Bund Deutscher Mädel, or BDM) take children from large families for an airing in the park while the mothers of the infants are at work.

Hitler's government introduced all kinds of programs to win favor with the majority of the population. Enormous publicity was devoted to job creation and massive public works programs. Many people still claim that Hitler "saved" Germany from the depression, and indeed, Nazi policies did accelerate the process of economic recovery. At the same time, many of Hitler's schemes continued what his predecessors had begun, and in any case, by 1933, the depression seemed to have bottomed out in Germany. Of course Hitler took credit for all improvements, and the Nazis even set up an agency called Strength Through Joy to organize workers' leisure activities and plan holiday trips. Strength Through Joy set up package tours, such as cruises to the Mediterranean or Scandinavia or short trips within Germany. It also sponsored mass production of the "people's cars"—Volkswagens—and set up savings plans so that workers could arrange to buy them. Even fun was to appear to be a gift of the führer.

Terror and Pageantry

The Nazi revolution claimed to restore order, but from the beginning it was enforced with terror. In March 1933, not even two months after Hitler became chancellor, Nazi authorities opened the first official concentration camp. Located at Dachau, just outside Munich, its initial prisoners were political—Communists arrested in the wake of the Reichstag fire—but it also held men charged with homosexuality and common criminals. Dachau Concentration Camp was no secret. To the contrary, the Nazi press covered its opening in detail, on the theory that merely knowing it existed would serve as a public deterrent.

Dachau and the network of similar camps that followed were under the control of Heinrich Himmler, one of Hitler's longtime associates, and the SS, Nazi's elite force. By July 1933 German concentration camps held an estimated twenty-seven thousand people in what was euphemistically called "protective custody."

Violence itself served the Nazi regime as a form of propaganda. In May 1933, Hitler's minister of propaganda, Joseph Goebbels, organized public book burnings, which presented intimidating spectacles of Nazi force. Thousands of pro-Nazi students proved especially eager to participate. They and other Nazi supporters made huge bonfires of books by such Jewish authors as Albert Einstein and the satirist Kurt Tucholsky. They also burned works by Communists and others associated with left-wing positions—for example, the playwright Bertolt Brecht and the writer Heinrich Mann; liberals such as Thomas Mann;

and foreigners, including the American Jack London. Such scenes must have communicated a clear threat to outsiders and critics of Nazism.

Pageantry was the flip side of Nazi terror, another show of strength. The first months of Hitler's rule featured endless torchlight parades with columns of marching men. Observers after the fact often interpret footage of those events as evidence of the unanimity of Germans behind Hitler. It would be probably more accurate to see those demonstrations as efforts on the part of the new regime to create an image of unanimity that itself worked to prevent opposition. It must have been a lonely and terrifying experience to be on the outside of a torchlight march looking in. What chance would one feel one had against that monolith of power?

The columns of Nazis often sang as they marched. Supporters wrote reams of new songs, everything from sentimental folk songs to outright vicious fighting songs, with lyrics about "Jewish blood" spurting from German knives. The most famous Nazi song was the "Horst Wessel Lied." It was named after its lyricist, a young Nazi Stormtrooper who had been killed in a brawl with a Communist in the 1920s. Set to a familiar folk tune, Horst Wessel's lyrics extolled the Nazi flag, called for unity against the foe, and praised the comrade-heroes who had died for the cause. During the Third Reich the Horst Wessel song became part of Germany's official national anthem. It was always sung with the right arm outstretched in the "Hitler salute."

A Revolution in Foreign Policy

As he had at home, Hitler used a combination of boldness and caution to bring about a revolution in foreign policy. He was a master of making his aims look safely conventional, even while his intentions were dangerously radical. Hitler railed against the Treaty of Versailles, but so had almost all German politicians since the war. He talked about restoring German boundaries to their "rightful" location; so had many German nationalists. Hitler's plans, however, were far more ambitious, and he wanted nothing short of world domination. Nevertheless, in the first stage of his rule he used diplomacy to work toward achieving his goals.

In this regard too Hitler chose his priorities carefully. His first major foreign policy success came in July 1933. That month Hitler's representatives signed an agreement called the Concordat with the Vatican in Rome. In exchange for recognition of his regime's legitimacy from the pope, Hitler promised to respect the rights of Catholics and the Catholic Church in Germany. The pope, for his part, hoped to protect Catholic interests within Ger-

*Three boys dressed in the uniform of the Hitler Youth
(Hitlerjugend, or HJ) learn how to salute.*

many and to use Hitler's Nazi regime as a defense against Communism all over
Europe. For Hitler the Concordat turned out to be an extremely effective way
to buy support both at home and abroad.

Germany's population in 1933 was almost 40 percent Roman Catholic,
and Hitler himself was raised in the Catholic Church. Nevertheless many German Catholic clergy were initially suspicious of Nazism. They saw Nazi ideas
as anti-Christian, especially the emphasis on race and blood and the obvious
disrespect for human life. Before the Concordat, some priests in Germany had
refused to administer the sacrament of communion to church members in
Stormtrooper or SS uniforms.

The Concordat pulled the rug out from under potential Catholic opposition in Germany. How could parish priests criticize a chancellor who had been
recognized by their pope? Meanwhile, abroad the Concordat added to the
prestige of Hitler's new regime. Even if the pope no longer wielded much
political power, he still had moral authority with Catholics all over the world.

Other foreign policy successes followed. By January 1934 Hitler's diplomats had negotiated a Non-Aggression Pact with Poland that was supposed to

last for ten years. Hitler had no intention of keeping that promise, but such deals bought precious time. Meanwhile, Germany withdrew from all its multi-lateral arrangements; most notably, in October 1933, it left the League of Nations.

Under Hitler Germany actively began to rearm. Because the Treaty of Versailles restricted German military power, rearmament at first had to be secret. In 1933 Hitler's government set up a phoney initiative called the Agricultural Tractor Program, which was a cover for a project that in fact built tanks. By 1934 Germany was producing explosives, ships, and aircraft in quantity. In 1935 Hitler dropped even the pretense of secrecy. Germany had become a military power once again, with an air force, a navy, and an army based on conscription.

The Nazi revolution was difficult to oppose because it occurred with a mixture of subtlety and force. The regime did not snap into place in January 1933 as a full-blown totalitarian prison. There was still room for Germans—at least those who were not considered handicapped, Jewish, or otherwise unwanted—to maneuver, even to criticize. Precisely those mainstream members of society, however, were the least likely to recognize the revolutionary nature of the new regime. Many of them stood to gain from the measures it introduced, and others were apathetic. What did any of it have to do with them? Sadly it was exactly those in the most vulnerable positions—Nazism's targets—who were the first to recognize what was at stake. They, however, had little power to do much about it, other than to warn people like them, who often preferred to hope for the best instead of heeding alarmists, or to try to convince a busy and often hostile world of their impending doom.

A Telling Incident

An incident recounted by a German waiter and recorded in Bernd Engel-mann's book *Inside Hitler's Germany* captures the dynamics of the early months of Nazi rule. In early 1933, the man worked at a restaurant in a small town. One day a group of Nazi enthusiasts came in. The editor of the town's Nazi newspaper was there, so were the chief Stormtrooper and the local party leader. At another table all alone sat an elderly, Jewish lawyer who had lived in the town all his life.

The group of Nazi functionaries got louder and drunker. Suddenly they summoned the waiter, a young man at the time, to their table and told him to deliver a note to the lawyer. Afraid to refuse, the waiter complied, but as he put the note down on the table he saw that it said something like: "Get out, you Jewish swine."

The lawyer read the note and began trembling with rage and shame. He stood up at his table and addressed the three men. How dare you, he challenged them: "I am a veteran of the World War. I risked my life for this country." The restaurant became deathly still. No one at any of the other tables spoke or even seemed to breathe. The waiter remembered being able to hear the sounds of pots and pans in the kitchen.

The three Nazis broke the silence. They taunted the lawyer again and turned back to their beers. The lawyer summoned the waiter and, still shaking, handed him money to cover his meal, then left the restaurant.

Later the waiter realized that the man had given him far too much money for his bill. He went to the lawyer's home to return the extra. There he found the man dressed in his hat and coat with a suitcase in his hand. He was leaving, he told the waiter, because there was no future for him in Germany.

What would have happened to any of the other Germans at that restaurant if they had spoken in defense of the Jewish man? At that point, in early 1933, probably very little. The aggressors were drunken bullies new to their roles. The observers likely knew them personally, as they did the lawyer. So why did they say nothing? Perhaps they did not want to risk an unpleasant, embarrassing scene. Maybe they would have taken the chance for someone else, a woman, say, or a Christian clergyman. In any case, they were silent, and their silence emboldened the ruffians. All over Germany the silence of others like them sent a message back up to Hitler: it was safe to keep pushing.

The Night of Long Knives and the End of the Revolutionary Phase

The end of Nazism's revolutionary phase can be marked with reference to a specific event—the so-called Night of Long Knives, also known as the Röhm Putsch, of 30 June 1934. Ernst Röhm (1887–1934) had been Hitler's associate since the early 1920s, when he had been instrumental in building up the Stormtrooper organization. By 1934 Röhm was head of 2.5 million Stormtroopers. A veteran of World War I, Röhm and his Stormtroopers had played a powerful role in destabilizing the Weimar Republic and consolidating Hitler's new regime. After some professional setbacks and personal scandals, Röhm immigrated to Bolivia in 1928, but Hitler brought him back to Germany in 1930 to reorganize the Stormtroopers.

After Hitler became chancellor, he began to view the Stormtroopers as a liability. Restless for action and disgruntled with what seemed a slow pace of change, many of them thought Hitler had sold out their movement's ideals for the sake of respectability. The SS, or Schutzstaffel (protective staff), Nazism's elite guard headed by Himmler, had grown more powerful and wanted the upper hand over its rival organization, the Stormtroopers. Meanwhile the army and Hitler's new conservative friends considered the Stormtroopers disreputable thugs who disrupted the public order.

Hitler had to choose. Would he cast his lot with the SS and the army or be loyal to his old brown-shirted Stormtrooper allies? He decided to drop the Stormtroopers. On the night of 30 June 1934, on Hitler's orders, the SS struck.

It is often said that a revolution devours its own children. Hitler's revolution was no exception. In a bloody rampage, SS men fanned out to kill Röhm, other old allies of the führer such as the Nazi ideologue Gregor Strasser, and Hitler's rivals, including former chancellor General Kurt Schleicher and, for some reason, Schleicher's wife. In general, Hitler and SS leader Himmler used the purge to get rid of people they found problematic. The list of dead even included a Catholic priest who had helped write *Mein Kampf* when Hitler was in prison. Perhaps that man was a victim of mistaken identity, or Hitler may have thought he knew too much to be trusted.

The total number of people killed is unknown. Some place it as low as 150; others estimate it in the thousands. At least eighty high-ranking Stormtroopers were shot. The numbers of more lowly individuals killed on local initiatives, that is, not on direct orders from Hitler or Himmler, may have been much higher. Hitler did not dismantle the Stormtroopers completely after the purge, but he clipped the organization's wings and subordinated it to the SS.

Hitler dressed the bloodbath in the guise of conventional morality. Ernst Röhm was openly homosexual. Hitler had known about Röhm's sexual preferences for years and never seemed to have considered them a problem. Now, however, in his bid for legitimacy, Hitler publicly reviled Röhm. The killings, Nazi press reports contended in lurid detail, were part of a cleanup of the movement, a necessary measure against decadence and perversion.

How did the German public react? You might expect shock or horror. In fact there was little of either expressed in Germany, at least in public. President Hindenburg sent Hitler a telegram of congratulation for restoring order, and German military leaders likewise praised what they considered appropriate measures in the interest of public safety. Members of Hitler's cabinet declared the purge retroactively legal. Many observers believed that now the Nazi regime had become an ordinary government, its dangerous, extremist days behind it.

Victor Klemperer, a German professor of Jewish background in Dresden, had a different opinion. After such blatant criminality, he was certain that the regime of brutes had to fall. Surely the old German elite would come to its senses and throw out the upstarts, he hoped, but Klemperer was wrong. The Night of Long Knives left Hitler stronger than ever.

PHASE II: ROUTINIZATION, 1934–1937

June 1934 marked a turning point in the Nazi regime. By no means did it signify the end of brutality, but it did usher in a new phase of routinization. Instead of uncontrolled, revolutionary shows of force, Nazi authorities concentrated on systematizing violence and normalizing coercion. They did so by centralizing power in the hands of a few and passing laws to make their measures at least look respectable. Inventing rituals and convincing people to police their own behavior in keeping with Nazi regulations were also parts of the process.

Centralization of Power

One component of routinization was centralization, which took many forms. One of the most significant was the centralization of police power under Heinrich Himmler and the SS. The Night of Long Knives brought the Stormtroopers under Himmler's control. In 1934, Himmler, along with his associate Reinhard Heydrich, who ran the intelligence office known as the Security Service, took over all political police, known in Germany as the Gestapo. By 1936 Himmler had pulled the criminal police into his orbit as well, so that the head of the SS and the concentration camps was now in charge of all police forces in Germany.

Himmler and his tens of thousands of SS men were crucial to the Third Reich. Unlike the German military, the SS was officially linked to the Nazi Party organization, not to the government of Germany. Throughout the Third Reich, the Nazi Party retained its own separate hierarchy with headquarters in the Brown House in Munich. Its status as attached to the party gave the SS an unprecedented degree of independence from any kind of authority that predated Hitler's rise to power. The SS was an ideologically dynamic organization that combined the functions of a conventional, repressive political police with a drive to implement the "führer's idea." Himmler saw his goal as defending "purity of the blood" and persecuting those who he believed threatened it:

Communists, Freemasons, Jehovah's Witnesses, homosexuals, Jews, Gypsies, and others.

In August 1934 President Hindenburg, the man who had appointed Hitler chancellor of Germany, died. In another act of centralization, Hitler united the offices of president and chancellor in his own person. That change did not substantially alter Hitler's actual duties, nor did the president's death remove a major obstacle to the expansion of Hitler's power. Hindenburg had done little to check Hitler's activities in the first year and a half of Nazi rule. Nevertheless, for some Germans the death of the old man Hindenburg meant the end of any hope that Hitler and Nazism would be stopped.

There were also practical repercussions to the uniting of the offices of chancellor and president in the person of the führer. According to the German constitution, still officially in force, the president was the supreme commander of the German armed forces. Hitler now claimed that position for himself and used it to require members of the military to swear an oath of personal allegiance to him.

Legalization

A second component of routinization involved legalizing Nazi measures. The goals of Hitler and the Nazi "true believers," as we have seen, were two-fold: "racial purity" and spatial expansion. In this phase of development after the Nazi revolution of 1933–1934, pursuing those goals meant revamping German law. Members of all professions—teachers, journalists, doctors—served the Nazi cause, but lawyers and judges played an especially important role in giving the regime and its measures a veneer of legitimacy that was important to at least some Germans.

The first minister of justice under Hitler, Franz Gürtner, was not a Nazi, although he supported authoritarian rule. Gürtner was prepared to sanction the blatant illegalities of the revolutionary phase, including attacks on Communists and the Röhm Putsch massacre. Justice Minister Gürtner also presided over laying the legal foundations for what would become mass murder of people considered handicapped and of Jews.

The key pieces of legislation when it came to attacks on Jews were the Nuremberg Laws, passed in the fall of 1935. The laws had two parts. First was the Law for Protection of German Blood and Honor, which forbade marriage or sexual relations between Jews and "Aryan" Germans. Jews could not fly the German flag nor employ German gentile women under age forty-five in their households. Such measures were intended to isolate German Jews from the rest of the population and stigmatize them as disloyal, destructive outsiders.

The second component was the Reich Citizenship Law of November 1935. This legislation defined, for the first time, who was to count as a Jew in Nazi Germany. According to Nazi ideology, Jewishness was a racial trait, but in fact there was no way to measure distinctions of blood, because they did not actually exist. In other words, there were no reliable markers of appearance, blood type, or any other physical traits that Nazi "experts" could use to separate Jews from "Aryans." Instead the Nuremberg Laws fell back on religion as the only way to define Jews.

Under the law it was not one's own religion but that of one's grandparents that mattered. People with three or more grandparents of the Jewish faith counted as Jews. Most Germans defined as "Jews" under the law lost the rights associated with German citizenship.

The Nuremberg Laws considered people who had two grandparents of the Jewish faith to be "Mischlinge," or "mixed bloods," a category that would remain in dispute throughout the entire Third Reich. Mischlinge who were Jewish by religion or who married people categorized as Jews also counted as Jews. Some Mischlinge who had no contact with Judaism or Jews likewise ended up being treated as Jews, perhaps because they looked stereotypically Jewish or had especially hostile neighbors or coworkers. There were, however, Mischlinge who managed to continue living in German society throughout the Nazi period, and a few of them even served in the German military in World War II. The law did not address people with one Jewish grandparent, but in practice some of them would also face disadvantage and discrimination of various kinds.

The Reich Citizenship Law offered no definition of "Aryan" other than the implied opposite of "non-Aryan" or "Jew." Thus, by default, Germans with four grandparents who were baptized into a Christian church were generally assumed to be "Aryans."

Most non-Jewish Germans gave little thought to the Nuremberg Laws. They seemed just one more bureaucratic measure that would have little direct impact on their lives. Nor did the international community regard the laws as especially significant. After all, every nation reserved for itself the right to determine who counted as its citizens, on what basis, and what rights they received.

Their mundane appearance notwithstanding, the Nuremberg Laws proved to be a crucial step toward the destruction of Germany's Jews. All kinds of attacks on Jews were now directly sanctioned, even mandated, by law.

Moreover, once Jews were defined, it would be much easier to isolate, rob, deport, and eventually kill them.

Although focused on Jews, the Nuremberg Laws had repercussions for other target groups as well. Regulations that followed meant that under certain conditions, Gypsies, as "alien to the Aryan species," could also lose the rights of German citizens. They too faced prohibitions on marrying so-called Aryan Germans. Eager German racists applied measures described in the Nuremberg Laws to Afro-Germans as well. One woman remembers how as a small girl she was sent home by a teacher who forbade her, as a "non-Aryan," to march behind the German flag.

The phase of routinization also brought increased measures against homosexuals. In June 1935, Paragraph 175 of the German criminal code was revised to expand the definition of "criminally indecent activities between men." The courts had free rein against anyone accused of homosexuality, and they used that power to impose a crackdown that brought thousands of men accused of homosexual behavior into prisons and concentration camps.

Meanwhile, Nazi sterilization developed its own routines, and new regulations extended the assault on those considered handicapped. For example, a 1935 law required any pregnant woman who should have been sterilized under the 1933 law but had not been to have an abortion. The laws and regulations already introduced against people deemed handicapped routinized worsening conditions in institutions and hospitals around Germany. What kind of treatment would you expect healthcare workers to mete out toward people whose government labeled them "useless eaters" and "unworthy lives"?

Ritualization

In addition to centralization and legalization, a third component of Nazi routinization was ritualization. After the first year, Nazi pageantry developed a ritualized rhythm. The largest event was the annual Party Rally, held each year in the southern German city of Nuremberg. It was an enormous spectacle, choreographed by propaganda experts to the smallest details. As with the early torchlight marches, these imposing shows of strength were supposed to create a sense of unanimity and invincibility so that any opponents of the system would feel isolated and helpless. In 1934 the German director Leni Riefenstahl filmed the rally and released it under the title *Triumph of the Will*. It has become one of the most famous propaganda movies of all time.

Later some Germans would describe their participation in these Nazi extravaganzas as among the high points of their lives. In particular children seemed very impressed. Alfons Heck, a member of the Hitler Youth from a small town near the French border, described his trip to the Nuremberg Party Rally in 1935 in his book *A Child of Hitler,* which he wrote many years later. Heck was awed by the pageantry, the uniforms, and the scale of the whole affair. No doubt those sensations contributed to his own devotion to the Nazi cause and his desire to share in such amazing power.

Of course, for others inside Germany Nazi spectacles brought other kinds of routines—predictable harassment and the drudgery of confinement. In preparation for the 1936 Olympics in Berlin, an event that Nazi organizers used to showcase the "new Germany" in all its splendor, police forced about six hundred Gypsies out of Berlin into detention in a camp near a sewage dump and the cemetery in the nearby suburb of Marzahn. Guarded by police and their dogs, the camp had only three water pumps and two toilets. Under those conditions, contagious diseases ran rampant. Doubtless the glories of the Third Reich looked rather different from the vantage point of what amounted to an overcrowded, filthy, open-air prison.

Self-Coordination

A fourth important aspect of routinization might be called self-coordination. In the years between 1934 and the beginning of the war, Nazism lost much of its momentum. Some people became disillusioned or bored with the new system, but most of the population, even those who were not overly enthusiastic, fell into the habit of going along with the regime. They grumbled in private, perhaps, or expressed their criticism in ineffective forms, such as jokes. In either case they posed no real threat to Nazi control.

One popular joke that poked fun both at Hitler's pretensions and at public gullibility went as follows. Hitler and Goebbels were driving through the German countryside when their car struck a dog. Hitler, who loved animals, was devastated. "Go and find the masters of that loyal German dog," he ordered his minister of propaganda. "Apologize to them in the name of the führer." Some time later Goebbels returned, beaming and bearing all kinds of gifts: bread, sausage, and beer. "What happened?" Hitler demanded. "Were they unhappy?" "Not at all, mein Führer," Goebbels answered. "All I said was 'Heil Hitler! Der Hund ist tot' [The dog is dead], and they began to celebrate."

Self-coordination also involved self-policing. Since 1933 a law called the Malicious Practices Act had banned remarks that offended or subverted Nazi authority. Such prohibitions can only be effective if people report one another, and they did so in Nazi Germany. Throughout the 1930s denunciations poured into the offices of the Gestapo, the political police in charge of crimes against the state. Some people denounced others in order to demonstrate their own loyalty to the Nazi cause. Others sought to better their positions, attack outsiders, or just carry out old grudges. The prevalence of denunciations and police raids inspired German wits to invent two new national "saints," Maria D'enunciata and Marie Haussuchung—that is, Holy Mary the Denouncer and Mary of the House Searches.

Fear of denunciation led people to develop what became known as the "German glance"—the quick look over the shoulder before one spoke to see who might overhear. The SD or Security Service employed an elaborate network of infiltrators and informers whose job it was to report in detail on the public mood across Germany. Nazi routinization depended on consensus and co-option as well as coercion.

Nevertheless Nazi Germany cannot simply be characterized as a "police state." Indeed, as the historian Robert Gellately has shown, there were in fact relatively few police per capita in Germany in the 1930s. A high level of cooperation from the general public, not an unusual number of men in uniform, made Nazi control possible. Smooth functioning of the system did not require all Germans—or even most—to share every tenet of Nazi ideology. Enough enthusiasts could always be found to stage enormous public shows of support, such as the annual Nuremberg Party rallies. On a day-to-day basis, the Nazi regime only needed most people to obey the law, try to stay out of trouble, and promote their own interests as best they could under the current circumstances.

Preparations for War

Even during the period of routinization Hitler did not lose sight of his goals of race and space. In various ways he presided over Germany's preparation for war. After two years of secret rearmament, in 1935 Hitler's government went public. It reintroduced conscription and revealed its new military machine to the world.

No one had altered the Treaty of Versailles, but German contravention of its terms had become routine under the Nazis. The victors of World War I were not in a position to risk a new conflict in order to check German violations. Impoverished by the war and the difficult years that followed and faced with their own problems at home, the British and the French had no desire to play the role of international police. The United States had retreated into isolationism, and most of its people opposed its government involving them again in the turmoil of European affairs.

In 1936 Hitler took his biggest foreign policy gamble so far. Under the Treaty of Versailles, the westernmost part of Germany along the Rhine River had been demilitarized to provide a buffer zone for France. A year after reintroduction of conscription, rumors began to circulate that Hitler intended to reoccupy the Rhineland with Germany's new military. For some months he seemed to waver, waiting until the Olympic Games in Berlin had ended and collecting the views of his inner circle, Germany's diplomats, and military leaders. By the beginning of March, he had made his decision.

Hitler made the announcement in a speech on 7 March to the Reichstag and, by radio, to the people of Germany. It was a lengthy and in places emotional speech, which denounced Versailles and railed against Communism. Hitler saved the punchline for the end. "In the interest of the primitive rights of a people to the security of its borders and safeguarding of its defense capability," he proclaimed, "the German Reich government has therefore from today restored the full and unrestricted sovereignty of the Reich in the demilitarized zone of the Rhineland." The six hundred deputies in the Reichstag, all in Nazi uniform, went wild, stretching out their arms in the Nazi salute and screaming "Heil!"

Meanwhile, German troops were approaching the Hohenzollern Bridge across the Rhine River in the city of Cologne. Propaganda minister Goebbels had arranged for planeloads of journalists to be on hand to record the event, and thousands of Germans crowded into nearby streets to cheer the soldiers as they crossed into the demilitarized zone. Even in this moment of national euphoria, Hitler and his advisers retained some caution. They made sure that the forward troops were instructed to withdraw if they met military resistance from the French. As Hitler had expected, the French did not respond by sending in their own troops. Instead the gamble paid off by giving Hitler's prestige at home its most enormous boost yet.

Even as he publicly pledged his commitment to European peace, Hitler announced to his inner circle in 1936 that Germany must be ready for war within four years. To that end he named his old associate Hermann Göring head of a "Four-Year Plan" to prepare the German economy and military for war. Göring took over economic planning, and the old minister of the economy resigned.

In the winter of 1937–1938, Hitler completed the routinization and consolidation of his rule by dumping the old elites who had been so instrumental in bringing him to power. Those old-fashioned conservatives had been useful throughout the phases of Nazi revolution and routinization. They had lent respectability to the regime when it needed it and had provided expertise and continuity as it consolidated its power. Now, as Hitler prepared to move to a more aggressive phase, they had become a burden.

In November 1937 Hitler met with leaders of the German army, navy, and air force. It had been two years since Germany had announced its rearmament. Since 1936 German forces had been involved in the Spanish Civil War on the side of General Francisco Franco and the enemies of the Spanish Republic. Hitler had pushed German intervention even though many Germans opposed it. Because the Soviet Union backed the Republic in Spain, support of Franco gave Hitler a way to attack Communism. Moreover, Mussolini was actively behind Franco as well. So Spain offered a chance for Germany and Italy to practice cooperation in the spirit of their leaders' mutual admiration. For the Germans the Spanish Civil War was also an opportunity to try out new military equipment. In particular they broke in their new air force by bombing Spanish towns and cities. Now Hitler was ready to risk more.

Hitler gave those gathered at the November meeting a lengthy harangue on Germany's need for more space. They were skeptical. How could Germany be ready for war? Hitler's response to their misgivings was typical. In early 1938 he launched a purge of the military leadership, replacing old conservatives with men more amenable to Nazi plans. He retired fourteen senior generals, replaced or pensioned approximately sixty others, and assumed command of the armed forces as minister of war.

Hitler made a clean sweep of all positions directly related to his plans for war. He replaced the conservative foreign minister Constantin von Neurath with the loyal Nazi Joachim von Ribbentrop. The Nazi general Walter von Brauchitsch became head of the army in place of Werner von Fritsch. There were new Nazi ambassadors to Rome, Tokyo, and Vienna.

Hitler's methods in early 1938 were quite different from those he had used to purge the Stormtroopers less than four years earlier. This time he employed less violent means, in keeping with the stature of the individuals involved and the spirit of routinization rather than revolution. But the tactics were no less vicious for all their bloodlessness. For example, Hitler disposed of the war minister Werner von Blomberg by stirring up a scandal around his new wife. She was a former prostitute, the Nazi press claimed; how could a man thus compromised hold a position of such responsibility? The fact that both Hitler and Göring had served as witnesses at the wedding was conveniently omitted, and Blomberg went abroad in disgrace.

Two years earlier, rumors of homosexual activities on the part of Fritsch, the head of the army, had been ignored. Now Fritsch had to go, and the old charges provided the perfect means to force him out. He, like the others, had served his purpose; he had supported Hitler's regime in its early stages and helped provide it with a veneer of legitimacy by linking the new system to familiar, experienced military leaders. After four full years in power Hitler had consolidated his position, and preparations for war were under way. It would become much more difficult to challenge Nazi rule now that not only the police but the military was firmly in hand.

Contrary to the image presented by Nazi propaganda—Germans marching in massive columns, their arms raised as one in the salute to Hitler—not all Germans fell into line. Friedrich Thimme, a trained historian and fervent German patriot who had headed the Foreign Office's division on the so-called War Guilt Question in the 1920s, railed in his private and not-so-private correspondence against Hitler and his henchmen and refused to break ties to his Jewish friends. Thimme's daughter Annelise, a teenaged schoolgirl in Berlin in the early years of the Third Reich, announced to her classmates that obviously the Nazis had lit the Reichstag fire themselves, and she scoffed at Nazified teachers who preached the party line in the classroom. With a group of high-spirited schoolmates, Annelise once played a trick on one of the worst offenders. One at a time the girls rode by the teacher, who was on her own bicycle, calling out "Heil Hitler" so that the woman repeatedly had to raise her right arm in salute until she lost her balance and fell. In a small way, that youthful prank reveals the continued presence in Hitler's Germany of people who for all kinds of reasons—family ties, personal loyalties, religious and moral principles, political allegiances—remained skeptical and even critical of their government and its actions.

In early 1938, however, most Germans were not thinking about challenging Nazi rule. Looking back on his youth in Germany, Alfons Heck can see some of the factors that made him an enthusiastic Nazi. There was the indoctrination in school and in the Hitler Youth, for example, and the unrelenting propaganda. But there were also concrete ways that Nazism benefited him. It promised action, rewards for his ambition, power, a chance to be an insider, and a role in something enormously successful. Heck, like many of Hitler's German supporters, was no brainwashed automaton. He was just one of millions of "ordinary people" who, for all kinds of ordinary reasons, endorsed and accepted a brutal system.

4

OPEN AGGRESSION: IN SEARCH
OF WAR, 1938–1939

By early 1938, Nazi rule had become a familiar routine for most Germans. For some, such as the eager young Hitler Youth member Alfons Heck, it was a comfortable yet exciting existence. Ambitious and enthusiastic, Heck could expect to realize his goal of becoming an airplane pilot. After all, was not Germany becoming richer and stronger? Its new air force beckoned him; his teachers and the books and newspapers he read assured him the future was his. Born in 1927, Heck could hardly remember the Nazi revolution. The normalization of Nazi power coincided with his development of political and social awareness. It was really the only world he knew.

For others, such as Victor Klemperer, professor of French literature in Dresden, routinization of Nazi rule meant an ever-tightening trap. The university dismissed Klemperer in 1935, even though he was both a convert from Judaism to Christianity and a veteran of World War I. One insult and deprivation followed another. Klemperer was forbidden to publish. He lost borrowing privileges at the library, and eventually library staff refused even to let him use the reading room. Over the years Nazi regulations robbed Klemperer of his car, his house, his driver's license, even his pets. If the years from 1933 to 1938 seemed to fly on magical wings for the young Nazi boy Heck, for the middle-aged "non-Aryan" Klemperer they crawled by, an endless drudgery of discouragement and abuse. The years ahead would be even worse.

Beginning in early 1938, Hitler's Germany entered the third phase of its development. After the euphoric phase of revolution and the consolidating phase of routinization, Hitler and his inner circle took off the gloves and began

81

actively seeking war. For Hitler war was more than military conflict; it was to be a decisive step toward realizing his ideas. By 1938 he had already prepared the ground by rearming, isolating target groups, and appointing loyal supporters in key positions. Now, open aggression would characterize developments in Nazi Germany even before the invasion of Poland in September 1939.

This chapter outlines some of the key events of that turbulent period in 1938 and 1939: annexation of Austria in March 1938; the Czech crisis later that year; the so-called Kristallnacht pogrom in November 1938; the Hitler–Stalin Pact; and the beginnings of a program to kill Germans deemed handicapped. In dramatic ways, Hitler began to realize his goals of race and space even before he got the war he wanted.

SKEPTICISM AND SUCCESS

Contrary to the stereotype, most Germans were not foaming at the mouth, eager for war, in 1938 and 1939. In fact, the German public as a whole, including many people who were enthusiastic about aspects of the Nazi domestic program, would greet with skepticism many of the moves that Hitler and his Nazi elite would make in this phase of open aggression. It was one thing to assert German strength and revolutionize conditions at home, but it was quite another to risk war when, for many Germans, memories of the previous war remained painfully fresh. Such uneasiness, however, was not enough to derail Hitler's plans. Instead he was able to use 1938 and 1939 to construct a unified front for the cause of race and space. He did so by resorting to such old loyalties as nationalism, patriotism, and solidarity against common enemies. Even more important, he built support through success.

It is often said that nothing succeeds like success. Certainly Nazi Germany seems to confirm that saying. Every time Hitler took a risk and won, he decreased the anxiety among the German people and convinced more of them to trust him. Many feared war because they dreaded bloodshed, personal and financial loss, and defeat. The wounds of world war and especially its bitter outcome in 1918 were still raw for most adults, but what they perceived to be Hitler's foreign policy triumphs in 1938–1939 did a great deal to relieve their concerns.

Events in 1938–1939 demonstrate how domestic and foreign policies were intertwined in Hitler's Germany. Foreign policy successes helped ease concerns and buy support at home. Meanwhile Hitler's regime pursued the goals of race and space on both fronts: abroad it attacked Germany's supposed enemies and took steps toward a military offensive; at home it enforced "racial purity" and trained its people for war.

THE ANSCHLUSS—GERMAN ANNEXATION OF AUSTRIA

The first of Hitler's string of foreign policy successes in 1938 and 1939 was the Anschluss, the German annexation of Austria in March 1938. The Treaty of Versailles had forbidden Austria and Germany from uniting. In 1936, in order to placate Mussolini's Italy, Hitler had issued assurances that Germany would not violate Austrian independence. Mussolini and some other Italians were worried about German designs on Austria because they hoped to annex parts of Austria themselves. Like all of Hitler's promises, that pledge to respect Austrian independence was made to be broken.

In early March 1938, the Austrian chancellor Kurt von Schuschnigg announced a plebiscite to show Austria's determination to resist Nazi power. The next day, Hitler called together his military leaders to address the possibility of German occupation. It took only hours to prepare a plan; Hitler ordered German forces to cross the border into Austria on 12 March.

The plan was no work of genius. Supposedly, German tanks had to stop at commercial gas stations to refuel on the way. Rumors were that one commander relied on Baedeker's guide, a popular handbook for tourists, to plot his route. Nevertheless the Germans arrived, greeted by cheering crowds.

Contrary to the impression created by the Hollywood movie *The Sound of Music,* most Austrians did not oppose the German invasion. In fact the Anschluss sparked vicious displays of antisemitism within Austria. Austrian gentiles, sometimes urged on by Germans but often acting on their own, seized the opportunity to assail their Jewish compatriots. They stole their property, harassed and beat them, and subjected many to public rituals of humiliation. For example, in Vienna, crowds took delight in forcing professors, artists, journalists, and other prominent Austrian Jews to scrub streets with toothbrushes. Decades after the war a small statue in Vienna commemorates the "Jew with a toothbrush" and reminds Austrians of the complicity of ordinary people from their country in the crimes of Nazism.

The other European and international powers did not try to stop the German annexation of Austria. Many foreign observers saw the event simply as Germans taking control of their own backyard. Meanwhile German authorities together with local supporters moved quickly to implement the Nazi revolution in Austria. Measures against Jews, Gypsies, the disabled, and others that had been implemented over five years in Germany were rushed through in the new Nazi lands within months. Members of target groups in Austria had even fewer options to help themselves than did their counterparts within the pre-1938 German borders.

Initially there were some popular misgivings about the Anschluss within Germany itself. Many Germans worried that this blatant defiance of the Versailles settlement could mean war. When the response instead was accolades within Austria and assent around Europe, they too welcomed this destruction of an independent nation as a legitimate expression of German strength. Once again Hitler had followed his familiar pattern, push forward hard and wait to see if anyone pushes back. If not, keep pushing.

Memoirs by Austrian Jews provide moving accounts of the impact of the Anschluss. In her memoir, *Still Alive,* Ruth Klüger, a young girl in Vienna in 1938, recalls the events of that year. She remembers lying in her bed hearing bands of men march by outside singing the song about "Jewish blood" spurting from German knives. One day her mother sent her to see the movie *Snow White and the Seven Dwarfs.* The girl was afraid to go; she knew Jews were not allowed in the cinema. Ridiculous, her mother insisted; no one would bother a child. They did bother, young Ruth learned. She ended up sitting next to

A member of the Reich Department of Health, Racial Hygiene, and Population Biology Research visits a Roma family in Vienna sometime in 1938 or 1939 to gather data. Such information was used to monitor Gypsies; for scholars it provided material for publications and career advancement.

the teenaged leader of the neighborhood Nazi girls' club, who threatened and shamed her. Sometimes children grasped more quickly than adults how things had changed.

THE SUDETENLAND CRISIS

Emboldened by success in Austria, Hitler made his next move against Czechoslovakia. He was willing to risk war; in fact he sought it and was disappointed in 1938 when it did not happen. With regard to Czechoslovakia the issue used to generate a crisis was the ethnic German minority in the Sudetenland, near the border with Germany.

In the summer of 1938, members of the ethnic German minority became increasingly vocal with complaints of mistreatment at the hands of the Czech government. Nazi agents from Germany encouraged and provoked their discontent. In response to reports that Hitler planned military action to rescue the ethnic Germans of the Sudetenland, the Czechs began to mobilize their own forces. They also appealed to the French and the British for help.

Alarmed at the risk of war, representatives of the European powers agreed to meet with Czech and German negotiators to seek a resolution. At the Munich Conference in September 1938, French and British delegates decided Czechoslovakia should cede the Sudetenland to Germany. The area had a substantial ethnic German population, they reasoned, and if they made this concession to Hitler's demands, he and his supporters would be satisfied.

Decades after the Munich Conference, it and its most famous spokesman, British prime minister Neville Chamberlain, are still synonymous with the term "appeasement." The term is almost always invoked with contempt, and Chamberlain is mocked for his triumphant announcement that he and his colleagues had achieved peace in their time. Some critics even suggest that the appeasers were somehow responsible for the Second World War, as if a harder line from them in 1938 would have melted Nazi aggression.

It is neither fair nor accurate to accuse Chamberlain and the others so harshly. They wanted peace, whereas Hitler was set on war. Instead of rejoicing at his successful maneuver, Hitler felt cheated when his representative, Göring, returned to Berlin with a negotiated settlement giving Germany control of territories that had belonged to Czechoslovakia. Hitler worried that the optimum moment for war might have passed him by, because Germany's enemies would now have time to prepare for confrontation. A show of force at Munich from the British and the French would not have prevented war. It would only have moved it to a timetable that Hitler himself considered preferable.

This time too there were misgivings at home. At the peak of the war scare, Protestant church leaders sponsored prayers for peace that landed a number of pastors in prison for their implied criticism of Hitler's actions. Within the army, some of the top brass worried about what seemed a slide toward a war they thought Germany could not win. There were even some tentative plans for a coup against Hitler in case it came to hostilities. All came to nothing. Instead Hitler's successful bid for the Sudetenland—although he regarded it as a failure—gave his prestige within Germany another substantial boost.

In 1939, just months after the Munich Conference granted Sudetenland to Germany, German troops entered the rest of Czechoslovakia. On Hitler's orders the state was dismantled. Parts were incorporated into the German Reich, and other parts were set up as a protectorate, a kind of colony. Slovakia became a semi-independent client state under the government of the anti-semitic Catholic priest Josef Tiso.

Those who blame the supposed harshness of the Treaty of Versailles for the rise and expansion of Nazism would do well to note the considerable territories the Germans had gained even before war began in 1939. By the end of 1938 Germany had already recouped most of its World War I losses. With the destruction of Czechoslovakia in 1939, Germany acquired lands it had never controlled before, but Hitler was not satisfied. His ambitions went far beyond merely revising the terms of Versailles.

THE KRISTALLNACHT POGROM

The year 1938 also signaled a heightened wave of aggression in racial policies. The most dramatic expression of this new stage of Nazism was the attack on Jews in Germany and Austria on the night of 9–10 November 1938. Nazi leaders called the pogrom the Kristallnacht (in English, the "night of broken glass"), and that name continues to be used.

In October 1938, the German government expelled more than fourteen thousand Jews who resided in Germany but were citizens of Poland. The order was a response to a decree issued by the Polish ministry of the interior requiring all Polish citizens living outside the country to revalidate their passports or lose the right to return. Worried that they would be stuck with these people, German authorities struck first. Transports dumped the Jews of Polish citizenship at the Germany–Poland border, where Polish authorities refused them entry.

Forced to spend desperate weeks in limbo, they were finally permitted into Poland after Jews inside the country promised to give them shelter.

The parents of Herschel Grynszpan, a seventeen-year-old student in Paris, were among those Jews thrown out of Germany. Enraged at his parents' treatment, Grynszpan went to the German embassy in Paris and shot an official there. For Nazi propaganda minister Goebbels, this incident provided the perfect excuse for a violent assault against Jews within Germany.

Nazi propaganda described the pogrom that followed announcement of

A Jewish woman, expelled from Germany in October 1938, washes clothes in the Zbaszyn refugee camp in Poland. Initially the homeless Jews found shelter in the stables of a military riding school and in a flour mill. Later Jewish relief workers organized a refugee camp, which remained open until the summer of 1939.

Herschel Grynszpan's shooting of the German diplomat as a spontaneous expression of hatred of Jews on the part of the majority German population. In fact the event was the carefully prepared culmination of a period of increasing pressure on Jews in Germany. Even the date was chosen with care—9 November, the date of Hitler's attempted putsch in 1923, was a holy day in the Nazi calendar.

Permission—and instructions—from above unleashed the hatred of Stormtroopers and other Nazi activists. All over Germany they torched synagogues and destroyed ritual objects associated with Judaism, such as Torah scrolls. Others joined in the attack, some driven by antisemitic fervor, others lured by the possibility of loot, still others just eager for action. Crowds smashed the windows of businesses owned by Jews; they vandalized and stole Jewish property. The attackers did not spare Jewish homes. They forced their way in, robbing, beating, raping, and demolishing. Memoirs describe the clouds of feathers that surrounded Jewish residences as the aggressors slashed bedding in their quest for valuables and their lust for destruction. They burned scores of synagogues all over Germany and Austria and killed about a hundred Jews. Nazi authorities rounded up some twenty-six thousand Jewish men and sent them to concentration camps. Those men seized in the Kristallnacht pogrom were the first Jews in Germany arrested simply for being Jewish.

Responses to the violence varied widely. Alfons Heck recounts how he and another boy eagerly joined a crowd singing as it stormed a synagogue. For them the pogrom was a chance to throw rocks and "smash some stuff." An outraged uncle caught them and dragged them away by the ears. Foreign journalists watched the event with horror. Their accounts differ considerably in the degree of popular participation they describe. Some observed how onlookers joined the rampage and plunder, whereas others sensed disapproval from ordinary citizens. (You can read some of those reports for yourself on the front pages of such well-known newspapers as the *New York Times*.) /

Certainly the German public as a whole was less enthusiastic about Kristallnacht than the pogrom's instigators had hoped. In this case it seemed that misgivings had less to do with fear of war or support of Jews than with a dislike of disorder. There was grumbling about the mess, the disruption, and the general impropriety of such open violence. Still such uneasiness did not produce a general outcry. At most it took the form of private aid to acquaintances. Peter Gay, a young boy in Berlin in 1938, recalls how a non-Jewish friend of the family hid his father from the police for weeks during and after the pogrom. Much more commonly, misgivings prompted non-Jews simply to turn their backs on the violence.

Nazi authorities, always alert to public opinion, noticed even that low level of disapproval. It is no coincidence that Kristallnacht marked the last open pogrom they organized in Germany and annexed Austria. In the future they would avoid having reluctant "Aryans" witness wide-scale violence at home. It would prove easy enough to move blatant attacks further from the public eye.

As in the cases of the Anschluss and the Sudetenland crisis, success made Kristallnacht more palatable for nervous Germans. Many Jews, terrified by the open attack and acutely aware of their vulnerability, became desperate to leave Germany. So-called Aryans benefited from that desperation as they scooped up Jewish property at bargain-basement prices. No doubt many who had shaken their heads at the unruly mobs on 9 November nevertheless were willing to share in the spoils. And once they had the goods those Germans had a stake in the continuation of Nazi anti-Jewish policies.

Afterward the German government added insult to injury by requiring the Jewish community to pay for the material damage of Kristallnacht. It

In February 1939 a carnival parade in the south German town of Neustadt mocks Jews. The float features a burning synagogue; the man in front represents Moses with the Ten Commandments. Note the large false noses on some of the men.

extorted an estimated $400 million from Jews for the death of the German diplomat and another $100 million for damages to property. That cynical policy no doubt furthered the false notion within Germany that the Jews were a bottomless source of wealth they did not deserve. Even the name "Kristallnacht," chosen by Goebbels, focused on the destruction of Jewish shop windows, as if the pogrom were somehow merely about correcting economic injustices within Germany. In fact it was the synagogues, sites of Jewish religious and communal life, that were the first targets of attack.

As for Jews themselves, how did they react? Between 1933 and the outbreak of war in September 1939, approximately half of the Jews in Germany—some three hundred thousand people—left. Much of this exodus took place in the wake of Kristallnacht, from what had been Austria as well as from all over Germany. For most European Jews it took enormous perseverance and ingenuity to get out, to find somewhere to go, and to figure out ways to start new lives.

Successful relocation also took luck. Many Austrian, Czech, and German Jews saw the threat of Nazism and tried to move beyond its reach. Some had the resources, connections, or relatives necessary to get to Palestine, the United States, Canada, Australia, or Britain. Others, often blocked from those most desirable destinations, took refuge in Cuba, the Dominican Republic, China, or Turkey. Many found their way to neighboring European countries: France, the Netherlands, and Poland. How could they know that within years, in some cases only months, they would end up in Nazi hands once again?

EXPANSION OF THE CONCENTRATION CAMP SYSTEM

Open aggression in 1938 and 1939 meant expanding the network of concentration camps begun in 1933 with the creation of Dachau. The history of the camps provides a kind of microcosm of the development of Nazi persecutions.

The German word for concentration camp is "Konzentrationslager," often abbreviated as "KZ" or "Lager." Throughout the 1930s the SS set up new camps so as to provide regional coverage. For example, Buchenwald, built in 1937, was located near Weimar; Sachsenhausen was not far from Berlin. Camps for women inmates, such as Ravensbrück, started up as well. After 1935 many German municipalities set up Gypsy camps into which police forced thousands of the country's thirty-five thousand Roma and Sinti, ostensibly in order to prevent crime. Those camps, parallel structures within the concentra-

A float in the Shrove Tuesday parade in the German Catholic town of Singen am Hohentwiel in February 1939 features members of the local jesters club feeding "Jews"—men wearing paper noses—to the "Jew Devourer," a voracious monster.

tion camp system, became sites of anthropological research and compulsory sterilization as well as sources of forced labor.

Concentration camps echoed the regime's ideological goals. Originally their founders described their purpose as re-education. In the camps, political opponents—Communists, Social Democrats, liberals—and so-called antisocial elements—vagrants, Gypsies, homosexuals, Jehovah's Witnesses, and others—were to be turned into useful citizens. Authorities also spoke of the camps as a place to put troublemakers into "protective custody for the restoration of law and order." Under that guise, the Nazi government gave itself the legal right to imprison suspects without a trial. From their start the camps were brutal places with terrible conditions for inmates. Torture, beatings, and deprivation were the order of the day.

As we have seen elsewhere, the move from Nazism's revolutionary phase to the consolidation of power did not mitigate the suffering of its targets. Instead that transition gave violence new forms backed by the full weight of the state and its institutions. The camps were an example. Between 1933 and 1939 the number of inmates skyrocketed, as attacks on target groups proliferated and increased in intensity.

The Nazi revolution of 1933 and 1934 brought large numbers of Communists into the camps. Homosexuals and Jehovah's Witnesses followed. The Sterilization Law of July 1933 brought a wave of arrests of supposed degenerates. Despite the Concordat with the Vatican, Nazi suspicion of the Christian churches also brought people into the camps. In violation of the agreement reached with the pope, Nazi authorities placed restrictions on Catholic priests, in particular regarding youth work. Some German priests refused to comply, and more than one hundred served terms in the camps as a result.

The period of routinization also enlarged the camps. When German courts and police tightened the enforcement of antihomosexual laws, they caused a jump in camp populations. At the same time the authorities became more proactive, arresting men and then pressuring them to reveal the names of their sexual partners, so that they could be charged as well. The Nuremberg Laws created a whole new category of crime, "Rassenschande," or crimes against the blood. The 1936 Berlin Olympics meant a "cleanup" of vagrants, prostitutes, pickpockets, and Gypsies. The result: more people dumped into camps. In some cases police created new camps, such as Marzahn, outside of Berlin, which was set up especially for Gypsies.

Persecution of Jehovah's Witnesses

German Jehovah's Witnesses added to the population of the concentration camps as well. Arrests of group members peaked in 1937 and 1938. German authorities cooked up many reasons to be suspicious of them. Their organization had international connections, in particular to the United States, although the same was true of the Church of Jesus Christ of Latter-Day Saints, whose members were not generally persecuted in the Third Reich. Because Jehovah's Witnesses emphasized the Old Testament and believed Jews had to return to the "Holy Land" before the world would end, their critics accused of them of being pro-Jewish and Zionist. Their door-to-door preaching made them an easily identifiable, unpopular, marginal minority whom other Christians ridiculed as a cult. Mockers dubbed them "Bible students," "Bible-worms," and "Bible-bees."

Perhaps most significant at a time when Germany was preparing for war, many Jehovah's Witnesses refused to serve in the military. Nor would they vote, give the Hitler salute, or do anything that would imply supremacy of the nation over God. Few in number, honest, and law abiding, Jehovah's Witnesses never posed a real threat to the stability of the Nazi German state. Nevertheless their insistence that their loyalty belonged to Jehovah alone and their firm refusal to abandon their beliefs made them dangerous in the eyes of a regime that tolerated no rivals for the allegiances of the German people.

Nazi authorities used their usual weapon—force—against the Jehovah's Witnesses, but with less success than they expected. Only about twenty thousand Jehovah's Witnesses lived in Germany in the 1930s; approximately ten thousand of them were arrested over the years and sent to concentration camps, where they were beaten and tormented like their fellow inmates. Some were executed for refusing military service. Some of those who managed to stay out of the camps had their children taken from them, many lost their jobs, their pensions, and their civil rights. Officials dragged them before special courts for refusing to enlist, to undertake air-raid watches, or to stop their preaching.

The Jehovah's Witnesses proved remarkably strong against assault. Camp authorities gave most of them the option of release if they signed a statement repudiating their beliefs. Very few did so. Instead they concentrated on building a strong network within the camps. They sang hymns, preached to the guards, and continued to meet as best they could to provide psychological and emotional support to one another. They interpreted ridicule and persecution as a fulfillment of prophecy, proof that they were correct in their faith. Those who remained outside tried to keep the faith as well. When police arrested one local leader, another took his or her place. They persisted in meeting and distributing literature, even to Nazi Party headquarters. In all, between twenty-five hundred and five thousand Jehovah's Witnesses were killed in German camps and prisons between 1933 and 1945.

One such victim was Wolfgang Kusserow. In 1942, Kusserow, a twenty-year-old Witness, was executed for refusing to perform military service. One of eleven children in his family, he assured his parents, brothers, and sisters in a farewell letter, "Our faith will be victorious."

Helene Gotthold also paid for her faith with her life. The mother of two children, Gotthold was arrested many times for continuing her Jehovah's Witness activities despite the government's ban. Condemned to death, she was beheaded in Berlin in 1944.

German authorities viewed the Jehovah's Witnesses more as an annoyance than a major threat. Nevertheless members of the group suffered terribly during the Third Reich. Their strength and resolve earned them a kind of grudging respect, even from some top Nazis. Himmler, for example, considered using them to resettle parts of the territories to be conquered by Germany. They were docile, obedient, and productive, he said, perfect qualities for pioneers. Inside the camps Jehovah's Witnesses sometimes functioned as personal

„Wir wollen kein Königreich Gottes Jehovas!
Wir haben unsere Kirche u. unsern Führer!"

Johannes Steyer, a German Jehovah's Witness, spent ten years in Nazi camps, prisons, and forced labor units. During the 1970s he painted a series of watercolors depicting his persecution under the Third Reich. In this scene, Steyer, preaching under surveillance, is told: "We do not want Jehovah God's Kingdom! We have our church and our führer!"

servants to the SS. Who else could be trusted as personal barbers wielding razors? Generally it seemed the Jehovah's Witnesses retained the respect of their fellow inmates and tried to do what they could within the camps to alleviate the sufferings of those even worse off than they were.

The third phase of Nazi development—open aggression in 1938–1939—added to the camp network in other ways too. The annexation of Austria meant building camps there; Mauthausen is the best known. The crisis around the Sudetenland brought some German Protestant clergy into the camps, mostly for short sentences. In November 1938 arrests of Jews during the Kristallnacht pogrom added about twenty-six thousand male inmates. Some died in the camps, many from being beaten; others were released in exchange for huge payments and often agreement to leave the country.

DIPLOMATIC INITIATIVES

Throughout this third phase of Nazi development—preparation for war—Hitler's approach to foreign policy was to talk peace and plan for war. His dip-

A Stormtrooper threatens the Jehovah's Witness Johannes Steyer: "I'll have you arrested."

lomats had been active during the 1930s making pacts that, like the Concordat with the Vatican and the Non-Aggression agreement with Poland, were intended to be broken. In 1935, for example, Hitler signed the Anglo-German Naval Agreement with Britain, which he then began spending enormous amounts of money to contravene. The agreement was supposed to prevent a naval arms race by limiting the German fleet to a certain percentage of the British navy. Instead it got the British to approve a German violation of the Treaty of Versailles. Meanwhile Hitler ordered construction of as many new superbattleships and aircraft carriers as he pleased, all designed to be used against Britain and the United States, on the assumption that the British would not discover the violations until it was too late. Although only two of the planned ships could be completed before the war was over, German intentions were nevertheless clearly the exact opposite of the peaceful arrangement promised by the agreement.

In May 1939 Germany signed the Pact of Steel with Italy, promising friendship and mutual aid. This arrangement would lay the foundation of what would develop into the wartime alliance called the Rome–Berlin Axis. The summer of 1939 also brought nonaggression treaties with Estonia, Latvia, and Denmark. The crowning achievement of this phase of preparation for war, however, came in August 1939 with the German–Soviet Non-Aggression Pact, sometimes referred to as the Hitler–Stalin Pact.

The deal had two parts. The first included public protestations of friendship and nonaggression between the two rival powers. To a world that had seen six years of Nazi attacks on Communists and the proliferation of German anti-Soviet propaganda, this part of the pact was shocking enough, but the second part went much further. In a secret arrangement, Hitler's and Stalin's negotiators agreed to divide eastern Europe between German and Soviet spheres of interest. They settled on a line through the middle of Poland as their secret boundary. The Baltic states—Estonia, Latvia, and Lithuania—fell to the Soviet side in the clandestine deal.

For Hitler the pact with the Soviet Union required some fairly dramatic reversals. In a sudden about-face he dropped his public anti-Communist stance to proclaim friendship with his ideological foe Stalin. Given Hitler's goals, the gains were well worth the inconvenience. By cutting such a deal Hitler secured the eastern border of Poland in case of war. Instead of worrying that the Soviet Union might attack invading Germans, he could rest assured that the Soviets would be busy securing their own designated sphere of interest. Germany would have a free hand in Poland, at least in the half that the secret pact reserved for German control. War with the Soviet Union, which Hitler believed was ultimately necessary to accomplish his mission, could wait.

In the meantime, Hitler and his henchmen spent the spring and summer of 1939 preparing for war. They conducted a massive propaganda campaign against Poland, accusing the Polish government and people of terrible violations of the rights of ethnic German minorities.

Already on 1 January 1939, Hitler had proclaimed his vision of the war to come to the German representatives in the Reichstag. As his speech made clear, it would be a war for race and space. "Europe cannot find peace until the Jewish question has been solved," Hitler told his audience. By the end of his remarks he had become more explicit:

> In the course of my life I have very often been a prophet, and have usually been ridiculed for it. During the time of my struggle for power it was in the first instance only the Jewish race that received my prophecies with laughter when I said that I would one day take over the leadership of the State, and with it that of the whole nation, and that I would then among other things settle the Jewish problem. Their laughter was uproarious, but I think that for sometime now they have been laughing on the other side of their face. Today I will once more be a prophet: if the international Jewish financiers in and outside Europe should suc-

ceed in plunging the nations once more into a world war, then the result will not be the Bolshevizing of the earth, and thus the victory of Jewry, but the annihilation of the Jewish race in Europe! (Noakes and Pridham 3:1049)

FLIGHT FROM NAZI GERMANY

Not everyone was deaf to Hitler's boastful warnings. Ever since 1933 large numbers of Germans had been leaving the country, fearful for their own safety. Finding a place of refuge could prove very difficult for all kinds of reasons. Thousands of German Communists fled to the Soviet Union after Hitler came to power. There some of them ran into troubles of their own with the paranoid and repressive regime of Josef Stalin. The purges of the 1930s did not spare these newcomers; Stalin and his associates had some evicted from the Communist Party, forced into labor camps in Siberia, imprisoned, and even killed. Still, to an important extent, German Communism would survive the Nazi era in the Soviet Union.

Other Germans also tried to get out or found themselves refused reentry by the Nazi government when they returned from trips abroad. Jews, liberals, pacifists, openly gay and lesbian activists, outspoken critics of National Socialism—all kinds of people went into exile. The writer Thomas Mann ended up in the United States as did the physicist Albert Einstein, the playwright Bertolt Brecht, the filmmaker Fritz Lang, and the actress Marlene Dietrich. In fact exiles from Nazi Germany played an enormous role in building the Hollywood film industry in the 1930s and 1940s.

The United States was not the only destination for exiles. International feminist activists and longtime companions Lida Gustava-Heymann and Anita Augspurg stayed in Switzerland after a trip rather than risk imprisonment back home. In the summer of 1939 some seventeen thousand Jews from Germany, Austria, and Poland made their way to Shanghai. Unable to get visas permitting them to enter places more culturally familiar to them, such as the United States and Great Britain, they seized the chance to get out of Europe even though it meant leaving behind almost everything they knew. Many of them would survive the war, including the Japanese occupation of China.

One family that left Germany for Shanghai in 1939 included seven-year-old Karin Zacharias. The Zachariases lived in a town in East Prussia not far from Königsberg (later the Russian city of Kaliningrad). Karin's father saw the writing on the wall early on with Hitler's government in Germany. Since the mid-1930s he wanted to get the family out of Europe, but his wife was not willing to go without her aging parents, who refused to leave their home.

Only in 1937, after the two older people both died, could the Zachariases begin to tackle the enormous project of getting out of Germany and finding a new home. Karin's father, educated as a lawyer, needed to learn a trade in order to get exit papers, so he became a welder. The family had to jump through endless bureaucratic hoops. To facilitate the process they relocated to Berlin. Finally in 1939 they left for China, where they would remain until 1948, when they were allowed to enter the United States. Karin, daughter of an assimilated German Jewish family, spent much of her childhood and her early teenage years in Shanghai. Half a century later Karin Pardo, as she is now called, lives in Chicago and still has vivid memories of the Chinese chapter of her life. Her experience is a reminder that the Holocaust was truly a worldwide event.

The Voyage of the St. Louis

An incident in 1939 illustrates just how hard it could be to escape even for those who recognized the dangers of Nazi Germany. That year, as in 1938, American immigration authorities decided to allow only around twenty thousand Germans and Austrians to immigrate to the United States. There was no separate quota for European Jews.

Of course a large proportion of the Germans and Austrians who applied for entry into the United States were Jewish. Only those who had relatives in the United States willing to sponsor them would be admitted. Sponsors had to demonstrate that they had enough money to support their European relatives once they arrived, if necessary. They also had to make their way through a mountain of red tape. Many Jews in Europe spent years trying to get visas to the United States, and most of them failed. It was no easier to get into Canada or Australia. In times of economic depression most people in those countries worried that immigrants would cost money and take away jobs.

In early 1939, the government of Cuba agreed to grant visas to a number of Jews desperate to get out of Europe. Between eight and nine hundred people set sail from Hamburg to Havana on board the steamship *St. Louis*. Before the ship came in, Cuban authorities changed their minds about the refugees; when the *St. Louis* arrived, they refused to allow the passengers to disembark. The ship remained offshore for days while representatives of the passengers tried to negotiate with the Cubans or find some alternative destination. Finally the *St. Louis* left Havana. Sailing slowly up the coast of Florida, its captain radioed to officials all along the way in the United States and Canada, but no one would permit the ship to dock.

The crew had no choice but to return to Europe. Negotiations by Jewish organizations managed to get refuge for many of the passengers from the *St. Louis* in Great Britain, France, and the Netherlands. In the years ahead some of those people, like most of those forced to return to Germany, would end up dead at Nazi hands, but some also found ways to stay alive. Careful research at the U.S. Holocaust Memorial Museum has traced all but a handful of the passengers of the *St. Louis*. Their stories show that foresight alone could not save a Jew from the Nazi trap. Connections, money, and determination were all factors, but so, above all, was luck, or whatever one might call chance at a time when no Jews could be counted lucky.

THE PROGRAM TO KILL
HANDICAPPED CHILDREN

Like Jews in Germany, people deemed handicapped also experienced the open Nazi aggression of 1938–1939. Hitler and other proponents of so-called racial purification would have to wait for the cover provided by war to implement murder on a mass scale, but by 1939 they felt confident enough to take steps in that direction. They began with the most defenseless segment of an already vulnerable group: the children.

In the winter of 1938–1939, a man named Knauer wrote to Hitler. He and his wife had a deformed baby. They wanted to have "this creature," as he called the child, killed. Hitler seized on the request as a way to begin having children who were considered "unworthy of living" killed. He assigned his personal physician, Dr. Karl Brandt, and the head of his personal staff in the Nazi Party, Philipp Bouhler, to deal with the Knauer case. Hitler instructed Brandt and Bouhler to inform the doctors involved that they could kill the child. Brandt and Bouhler were to tell the doctors that if any legal action were taken against them, it would be thrown out of court.

Hitler authorized Brandt and Bouhler to deal with similar cases in the same way. They recruited a group of officials and doctors who were positively disposed toward such ideas. The group's official title was the Reich Committee for the Scientific Registration of Serious Hereditarily- and Congenitally-based Illnesses. By August 1939 the Reich Committee required all midwives and doctors to report the existence of any children with deformities. It passed the forms on to three pediatricians. They marked each form with a plus or a minus sign to indicate whether the particular child was to die or be allowed to live. Those doctors never saw the children whose fates they decided.

Brandt, Bouhler, and their committee were not confident that most of the German people would support the killing of children with deformities, so they shrouded the process in secrecy. Still they had no trouble finding enough personnel to participate in these early stages of the program. The program to kill deformed children served Nazi planners as a kind of trial balloon, sent up to test reactions. The responses they perceived indicated that it was safe to go even further in attacks on people considered handicapped.

5

EXPERIMENTS IN BRUTALITY, 1939–1940: WAR AGAINST POLAND AND THE SO-CALLED EUTHANASIA PROGRAM

In 1939 Hitler got his war. It would not be against Czechoslovakia as he had hoped but against Poland. Still Poland was not a surprising target; along with many of Germany's leading military men, Hitler had always considered existence of an independent Polish state to be anathema, and of course for Germany, Poland was the gateway to the east, where Hitler intended to find Lebensraum—living space—for his superior "Aryan race."

With the German invasion and conquest in 1939, Poland would become a laboratory for experiments in spatial expansion and racial ideology. In Poland the Germans seized control of large numbers of Slavs, Jews, and Gypsies; those people Nazi teachings described as subhuman. In Poland, German planners began to implement schemes to recast the face of Europe. They forced millions of people to move, resettled those they deemed desirable, and robbed, evicted, enslaved, and eventually killed those they did not want. For two years, even before construction of the first killing centers in 1941, the German occupiers of Poland tried out various solutions to what they considered their population problems, above all their self-made "Jewish problem."

This first stage of the war also brought experiments of another kind—in the murder of people deemed handicapped. In 1939 and 1940 the so-called Euthanasia Program got into full swing within Germany. The word "euthanasia" comes from the Greek for "good death" or "good dying." In the Nazi case the label itself was a lie, suggesting as it did that the killings had something to do with concern for the patients' well-being. They did not. The program's initiators did not care about the suffering of their targets but asked only whether those people could contribute to the supremacy of the "Aryan race."

As in Poland, planners and functionaries in the Euthanasia Program tested methods and developed techniques to implement the teachings of race and space. Their goals involved learning how to kill large numbers of people and then dispose of their bodies most easily. In the years ahead the lessons of this early program against handicapped people would be applied again and again.

This chapter traces Nazi German experiments in brutality in 1939 and 1940. From the outset we can identify two principles that seem to have guided German policy, both in defeated Poland and with regard to people deemed handicapped. First, Nazi leaders encouraged experimentation—even rivalry and organizational confusion—among the people who carried out their plans. Rather than easing the situation of those targeted for persecution, such chaotic conditions often increased the victims' vulnerability and exacerbated their suffering. Second, German decision makers endorsed the notion of divide and conquer. Whenever possible they stirred up dissension and hatred among those over whom they ruled in order to advance their own cause. That kind of cynical manipulation by Nazi overlords of their subject peoples added to the wartime misery too, first in Poland and later throughout Europe.

THE GERMANS IN POLAND

Blitzkrieg

On 1 September 1939 German forces invaded Poland. German planners tried to disguise this act of aggression as a defensive measure. They dressed 150 concentration camp inmates in Polish uniforms and used them to stage a mock attack on a German radio station near the border. The corpses of those men then served as "proof" of Polish belligerence and justification for attack.

Hitler and his inner circle were not confident that the German public was ready for war. They had already spent the summer of 1939 rousing anti-Polish sentiment in Germany, using the newspapers to publicize wild accusations of Polish crimes against the ethnic German minority in Poland. Still, within Germany the initial reaction to war was cautious. When Hitler appeared on his balcony in Berlin following announcements of the attack on Poland, he expected to be greeted by throngs of zealous supporters. Instead the crowd was so small that he went back inside to avoid embarrassment.

The assault of 1 September 1939 did not take the Poles completely by surprise, because they had had plenty of opportunities to observe German saber-rattling in the preceding months. They were, however, stunned by the rapidity of the German advance. The Germans' technological advantage enabled them to wage a blitzkrieg—a war at lightning speed. First their planes pounded the Poles from the sky. Then tanks rolled in to crush resistance and clear the way for occupying troops. With 11 cavalry brigades, a single tank division, and 750 armored vehicles, the Poles were no match for the Germans, who smashed into Poland with 15 tank divisions and some 3,600 armored vehicles. Jack Pomerantz, at the time a young Jewish man in the Polish town of Radzyn, recalls that he had never seen an airplane until the German attack on 1 September 1939. That day the sky was black with them.

The repercussions were enormous. France and Britain declared war on Germany, although for the time being they remained outside the fray. The Hitler–Stalin Pact of August 1939 assured the Germans of nonaggression from the Soviet Union. As the secret arrangements had anticipated, the German offensive was followed within weeks by a Soviet advance into Polish territory from the east, up to the line previously agreed upon. By early October, the Germans had forced the Poles on their side to surrender. Meanwhile eastern Poland would remain in Soviet control until mid-1941.

In the 1939 attack Germans killed at least seventy thousand Poles. German losses were much lower but still considerable, some eleven thousand men. At least 1 million Poles were taken prisoner—many by the Germans but also a substantial number by the Soviets.

The Polish leadership fled to London to establish a government-in-exile. Members of the Polish army buried huge caches of arms rather than relinquish them to the Germans. Those weapons would provide the nucleus for the underground armies in the half decade of struggle that still lay ahead for the Poles.

Division of Poland

From the outset, "divide and conquer" was the German byword in Poland. The arrangement with the Soviet Union reflected that approach as did the German decision to divide its own part of conquered Poland into two parts. The western areas, known as the "incorporated territories," were annexed by the Greater German Reich. This area included such important cities as Danzig—now called Gdansk—and Lodz, which the German leadership would later rechristen Litzmannstadt. The incorporated territories were home to 10 million people, around 80 percent of them ethnic Poles. Also living there were ethnic Germans, Jews, and small numbers of other groups, including Gypsies, Czechs, and Ukrainians.

The Germans called the remaining part of their Polish territory the General Government and administered it like a colony. Warsaw, Krakow, and Lublin were its major cities. Under the leadership of Governor General Dr. Hans Frank, a longtime associate of Hitler, the General Government became a key site of Nazi brutality. Much of the mass killing of Jews after 1941 would be done there; plans to reduce Poles to slaves of Germany also found early implementation in the General Government.

Competing Authorities and German Plans for the Poles

Germans, in particular Nazi Germans, are often described as hyperefficient and organized. German rule in the territories of occupied Poland, however, contradicts that stereotype. Rather than orderly, it was chaotic, characterized by overlapping jurisdictions and competing authorities. The German military was involved as was the SS under Heinrich Himmler. Hans Frank and his administration in the General Government played an important role; so did Hermann Göring, Hitler's deputy and head of the Four-Year Plan for the German economy. Local Nazis got involved, especially in the incorporated territories, as did German police and representatives of the interior ministry.

Almost every ambitious German Nazi activist, military man, and bureaucrat wanted a piece of the action. For them defeat of Poland meant new career opportunities. Whether in the incorporated territories or in the General Government, they tried to distinguish themselves from their colleagues and rivals by being more effective—that is, harsher—and more ambitious—that is, more brutal—in their treatment of the local populations.

Hitler and his inner circle had grandiose plans for Polish territories. Initially they intended to force the ethnic Poles farther east, to confine Jews to some desolate reservation, and to establish an area of pure "Aryan"/German settlement. Although details remained vague, implementation began immediately.

On 7 September 1939, Reinhard Heydrich, head of the German Reich Security Main Office, issued an order to the special units of police and SS under his jurisdiction. It would be necessary, he instructed, to destroy the leadership class in Poland and expel all Jews from areas in German hands. In short, as he told a subordinate, the "nobility, clergy, and Jews must be killed."

Heydrich's position was in line with the views of his bosses Hitler and Himmler. They wanted to reduce the Poles to a people of slaves, to destroy their intellectuals and their sense of tradition—anything that might give them a way to organize against Germany. Accordingly they encouraged German forces to target Polish Catholic priests. In the opening months of the war, Germans shot fifteen hundred priests and imprisoned countless others. They also humiliated, arrested, and murdered many other prominent Poles—for example, journalists, professors, and artists.

German authorities prohibited any activities that advanced the education of Poles, fostered communal ties, or promoted national feelings. They imposed curfews and seized Polish businesses. They shut down Polish newspapers and used forced labor and public hangings to make examples of Poles who defied them. Members of the SS, police, and regular military, along with local collaborators, also terrorized Poles in less organized ways that included theft, beating, castration, and rape.

The war in 1939 brought massive expansion of the network of concentration and labor camps. Some Poles were forced to build roads and dams in labor camps, where the terrible conditions were often deadly. Others were sent to

The execution of Piotr Sosnowski, a Catholic priest, by the SS and local ethnic German militia in October 1939 near Bydgoszcz (Bromberg). Forty-five Poles, including Father Sosnowski, were forced to dig a grave in the forest and then were shot into it.

Germany. The existing camps in Germany could not hold all of the new inmates, so German authorities also set up camps in their newly acquired territories—places such as Majdanek, near Lublin, or Plaschow, outside Krakow, depicted in Steven Spielberg's movie *Schindler's List.*

Officials also introduced a whole range of measures intended to differentiate Poles and Germans, two groups that in fact were not always easy to separate in a part of Europe that had traditionally been ethnically mixed. Poles were not permitted to say "Heil Hitler," nor could they serve Germans in shops. Laws forbade friendships between Germans and Poles and criminalized sexual relations. Nevertheless, sexual assault of Polish women by German men was common. Later in the war German military authorities would force some Polish gentile women into brothels to serve German men and non-Germans who fought for the Reich.

Most of these measures applied to Polish gentiles and Jews alike, but sometimes the Germans showed additional, often improvised brutality toward their numerous, new Jewish subjects. In the 1930s far more Jews lived in

In late 1939 SS personnel lead Polish women from the Pawiak and Mokotow prisons in nearby Warsaw into the forest to be killed. Members of the Polish underground sent this photograph to the Polish government-in-exile in London to illustrate Nazi terror in occupied Poland.

Poland than in Germany. Germany's half million Jews in 1933 made up less than 1 percent of the population; Poland's more than 3 million Jews in 1939 represented approximately 10 percent.

The first phase of the war became a kind of open season against Polish Jews for Stormtroopers, SS, Nazi Party members, and unruly soldiers. Undisciplined and often drunk, they roamed around Polish territories burning, looting, and raping. The distinctive appearance of Orthodox Jewish men made them favorite targets for ridicule and violence. Rowdy Germans pulled out their beards and forced them to crawl in the street. Thugs attacked synagogues, where they desecrated ritual objects and abused the observant.

Hostage takings and demands for ransom were common. On 18 October 1939, Germans murdered one hundred Jews in a café in Lodz and forced others to pay for their lives. Similar incidents occurred in many cities and towns.

Ethnic Germans and Resettlement Schemes

Nazi racial policy had two sides: attack on people deemed undesirable and advancement of those considered "Aryan." In 1939 and 1940 the second part of that scheme included locating ethnic Germans, people living outside Germany who identified themselves culturally as Germans (but not as Jews). In 1939 German experts estimated there to be about seven hundred thousand ethnic Germans in Poland alone.

German forces used the ethnic Germans to increase the terror of the early months of the war. Some ethnic Germans were killed by their Polish neighbors for helping the invading Germans. The numbers are unclear; respectable estimates range from two to five thousand such casualties, but official German reports claimed that vengeful Poles had slaughtered fifty-eight thousand ethnic Germans. That charge served to whip up hatred against Poles within Germany and also helped the SS form ethnic Germans into vigilante groups that attacked Poles and stole their property.

Many German officials who flocked into the newly conquered Polish territories busied themselves drawing up lists of people who should count as ethnic Germans. They organized programs to relocate them to the most desirable areas and evict the Poles who had been living there.

Plans for resettlement went even further. In October and November 1939 German diplomats worked out deals with Estonia, Latvia, and the Soviet Union so that ethnic Germans in those parts of Europe would also be brought "home into the Reich." The idea was to move those ethnic Germans out of the Baltic states and eastern Poland into the newly incorporated territories. Of course moving ethnic Germans in meant moving other people out.

By 1940 some two hundred thousand ethnic Germans who had signed up for resettlement needed homes. That year German police forced 325,000 Poles to leave the incorporated territories for the General Government. Often they were given only hours to get out, with instructions to leave their houses swept and the keys in the cupboard for the new inhabitants. Meanwhile, in the General Government nothing awaited the deportees but misery.

In late 1939 and 1940 German police evicted tens of thousands of Polish Jews from their homes and squeezed them into ghettos in the cities. The most desirable residences and businesses went to ethnic Germans or Germans from the Reich. Poor properties were allotted to Polish gentiles.

Individual Initiatives—The Eichmann Example

Some German officials took their own initiatives against people whom Nazi ideology deemed inferior. By doing so they hoped to catch the attention of their bosses and advance their own careers. For example, in the fall of 1939, Adolf Eichmann (1906–1962), an ambitious bureaucrat in Heydrich's Reich Security Main Office, began to organize transports of Jews to the General Government—from Vienna, from Silesia in the incorporated territories, and from parts of the former Czechoslovakia.

After the war, when he was tried in Israel for his role in the Holocaust, Eichmann would insist that he had never been an antisemite. It does seem that in Eichmann's case, careerism was a more powerful motivation than antisemitism. In any case Eichmann played a central role organizing forced emigration of Austrian Jews in 1938 and of Czech Jews a year later. Throughout 1942 and 1943 he would be instrumental in arranging transportation of Jews from all over Europe to killing centers. He also coordinated deportation of Hungarian Jews to Auschwitz in 1944. In 1962 Adolf Eichmann was hanged in Israel.

Eichmann, trained as an expert in Jewish affairs, had no formal authorization for his project. Nor had he made any arrangements for the Jews when they arrived. Instead his men simply dumped their prisoners off at a place called Nisko, near the city of Lublin, and told them to get lost. Most of the Jews fled into the woods, and the Germans shot those who returned.

As the Nisko incident illustrates, competition among German authorities often made the situation of the people they targeted worse. Sometimes, however, the resulting disorganization also undermined the Germans' ability to achieve their goals. By early 1941, top Nazis had to stop deporting Poles to the

General Government, because the situation had become too unstable. Hans Frank announced he could not take any more Poles in his area. Göring agreed that it was economically unwise to keep up the deportations. Neither man was motivated by humanitarianism. Both were interested above all in expanding their own power, and during 1941 both would be instrumental in moving German policy from the confused resettlements and deportations of 1939 and 1940 to the so-called Final Solution of the Jewish Question: annihilation.

Policies of Divide and Conquer and Protests against German Brutality

All of the German schemes in Poland relied on the notion of divide and conquer. Privileging ethnic Germans turned their neighbors against them. Dangling promises of Jewish property in front of gentile Poles gave them a stake in attacks on Jews and encouraged them to betray Jews to the Germans.

SS leader Himmler explicitly encouraged his men to do all they could to turn ethnic groups within Poland against one another. It was a good idea to recruit local policemen and mayors from minority groups, he suggested. That way the majority's anger would be diverted from the Germans onto those petty officials. Accordingly Germans in the General Government often used Ukrainians and Belorussians against ethnic Poles and Jews. In many cases German authorities relied on local Polish gentiles to point out who was Jewish.

Some people spoke out against German atrocities in Poland. Shocked by the slaughter of Polish Catholic priests, Roman Catholic leaders in Germany appealed to the Vatican. Perhaps Hitler would listen to the pope, they reasoned.

Polish clergymen also begged the pope to take action, but Pope Pius XII remained silent. His reasons are unclear. He may have believed that a strict policy of neutrality was the most powerful position the Vatican could take. Perhaps he feared reprisals against Catholics within Germany, or against the Vatican itself. A staunch opponent of Communism, he may have thought that Nazi Germany—even given its excesses—was still preferable to Soviet domination of Europe. In any case, his silence in the fall of 1939—when the victims of German aggression were priests in his own church—would make it hard for him to speak out later in the face of crimes against Jews.

Some members of the German army also protested the brutality around them. The best known case involved General Johannes Blaskowitz, commander of a military region in occupied Poland. In early 1940 Blaskowitz sent a long memorandum directly to Hitler. It provided specific examples of German crimes against civilians. For example, Blaskowitz described how a drunk

German policeman beat a Polish man to death and forced a woman who may have been his wife to bury the body while scores of Germans and Poles looked on. Blaskowitz also told about some German soldiers who raped a teenaged Jewish girl in a cemetery. His account included many other cases of viciousness on the part of German police and SS men.

Such behavior was counterproductive, Blaskowitz warned. It would lead to demoralization and a breakdown in discipline among the German forces. It would stir up bad press abroad, he wrote, and alienate even those elements of the population that might otherwise have been sympathetic to the Germans. According to Blaskowitz, German abuses would drive Polish Jews and gentiles together. Polish gentiles were particularly worried by German brutality toward the Jews, Blaskowitz reported, because they feared that anything done to Jews would eventually be done to them too.

Hitler dismissed Blaskowitz's memorandum as childish and naive. One could not "win a war with Salvation Army tactics," he allegedly responded. You might expect that Blaskowitz was shot or imprisoned for daring to send his report, but he was not. Instead he was merely transferred out of Poland. Others were happy to take over his powerful position there.

Over time such protests ceased. Other military men who felt as Blaskowitz did in the fall of 1939 probably got used to conditions or forgot their misgivings in the face of Germany's dramatic military triumphs. Meanwhile, those who showed they were willing or even eager to fight a war of atrocity found themselves favored for promotions. By consistently rewarding behavior that furthered the goals of race and space, the Nazi leadership made sure that it always had a supply of ambitious, loyal individuals at every level of the hierarchy.

As the case of Blaskowitz indicates, Nazi Germany did not need unanimity in order to function. The Third Reich was not merely the work of "true believers"—fanatics who blindly endorsed every detail of Hitler's ideology. It also built on the efforts of critical Nazis and even opponents of Nazism, people who grumbled about some of its excesses even while they applied their energies and abilities to ensuring its stability. Not mass brainwashing but the participation of ordinary people of all kinds enabled the Nazi system to operate as it did.

Ghettoization of Polish Jews

At first German decision makers were not sure what to do with the many Jews who fell into their hands in 1939. Not until 1941 would they cross the line to regarding total mass murder as the "solution" to the "Jewish problem." From the outset, however, they did all they could to isolate Polish Jews from the rest of the population. They targeted Jews in particular ways in order to make them so vulnerable and contemptible that non-Jews would lose any sympathy for them and would worry only about how to avoid being treated that badly themselves.

Ghettoization, the stopgap measure that German authorities developed in late 1939 and early 1940, was a logical extension of the approach of divide and conquer. All over Polish territories German officials forced Jews out of their homes, in villages, small towns, and cities, into designated urban areas called ghettos. There the Jews were to be concentrated and isolated. Meanwhile German authorities seized Jewish property to dispose of as they saw fit. In some cases eager non-Jewish neighbors rushed in before them to pick up the spoils. The Germans also forced many Jews in the ghettos to work for them producing supplies for the war.

German planners always considered ghettoization a temporary measure, a sort of holding pattern until subsequent steps could be taken. But what were those steps to be? In 1939 and 1940 some Nazi decision makers were still talking about a Jewish reservation in the east, near Lublin. Officials in the German Foreign Office would propose another scheme, the Madagascar Plan, to ship all of Europe's Jews to an island off the coast of Africa. Others floated different ideas such as using the Jews in the ghettos as enslaved labor or allowing them to die of starvation and disease there. The Nazi leadership encouraged every plan as long as it aimed to destroy Jewish life in Europe.

Between 1939 and 1941, during this phase of experimentation and uncertainty with regard to German policy toward the Jews, over half a million Polish Jews died in ghettos and labor camps. Many starved to death; many also died of diseases brought on by the crowding and terrible sanitary conditions. Police, guards, and overseers shot and beat others to death—for trying to escape; for stealing, as if the Germans themselves were not thieves on the largest conceivable scale; for failing to work to the level demanded; or simply for sport. The ghettos were not yet a formal program of annihilation, but they proved deadly enough for hundreds of thousands of Polish Jews of all ages.

In 1940 a visitor to the Warsaw ghetto offered the following description of living conditions there:

> On the streets children are crying in vain, children who are dying of hunger. They howl, beg, sing, moan, shiver with cold, without underwear, without clothing, without shoes, in rags, sacks, flannel which are bound in strips round

the emaciated skeletons, children swollen with hunger, disfigured, half conscious, already completely grown-up at the age of five, gloomy and weary of life. They are like old people and are only conscious of one thing: "I'm cold." "I'm hungry." (Noakes and Pridham 3:1067)

The German government-run leisure organization Strength Through Joy organized bus tours to the ghettos so that members of the supposed master race could see the degeneracy of their alleged inferiors. No matter that the Germans themselves had created the filth and desperation evident there. That squalor was offered as proof that Nazi theories of race and space held true.

THE EXAMPLE OF LODZ

One of the largest ghettos was established in Lodz in the incorporated territory in the winter of 1939. By April 1940 it had been sealed off completely from the rest of the city. The Lodz ghetto lasted in part at least until August 1944, when the Jews remaining there were shipped to Auschwitz. Although every ghetto was different, Lodz illustrates some general conditions.

In Lodz, as elsewhere, German authorities had varying opinions about the nature of the ghetto. Was it primarily for forced labor? Was it to be self-

A postcard from the Lodz ghetto in 1940 or 1941 showing the entrance and a sign forbidding non-Jews from entering the ghetto.

supporting? If so, how, when it was allocated no resources? To what extent was it to be self-administered? All of this uncertainty added to the misery of those imprisoned within the poorest parts of the city.

The ghetto was disastrously overcrowded. In Lodz, an average of seven people occupied a single room—that is, in 1940 an estimated 230,000 people were crammed into some 30,000 apartments, most of them one room only. Only about 725 of those lodgings had running water. Many had electricity, but it did little good; police forbade those in the ghetto from using their lights most of the time.

Lodz was one of the most isolated of all of the ghettos. A kind of no one's land surrounded it, so smuggling anything in or out was almost impossible. Because it was in an industrialized region, there was no forest nearby to which the ghetto Jews could escape. The city of Lodz itself was slated to be "Germanized"—that is, German planners intended to remove ethnic Poles, Jews, and others from the area and replace them with Germans from the Reich and ethnic Germans from elsewhere in Europe. As a result, previous contacts in the city were of little help to Jews in the Lodz ghetto.

Food was extremely scarce—potato peels became a prized item. Lice and rats thrived; such diseases as typhus and tuberculosis ran rampant. Nevertheless hard work was required of everyone in the ghetto who wanted a chance to stay alive. By 1943 ghetto workshops were churning out uniforms, boots, underwear, and bed linen for the German military; ghetto workers produced goods of metal, wood, leather, fur, down, and paper, and even electrical and telecommunication devices. Children as young as eight slaved away for pathetically small rations of food.

Under these conditions it is no surprise that people died in terrible numbers. In 1940, some six thousand Jews died in the Lodz ghetto. By the following year the number had almost doubled, to eleven thousand. In 1942 there would be eighteen thousand dead. Of course, by the end of 1941 the primary cause of Jewish death would no longer be starvation and illness in the ghettos but deportation to the new killing centers.

German racial experts came to think of the ghettos as repositories for people they considered human trash. Beginning in 1941 they dumped Jews from all over Europe—Luxembourg, Germany, Austria, Czechoslovakia—in Lodz. German officials also deported some five thousand European Gypsies to the Lodz ghetto, where they inhabited a specially designated area and, like the Jews, suffered beatings, starvation, and disease. In December 1941 and January 1942 those Gypsies still in Lodz were gassed at Chelmno. It is said that no

Roma survived the Lodz ghetto. Nazi authorities also sent Gypsies to Jewish ghettos in other cities, for example, Warsaw, Lublin, and Bialystok.

THE JEWISH COUNCILS

German officials saved themselves work by setting up Jewish Councils to administer aspects of the daily lives of the ghettos. They appointed recognized Jewish leaders—prominent local people, businessmen, teachers, lawyers—to these boards and assigned them the task of carrying out German orders within the ghetto. In each ghetto the Jewish Council also organized social life, set up charities, and tried to find ways to maintain some kind of human community.

The autonomy of the Jewish Council, often referred to by the German word Judenrat, was more apparent than real. It could not escape German goals and priorities. In cases when members of the councils refused to cooperate, German officials dismissed them or had them shot and then replaced them with more compliant men. In Lodz, for example, the Germans had some trouble recruiting twenty-four members because the first Council of Jewish Elders set up had been summoned to the Gestapo and never seen again.

The Jewish Councils have often been criticized, and some people have suggested that the Jewish leadership in eastern Europe formed part of the machinery of destruction. Hannah Arendt, a political philosopher and refugee from Nazi Germany, was accused of taking that stance in her famous study *Eichmann in Jerusalem*. Arendt drew attention to what she considered the complicity, even collaboration, of the Jewish leadership with the Germans. Publication of her book in the early 1960s sparked a heated controversy.

Instead of viewing the Jewish leaders, especially those in the Jewish Councils, primarily as agents of Nazi destruction, it is more accurate to see them as caught between conflicting sets of demands. Above them loomed German orders; below them spread the ever more desperate needs of the Jewish communities of eastern Europe. Members of the Jewish Councils had to respond to German demands for funds, goods, information, a labor force. If they refused or failed to do so, German officials would come and take whatever they wanted anyway. On the other hand, the Jewish Councils tried to help their people, to maintain order, to save lives, and to feed, clothe, and doctor the Jews in the ghettos.

It was impossible to reconcile these two sets of goals in a situation where the German priority was destruction of the Jews. In the conditions that the victorious Germans created in Poland, however, the two tasks of the Jewish

Councils could not be separated either. Attempts by Jewish leaders to accomplish both in some way led to hostility on the part of their own people; in many cases it also pushed them to behave in ways counter to their own principles. Once again we can see the familiar notion of divide and conquer at work here.

The tasks the Germans set the Jewish Councils were straightforward. They were to make lists of the people and property in their ghettos and, as required, turn over the money, things, or people demanded. The tasks the Jewish Councils set themselves were more ambitious. They hoped to maintain order and sustain life in the ghettos. They intended to mediate with the Germans, to reason and plead on behalf of the Jews as a whole, and they tried to maintain productivity, to make the ghettos valuable to the German war effort so that Germans would want to keep Jews alive.

Critics of the Jewish Councils often imply an additional task—the councils should have warned their people. Is this charge justified? Could and should the Jewish Councils have done more to warn Jews in the ghettos of German intentions or to rouse resistance?

The case of the ghetto in Lublin illustrates the complexity of this issue. In 1939 there were thirty-eight thousand Jews in Lublin, 21 percent of the city's population. It was one of the oldest Jewish communities in Poland. After the German invasion in September, Jewish refugees flooded into the area. The Germans set up a ghetto and a Jewish Council, one of whose most prominent members was a lawyer named Mark Alten.

Alten believed that the terror of late 1939 was a temporary, local aberration. Things would get better once German power was centralized and control established, he assumed. Alten worked hard to cultivate contacts with Germans and used his influence to plead for exceptions, to urge a stop to arbitrary violence. More than once Alten was arrested for his efforts.

In the end everything Alten did was futile. In 1942 almost all the Jews of Lublin were murdered, just like their counterparts all over Poland.

Alten has been accused of ingratiating himself with the Nazis, the very people who would seek to kill every Jew alive. There is no doubt that Alten misread the situation, although his misjudgment came out of predictable, human tendencies. He looked to the past as people do when seeking guidance for the present. He saw persecutions of Jews, pogroms, and isolation. From that history he took the lesson that this attack too would pass, if the Jews could just hold on. Alten was wrong, but can he be faulted for failing to anticipate something that had never happened before? Can the Jewish Councils be blamed for not realizing in 1939 or 1940 what even top Nazis did not grasp until sometime in mid-1941, that this time the goal would be annihilation of every Jew in Europe? To decent people such a thing would long be unimaginable.

The Jewish Councils are sometimes charged with having handed Jews over to their deaths. There is no denying that German officials used the Jewish Councils to their own ends; they had been created for that purpose. Beginning in late 1941, the councils prepared lists for transports out of the ghettos—to killing centers. Often they used their own police forces to help round up those slated for destruction. Not surprisingly, they generally sent first those people in the ghetto they viewed as least useful: the sick, old, very young, and weak. Outsiders such as Gypsies could also expect to be on the early transports.

Nevertheless Jewish leaders varied considerably in their responses. Sometimes they even managed at least temporarily to thwart Nazi designs. Several brief examples give an idea of the kinds of activities possible among the councils.

By 1940 the Jewish Council in Lublin was dealing not only with the ghetto in that city but with about fifty work camps. Under the crowded and desperate conditions, food, medicine, and doctors were all woefully inadequate. Overwhelmed, the Jewish Council resorted in some cases to bringing in auxiliary police recruited from local ethnic Germans to keep order. Known for their viciousness toward Jews, those police contributed to the hatred that many Jews felt for the Jewish Council. Eventually the Lublin Council formed its own Jewish Order Police. To inhabitants of the ghetto, those enforcers, whether Jewish or not, were detested as the most visible representatives of German authority.

In Warsaw the head of the Jewish police, Jozef Szerynski, was a convert to Christianity who had been trained in the Polish police force. He was indifferent and even hostile to Jewish traditions. Most of the population of the ghetto regarded him and his seventeen hundred policemen as tyrannical. The requirement to pay a special police tax roused particular bitterness. In Riga, in contrast, the Jewish police were recruited from among the Zionist youth. They included some of the best of Jewish society. In the ghetto they were widely respected and viewed as helpers.

Some Jewish Councils were involved in resistance activities. For example, in the summer of 1941, during a search on a train, German police discovered copies of a Jewish underground newspaper. The courier was a Polish gentile woman who was carrying addresses, including some linked to the Jewish ghetto in Piotrków Trybunalski in the incorporated territories. The Gestapo found that the Jewish underground there was connected to the heads of the

Jewish Council. They had the chairman and almost all of the community leaders arrested and tortured. In September they were sent to Auschwitz.

Critics of the Jewish Councils note that some of the Jewish leaders enriched themselves and relished the taste of power that their positions in the ghetto gave them. Here too the record is mixed. One can find cases of Jewish leaders who suffered from delusions of grandeur. Moishe Merin, the thirty-year-old head of the Central Council of Elders for Eastern Upper Silesia, fancied himself a kind of dictator of the European Jews. Chaim Rumkowski, head of the Jewish Council in Lodz, was even more blatant. He had money and stamps printed bearing his image; he encouraged a kind of cult of personality around himself. Still, both men tried to save the Jews in "their ghettos," not merely to expand their own power.

Jewish leaders came to recognize their powerlessness too. In 1943 Merin would address the remaining survivors of his jurisdiction with the following words: "I stand in a cage before a hungry and angry tiger. I stuff his mouth with meat, the flesh of my brothers and sisters, to keep him in his cage lest he break loose and tear us all to bits" (Hilberg, 197).

For most Jewish elders, leadership was a burden, not a reward. At first they were not paid but served in the tradition of volunteer community leadership. By 1940 they received some pay, and although it was meager, like that of the Jewish police, it still sparked resentment in a time of such terrible want.

Most Jewish leaders worked hard and suffered a great deal. Some, like Adam Czerniaków in Warsaw, saw no way out of their desperate situation but suicide. Few withstood the temptation to try to use their positions to save themselves and those close to them. Nevertheless in the end their thankless task guaranteed nothing. Jacob Gens spent years as head of the Jewish Council in Vilna, doing all he could to increase the productivity of the ghetto. He was shot anyway by the Germans in 1943 when they liquidated the ghetto. Rumkowski, for all his pomp, ended up in a transport from Lodz ghetto to a killing center. He too died with his people; rumor had it they killed him themselves.

Hell, according to the French philosopher Jean-Paul Sartre, is a self-service cafeteria—the worst suffering, in other words, is that which you inflict on yourself. Nazi planners seem to have understood that concept instinctively. By forcing Jewish leaders to involve themselves in decisions about the fate of people in the ghettos they both lightened their own sense of responsibility and increased the suffering within the Jewish community. Powerless as they were, the Jewish Councils had painfully few options. In a lose–lose situation where the options were destruction or destruction—death or death—there could be few, if any, right decisions.

Jewish–Christian Relations in Poland

Poland occupies a particular place in the history of the Holocaust. Half of the Jews murdered during the Nazi era were Polish, and much of the actual killing occurred in territories taken from Poland. The killing centers built after 1941 were concentrated there, although in the case of Auschwitz, the camp was in the part of Poland that was incorporated into the German Reich and most of the Polish locals were forcibly removed from the surrounding area. Of course there were also significant sites of slaughter elsewhere; for example, the killing fields in Transnistria, where many Romanian Jews were killed, and the shooting pits in Lithuania and Ukraine. There is also evidence that German planners intended to build a killing center near Minsk in Belorussia but decided against it. Nevertheless, the significance of Poland demands a special look at relations between Polish gentiles and Jews.

The topic remains very emotional. The most common interpretations can be categorized into three main groups. One idea might be called the "Poles as arch-antisemites" theory. Some observers argue that Polish gentiles in the early decades of the twentieth century were raised on the principles of antisemitism. According to this view, Polish Christians were even more hostile to Jews than were Nazi Germans, and Polish antisemitism was an essential factor in the Holocaust. The fact that many Polish gentiles benefited materially from German attacks on Jews might seem to support this view. Although this interpretation may be emotionally satisfying in some ways, however, it oversimplifies the past and neglects in a cruel way the terrible situation of all Poles under Nazi rule.

At the other end of the scale is a position one might label "all Poles were victims of the Holocaust." Proponents of this view maintain that almost 6 million Poles died in the war—about 18 percent of the population—and they sometimes fail to mention that half of the Polish dead were Jewish. They argue that Polish gentiles had no real choice in how they behaved under German rule. They did all they could for their Jewish neighbors under circumstances in which they too were victims. Scholars who take the stance that all Poles were victims may concede some uniqueness to the Jewish experience but consider it wrong for Jews to claim the Holocaust as their own. Some criticize the scholarship of Jewish historians as a kind of special pleading; some blame Jews themselves for the fact that Polish Christians did not do more to help them. Had the Jews not rejected assimilation into mainstream Polish society, they suggest? Were they not richer than their Christian compatriots? Did they not tend to be pro-Communist? Studies written from this perspective have done important work to draw attention to the suffering of Polish gentiles during World War II. They sometimes do so, however, by downplaying Jewish victimization or even reproducing antisemitic ideas.

A third alternative can be called the "unequal victims" theory. According to this view, Nazi Germany attacked Polish gentiles and Polish Jews, but in different ways and to different extents. Here too the numbers are instructive. Approximately equal numbers of Polish Christians and Jews were killed during the war, about 3 million each. In the case of non-Jewish Poles, the estimate of 3 million includes many people killed by the Soviets as well as by the Germans. That number—3 million—computes to over 10 percent of Polish gentiles, a terrible toll. It amounts to more than 80 percent of Polish Jews, a total catastrophe. The "unequal victims" approach has validity, but as the label itself suggests, it all too easily disintegrates into a kind of competition in suffering or a numbers game in which human agony is quantified in ways that do not really make moral sense.

These debates intensified with the publication of a book called *Neighbors* by Jan Gross. In graphic detail, Gross recounts how on one day in July 1941, half of the residents of the Polish town of Jedwabne murdered most of the other half. In Jedwabne, according to Gross's account, Poles, not Germans, initiated and carried out the slaughter of more than fifteen hundred local Jews. Gross's study, however, is not simply one more accusation of some kind of intrinsic, uniquely Polish antisemitism. Instead he shows the complex interplay of forces in a region first terrorized by Soviet rule between 1939 and 1941, then overrun by the Germans. Poles accused Jews of collaborating with the Soviet oppressors, but in fact it was often precisely those Polish gentiles most deeply implicated in Soviet crimes who were quickest to take the lead in attacks on Jews—attacks that would serve both to deflect the anger of their neighbors and to curry favor with the new German occupiers.

Gross's analysis and the best of the controversy it has sparked caution against generalizing and emphasize instead the wide range of actions and experiences on the part of Poles during World War II. Some collaborated with the Soviets, some with the Germans; some helped their Jewish compatriots, often at great risk to themselves. The fates of Polish Christians and Polish Jews under Nazi occupation were linked in complicated ways that we cannot understand if we study those groups of people in isolation from each other.

Particular Features of the Polish Situation

As a whole Polish gentiles, unlike their Italian, Danish, or Bulgarian counterparts, did not obstruct Nazi plans to isolate, expropriate, and eventually annihilate the Jews. What factors might help us understand the Polish situation?

*A Polish gentile woman and two Polish Jewish men are forced to walk together,
probably to an execution site, sometime in the 1940s. The sign around the
woman's neck reads, "For selling merchandise to Jews."*

One important point involves chronology. Poland came under German
domination very early—in 1939—and remained, at least in part, in German
hands until early 1945. Unlike the Italians, who began to contend with German occupation only in 1943, the Poles were broken down by years of abuse
and persecution.

A second factor was ideological. Nazi racial theory considered Poles, like
all Slavic people, to be Untermenschen—"subhumans." Polish gentiles occupied a higher position on the ladder of Nazi racial theory than did Jews, but
they nevertheless counted in German eyes as inferiors, worthy at most to serve

their "Aryan" masters as slaves. Hitler's Germans considered the northern Europeans over whom they would come to rule—the Danes, Norwegians, and Dutch—to be racially related. Accordingly they tried to preserve what they considered their valuable "Nordic blood" and to co-opt them into their system of world domination, but they had no such intentions for the Poles, whose lives they regarded as worthless.

Demography—ethnic division within Poland—was a third factor that shaped the Polish situation. Many of the inhabitants of Poland in 1939 were not ethnic Poles. For example, the area seized by the Soviets in 1939 and held until 1941 was particularly mixed. Its 12 million inhabitants included only about 4.7 million ethnic Poles. The rest were Ukrainians, Belorussians, Russians, Jews, and others. Relations among these groups were not always harmonious, and as we have seen, the German invaders would prove adept at turning ethnic groups against one another to further their own ends.

The 1939 division of Poland between Germany and the Soviet Union seemed to have deepened hostilities between Polish gentiles and Jews and exacerbated Polish antisemitism. It is unlikely that either Hitler or Stalin foresaw that outcome when the pact was signed in August 1939, but both stood to gain from anything that helped them divide and rule the Poles.

Both the Soviet Union and Germany were traditional enemies of Poland. Many Soviet leaders, like Hitler, opposed the existence of an independent Polish state. So when Soviet forces took over eastern Poland in 1939, they sent many prominent Poles to forced labor in Siberia. Moreover, in the decades since the Bolshevik Revolution, the Soviet Union had developed a reputation for attacking Christianity and the churches. No wonder then that many Poles, especially the wealthy, staunchly nationalist, or devoutly Catholic, considered Soviet rule the worst tragedy that could befall them. In the fall of 1939 some fled to the parts of Poland under German control.

Polish gentiles would find little to choose between regarding Soviet and German rule. As we have seen, policies of resettlement and Germanization meant that hundreds of thousands of ethnic Poles were forced out of the incorporated territories. Meanwhile life in the General Government became increasingly untenable as the Germans targeted Poles for impoverishment and forced labor. Still, at least initially, many Polish gentiles considered their chances better with the Germans than with the Soviets.

In 1939 Polish Jews, in contrast to their gentile neighbors, tended to regard Soviet rule as a lesser evil than Nazi German domination. At least in theory antisemitism did not exist under Communism. Even in practice, Jews had possibilities to make lives for themselves in the Soviet Union, including as officers in the military. Nazi Germany offered no such option. So while some Polish Christians fled west to the Germans, many Polish Jews, like the young Jack Pomerantz, took their chances by running east.

Suspicious Polish gentiles interpreted as a betrayal the tendency of some Polish Jews to cast their lot with the Soviets. Antisemites had long accused Jews of being Communists; here they could claim to have found proof. Some Christians had always charged Jews with trying to destroy Christianity; now they could say they had evidence of an atheist conspiracy. We tend to assume that shared hardships draw people together. Often, however, quite the opposite occurs. In the early stages of World War II, the tribulations faced by all Poles tended to drive wedges between Christians and Jews.

Polish Jews who welcomed the Soviets in 1939 would be disappointed. Their new rulers had no intention of protecting them. Instead they shut down Jewish community institutions, banned organized activities, and confiscated private assets from Jews as well as non-Jews. In some cases, they evacuated Jews to the interior of the Soviet Union and to distant regions as laborers.

Soviet authorities required all young men in the areas under their control to enlist in the Red Army. Some Poles—Jewish and gentile—chose that option. Others went west rather than risk being stranded in the Soviet Union and separated from Poland and their families forever. In 1939 they could not know that, within two years, for a Jew to be trapped anywhere in Poland would amount to a death sentence. At least in the Soviet Union Jews could keep moving east. From Poland there would be no place to go.

The Role of Property

Some scholars suggest that Polish antisemitism was not primarily religious or racial but economic—that is, Polish Christians' hatred of Jews was fueled by material resentments, often based on their own deprivation and fantasies of Jewish wealth. In this view it was not greed but pauperization that led to Polish gentiles taking advantage of German aggression to grab Jewish property.

Certainly the poverty of many Poles played into the hands of the Germans. In retrospect one is struck by the pathetically small stakes that induced some gentiles in Poland to betray Jews to the Germans or even kill them themselves. Life seems to have been worth very little. For example, in one Polish town during the war Germans promised a kilogram (2.2 pounds) of salt to anyone who brought in the head of a Jew. Local Ukrainians fanned out through the nearby forests and returned clasping severed heads. In other cases, bags of sugar served as a reward. Sometimes just the promise of whatever possessions the Jews carried with them sufficed.

Discussion of the role that greed played in the Holocaust draws our attention to the "banality of evil." Hannah Arendt first used that phrase in her book *Eichmann in Jerusalem*. Most of the people involved in mass killing—as perpetrators, onlookers, and beneficiaries—were not crazed maniacs but ordinary people with familiar motivations. There were Polish peasants who deplored German brutality but willingly took the property of Jews forced into ghettos. There were ethnic German families who moved into homes from which the Polish owners had been evicted and eagerly accepted the booty for themselves. Such people did not necessarily initiate destruction, but they profited from it and developed a stake in its continuation.

Nevertheless one can also find many accounts that show Poles who risked their lives for others, including Jews. Yad Vashem, the Holocaust memorial and archive in Israel, honors non-Jews who rescued Jews from the Holocaust as "the righteous among nations." One of the criteria for being recognized as one of the righteous is that the person received no monetary benefit for what she or he did. Of all the countries of Europe, Poland has the greatest number of gentiles recognized for heroism toward Jews—as well as the largest number of Jews killed in the Holocaust.

An important example of Polish rescue efforts is the organization known as Zegota. Its network of operatives provided aid, food, and medication to Jews all over Poland. Zegota also produced scores of forged documents. Its work is credited with saving the lives of forty to fifty thousand Jews.

The Polish Underground Army

War did not end in Poland with the German defeat of the Polish army in 1939. Instead many Poles fought on in the underground army. There were actually two variants of the Polish underground army, one nationalist, the other Communist.

The Polish nationalist army, know as the Home Army, or AK, maintained links to the Polish government-in-exile in London. Its leaders were prewar Polish officers, and it was quite well organized and equipped. For the most part the Home Army was not particularly sympathetic to the sufferings of Polish Jews. Some of its officers were themselves antisemitic, and in any case their priorities lay elsewhere. They generally refused to shelter Jews or to arm them, although there were exceptions, for example, in Warsaw where the Home Army passed some revolvers to the Jewish underground. In some cases members of the Home Army even participated in killing Jews themselves in the forests. Nevertheless the Home Army did devote considerable attention to learning about what was happening to the Jews in Poland. Its intelligence assumed that any methods applied to Jews would later be used against Polish gentiles.

Generally the Communist underground army was more open to Polish Jews, at least to those who wished to join its ranks. However, it was rather weak and disorganized in many places and had little time for people ill equipped to take part in fighting: children, elderly people, and the unarmed.

In some places Jews would form their own underground fighting organizations. At least one of those, the Bielski partisans in western Belorussia, did accept older people, women, and children. Led by the dynamic Tuvia Bielski,

In August 1942 Bronia Szyr (later Brenda Senders) escaped from the ghetto in Sarny, a town in eastern Poland. She joined a Russian partisan group and spent the rest of the war fighting the Germans. This photograph was taken in April 1944 in Ukraine.

that forest community combined fighting and rescue activities. By 1944 it included more than twelve hundred Jews. Nechama Tec describes its efforts in her aptly titled book *Defiance*.

The Complexity of Polish–Jewish Issues: An Illustration

In his book *Anton the Dove Fancier*, Bernard Gotfryd recounts a story that shows how the lives of Polish Jews and gentiles were intertwined. When the war began Bernard was a young Jewish boy living in the Polish city of Radom. His neighbor Anton was a Polish Christian who raised and trained pigeons.

Anton was a rough man. He drank, threatened to cook his beloved birds, and neglected and scolded his wife. One day German officials requisitioned Anton's pigeons for the Reich. Instead of turning them over to the enemy, Anton killed every one of them. He was arrested for disobedience and sent to a camp.

Later during the war Bernard himself ended up in the concentration camp of Majdanek. There he saw Anton, now wearing the uniform of a kapo. A kapo was a prisoner whom the Germans had elevated to a position of authority over other prisoners. Many kapos were known for their extreme brutality.

Anton recognized Bernard and gave him some warm clothes and extra bread. Later he provided Bernard with water, cigarettes to barter, and advice. Somehow Bernard Gotfryd lived through the war. While he was still in a camp he learned that Anton had been killed by his fellow prisoners in revenge for his cruelty.

Gotfryd returned to Radom, where he saw Anton's wife. She told him that she too had been born Jewish. As a child she had been orphaned and taken in by Anton's mother. Anton had never known about her origins. Now she planned to leave for Palestine.

This case shows the danger of assuming clear-cut categories when studying a situation as complicated as that in Poland during the war. As Anton demonstrated, the same person could be a resistance figure, a perpetrator of brutality, a hero, and a victim of Nazi aggression. As his wife's experience suggests, even the line between "Christian" and "Jew" could be blurred. There is little that is simple about Polish–Jewish relations during the Nazi era.

MURDER OF THE HANDICAPPED

Hitler's Germany first crossed the line from persecution to mass murder not with Jews but with people considered handicapped. The year 1939 would see initiation of a program to murder people defined as "lives unworthy of living." Here, too, experimentation would characterize the early stages of implementation, and the outbreak of war provided both cover and justification for the killers.

As we have seen, the idea of "purging" the population of elements considered undesirable predated Nazi rule and was not exclusive to Germany. Such notions, however, got a big boost with Nazi ideology and its idea that the "collective good"—at least the well-being of those judged superior—overrode the good of the individual. Nazi planners measured the value of a human life by its contribution to the national community, not by some inherent worth.

The T-4 Program

Even before the war began in 1939 Hitler had authorized Dr. Karl Brandt and Philipp Bouhler to organize a children's "euthanasia" program. Under this scheme children selected for killing were sent to special clinics where medical personnel starved them to death or gave them lethal injections. Doctors and research scientists also used some children for experiments that they hoped would advance their own careers.

In the summer of 1939, Hitler instructed another physician, Dr. Leonardo Conti, to organize a similar program for adults. Conti, the Reich Doctors' leader and state secretary in the interior ministry responsible for health matters, set up a huge administrative machinery that involved doctors, professors, social workers, nurses, and other healthcare professionals. Their main target would be institutionalized adults with mental illnesses and disabilities. Codenamed "T-4" for the address of its headquarters in Berlin, Tiergartenstrasse 4, the program was operating by October 1939.

Even before killings began, Conti's people developed a target number by using the following formula. Of every one thousand people in the German Reich, they estimated, ten needed psychiatric treatment. Five of those were institutionalized. One of those five was assumed to qualify for what was euphemistically called euthanasia. In fact, it was murder. That formula—1000:10:5:1—yielded between sixty-five and seventy-five thousand target cases in Germany. Conti's committee prepared forms to be sent to all mental institutions. The form was short and asked such questions as whether the patient received regular visitors or had any "non-Aryan" blood. Obviously the criteria for selection had little to do with the actual health of the person in question.

Teams of medical evaluators examined the forms. They marked with a red plus sign those people to be killed; they used a blue minus sign to specify who was to be left alive. Some doctors refused to participate. For example, the director of one asylum declined with the explanation that he was "too gentle" for such work. He and others like him did not suffer any consequences. It was no problem to find enough ambitious professionals to keep the program running smoothly.

The T-4 experts experimented with various methods of killing. They used injections and poison in the early months but soon sought quicker means. By January 1940 they had conducted the first successful gassing, at an asylum not far from Berlin.

Some of the earliest gassings were carried out at Grafeneck, a former palace in Württemberg that had been made into a hospital for physically handicapped people. State authorities moved the patients out and took over the building, which they revamped as a killing center.

An employee at the killing center of Hadamar, in Hesse, described viewing a gassing there. He "looked through the peephole in the side wall," he remembered:

> Through it I saw 40–45 men who were pressed together in the next room and were now slowly dying. Some lay on the ground, others had slumped down, many had their mouths open as if they could not get any more air. The form of death was so painful that one cannot talk of a humane killing, especially since many of the dead men may have had moments of clarity. I watched the process for about 2–3 minutes and then left because I could no longer bear to look and felt sick. (Noakes and Pridham 3:1027)

Meanwhile, other initiatives began against the mentally ill in Poland. Already on 29 September 1939, Germans began shooting Polish mental patients in the district of Bromberg (the Polish name is Bydgoszcz). By 1 November they had murdered almost four thousand people this way.

Elsewhere in territories conquered from Poland, SS execution squads murdered residents of mental institutions in order to empty out buildings for their own purposes. Sometimes they responded to requests from bureaucrats in the resettlement offices who needed beds for ethnic Germans being brought into an area. One SS special commando used a van labeled "Kaiser's Coffee" as a mobile killing unit. Carbon monoxide gas was fed from a container in the cab into the back of the van to asphyxiate the passengers. During December 1939 and January 1940 the SS special commando murdered hundreds of patients from Polish asylums in that van.

Hitler's Backdated Authorization and Efforts to Maintain Secrecy

Worried about possible repercussions for their activity, the organizers of the T-4 program approached Hitler for formal authorization that would serve to cover them should objections be raised. Sometime in October 1939 T-4 officials persuaded Hitler to sign a short statement that was printed on his personal notepaper rather than as an official document. The statement read: "Reich leader Bouhler and Dr. Brandt are charged with responsibility to extend the powers of specific doctors in such a way that, after the most careful assessment of their condition, those suffering from illnesses deemed to be incurable may be granted a mercy death" (Noakes and Pridham, 3:1021).

It is significant that Hitler backdated this note to 1 September 1939, the day of the German invasion of Poland. Presumably he did so in order to link the decision to begin killing people deemed handicapped with the demands of war. In fact the murders were not a response to the exigencies of war; they were an expression of the ideology of race and space. The upheaval of wartime, however, provided the opportunity to carry out such plans with reduced public scrutiny. At the same time war increased Hitler's ability to appeal to the German nation to support his cause.

The program's organizers tried to keep the killings secret, but total concealment was impossible. There were simply too many people involved and too many ways for information to leak out. Staff at hospitals and asylums saw patients taken away for killing. Family members received letters that announced the deaths of their loved ones. In some cases officials made errors; for example, they wrote that someone had died of appendicitis when the person's appendix had been removed years earlier; they listed another cause of death as spinal disease, but the relatives had just seen the man and he had been in perfect health. The patients themselves in some cases figured out what was going on and pleaded for their lives.

News also circulated in the German communities near the killing centers and beyond. Employees of such places sometimes frequented local bars, where they spouted off about what they had seen. The stench of bodies burning in crematoria drifted beyond fences and walls that enclosed the sites of killing. Even small children playing teased one another about being taken away in the buses with the darkened windows if they acted retarded.

Protest against the Killings

News of the killings of handicapped people upset many Germans. Relatives of some of those murdered launched protests of various kinds. Some wrote directly to Hitler to express their disapproval. Some shared details with their pastors or priests. Probably the ease with which the program got started had convinced Hitler that the public would be indifferent. Perhaps most people were, but those opposed made their views known.

Church leaders in both the Catholic and the Protestant churches in Germany learned about the killings in direct ways: many asylums were run by the churches. Most of those institutions and their personnel cooperated with the program, although there were exceptions. Nevertheless, it was from church circles that the most concerted protests to the killings would emerge.

Some local Protestant and Catholic clergy made public calls to respect the sanctity of human life. In December 1940, Pope Pius XII issued a statement that denounced "killing of an innocent person because of mental or physical defects." The most pointed protest did not come until the summer of 1941. By then between seventy and eighty thousand people had been killed in the program in Germany alone. The number of Polish handicapped people murdered is unknown, but in all it is estimated that by 1945 the Germans murdered some 275,000 people they deemed handicapped from all over Europe.

In August 1941 the Catholic bishop of Münster, Cardinal August Count von Galen, decided to take a stand against the killings. He preached a sermon in which he made it clear that he knew exactly what was going on and considered it a crime against humanity. Galen quoted the German Penal Code's prohibition against murder and warned the government that its policies would backfire. He told of a German soldier whose father had been institutionalized for some mental disturbance. As the younger man went off to defend his nation, his father in Germany was being killed by his German national comrades. Whose life would be safe in such a society? Galen asked his parishioners.

Galen's sermon was duplicated and circulated all over Germany and even abroad by sympathetic elements within the Christian churches. Nazi leaders were furious, but they dared not take action against Galen. He was too well known and too popular. In wartime the government could not risk alienating its own population, so Galen kept his post.

Late in August 1941 Hitler gave an order to halt the "Euthanasia Program." That order was little more than a ploy. It is now known that the killings did not stop—nor did Hitler intend them to. The secrecy around them was increased, however, and some of the killing operations were moved outside Germany.

It is not clear to what extent Hitler's order to halt was a response to protests such as Bishop von Galen's sermon. Certainly the stepped-up efforts at concealment were intended to placate the public. German authorities also had an eye to morale in the military. During wartime the last thing soldiers needed was the worry that they would be killed by their own government if they were injured. In any case, the T-4 experts had already made their quota. More blatant "cleansing" of those "flawed" elements from the "Aryan race" could wait until after the war.

Sweden

*Baltic
Sea*

Riga

Latvia

Lithuania

Kovno
(Kaunas)

Danzig
(Gdansk)

Königsberg
(Kaliningrad)

East Prussia

Vilna
(Vilnius)

Grodno

Minsk

Bydgoszcz
(Bromberg)

Jedwabne

Bialystok

Vistula

River

Zbaszyn

Poznan

Incorporated Territories
(Annexed by Germany)

Oder River

Lodz

Radom

Warsaw

Bug

Soviet-Occupied Territory
September 1939 - June 1941

Lublin

River

**German - Soviet
Line**

Breslau

Piotrkow Trybunalski

General Government

Dubno

Germany

Katowice

Krakow

Lvov

Dniester River

Slovakia

Romania

Danube

Vienna

River

Budapest

Hungary

Division of Poland
September 1939

Former Polish Border

0   100 miles

0   150 kilometers

Map by Michael J. Fisher, cartographer

6

EXPANSION AND SYSTEMATIZATION: EXPORTING WAR AND TERROR, 1940–1941

The previous chapter described the first year of the war as a period of Nazi experiments in conquest, persecution, and mass killing. Just as Nazi revolution in 1933 had been followed by routinization, the experimental phase in 1939 gave way to what might be labeled a time of expansion and systematization. During 1940 and 1941 the size of Hitler's empire increased tremendously as German forces overwhelmed more and more of Europe. After Poland the Germans first turned their military attentions to the north and west, attacking Denmark, Norway, the Netherlands, Belgium, Luxembourg, France, and Britain in the spring and summer of 1940. Able to conquer all but the British, they moved south and east—against Yugoslavia and Greece in spring 1941, and then in June 1941 against the Soviet Union.

Terror and suffering grew along with Hitler's empire as programs of killing became both much larger and more efficient. By the end of 1941 German mobile killing units would have murdered close to a million Jews in eastern Europe—men, women, and children—many of them shot into mass graves. Preparation of killing centers to massacre even more stunning numbers of people would be under way. Millions of Soviet prisoners of war would be dead or dying in German captivity.

This chapter surveys the German campaigns of 1940 and 1941 that brought most of Europe under Nazi control. It explores the repercussions as Nazi Germans took their projects of supposed racial purification and territorial expansion ever farther from home.

WAR IN THE NORTH AND WEST

Within days of the German invasion of Poland on 1 September 1939, both Britain and France were officially at war with Germany. Bound by agreements to Poland, the British and French declared war on Germany on 3 September but initially remained fairly inactive. This early phase was known in Britain as the "phoney war." The French referred to it as a "drôle de guerre"—a "funny war"—and the Germans spoke of a "Sitzkrieg," an immobile "war of sitting" in contrast to the rapid "Blitzkrieg"—"lightning war"—in Poland.

There were a few skirmishes on the border between France and Germany in 1939 but nothing otherwise on land. Siegfried Knappe, a young German artillery officer, describes in his memoir *Soldat* how he spent much of the fall and winter of 1939–1940 in western Germany, mere miles from the border with Luxembourg. Days and then weeks passed as the Germans prepared for an attack from the French that never came. Rather than the dangers and strains of combat, Knappe and his men faced the challenge of readying their horses and themselves for action, tasks that left plenty of time to celebrate German victories in Poland by drinking beer and dancing with the locals. Knappe especially enjoyed an invitation to the Bismarck estate, where he and a group of fellow officers sipped cocktails and chatted with the vivacious, young granddaughter-in-law of Otto von Bismarck, the hero of German unification in 1871. From Knappe's vantage point, it must have been easy to view Hitler's early triumphs as confirmation of German superiority.

At sea there was more action as the Germans began their attack on Allied shipping. In return the British navy organized a convoy system and began actively breaking German codes. By mid-1940 this phase of the "phoney war" in the west would come to an abrupt halt.

In the spring of 1940, after a winter spent consolidating their hold on Poland and continuing preparations for further offensives, the Germans moved north and west. Hitler and his generals knew that their plan to dominate Europe remained impossible unless they crushed and subordinated the European powers of France and Britain. That goal could only be achieved through war.

For Hitler war in the west was a prerequisite for grabbing land in the east. It had been part of the plan all along. The western conflict, however, did not take quite the form Hitler had foreseen. Already in 1938 Hitler believed Germany was ready for war against France and Britain. He had expected that war to precede hostilities with Poland. The German air force—the Luftwaffe—had been built up under Hermann Göring with an eye to campaigns in the west. It was in the west that Hitler anticipated the most difficult fighting for the Germans. After all, in Nazi eyes, Europeans to Germany's east were racial inferiors, surely easy opponents for members of a master race.

In keeping with Nazi racial theories, German warfare in the west would be less excessive than in the east. Nazi ideology regarded western and northern Europeans as "racially valuable" people, suitable partners for German "Aryans." Still, Germans would do much stealing and plundering in these parts of Europe too. For leaders who believed that Germany had lost the previous war because of public discontent—the stab in the back from the homefront—nothing was more important than placating the people back home. What easier way to do so than to let them enrich themselves at the expense of others?

In April 1940 German forces entered Denmark, and that small nation surrendered without a struggle. The Germans moved on to Norway, where they had to fight their way in, but by June 1940 they had defeated the Norwegians too. The British and French tried to help Norway, but without adequate air support and thorough coordination their landings failed.

The Norwegian government fled to London, where it established itself as a government-in-exile. Norwegian merchant ships also escaped to Britain, where they could be used in the war effort against Germany. A local fascist leader, Vidkun Quisling, took power—or more accurately, became the German puppet—at home. His name, "quisling," has become a synonym for "cowardly collaborator." The Norwegians would execute Quisling as a traitor in 1945.

What did German military planners want with Denmark and Norway? A look at a map gives some explanation. The Germans needed to secure the supply route of Swedish iron ore for their war machine. They also sought to broaden their base for a sea war with Britain, and Scandinavia would provide naval bases from which to attack the British with submarines.

In May 1940, just a month after the offensive against Denmark and Norway began, German forces invaded and conquered the neutral nations of the Netherlands, Belgium, and Luxembourg. Here too victory was swift.

For example, in the Netherlands, German armored forces penetrated the borders, while airborne units took strategic airfields and bridges. The Dutch soon surrendered. First, however, there were some significant developments. The queen and her government left Holland for Britain, where they too formed a government-in-exile on the side of the Allies. The Dutch were important to the French and British cause because they controlled a large colonial empire and a substantial merchant fleet, both of which would prove valuable in the war effort.

On 14 May the Luftwaffe bombed the Dutch city of Rotterdam in an attempt to terrorize the Dutch into surrender. The Germans clearly aimed at civilian targets to intimidate and demoralize their opponents. They destroyed the center of the city and killed hundreds of civilians. At the time, the panicked British press reported the inflated figure of thirty thousand Dutch casualties. For the Allies, the bombing of Rotterdam provided an early manifestation of German brutality and introduced a new kind of warfare: unlimited war from the air. Within a few years the Germans would reap what they had sown with the destruction from the air of their own cities.

One of the eyewitnesses to the German conquest of the Netherlands was Anne Frank, a young girl living in Amsterdam. Her family were German Jews who had left Frankfurt for Holland after Hitler came to power. As it turned out, they had not fled far enough. Unable to get out of Europe in 1940, their only option would be to try to disappear within the city of Amsterdam.

Anne's father began to use his contacts to prepare a hiding place for his family and some acquaintances. It was in their "secret annex" between July 1942 and August 1944 that Anne would write a diary, now one of the most famous documents of the Holocaust. Betrayed by an anonymous tipoff to police, the Franks and the people in hiding with them were sent first to the Dutch transit camp of Westerbork and then on to Auschwitz. A group of them were later moved to the Bergen-Belsen concentration camp in Germany, where Anne died in March 1945. Of the eight residents of the hiding place, only Anne Frank's father, Otto, survived the war.

German Victory over France

In May 1940 German troops entered France. They came through Belgium from two directions, the north and also the south. The French had concentrated their best forces in the north and were unprepared for a German attack through the Forest of Ardennes in southern Belgium. By 12 May, German soldiers were on French soil, and by 20 May, they had broken through to the sea, to the coast of the English Channel. In effect German forces cut the Anglo-French troops in two.

The Germans prepared to surround and annihilate the Allied forces converging on the French seaport of Dunkirk. Between the end of May and early June 1940, however, the Allies managed to evacuate some 338,000 of their own soldiers. Using merchant ships, motorboats, fishing boats, private yachts, destroyers, and any other craft they could muster, the British rescued their men from the beaches of Dunkirk while under continued attack from the Germans. They had no choice but to leave most of their equipment behind.

By 14 June, German troops marched triumphantly into Paris. Hitler danced the jig that became famous from the newsreels when he visited Paris for the first time. Unlike the Dutch and Norwegian governments, the French government did not go into exile. Instead it remained and signed an Armistice Agreement on 22 June 1940. Under the terms of the armistice the Germans divided France into two parts: an occupied zone and an unoccupied zone known as Vichy France because its capital was located in the small, southern city of Vichy. Much of the French army entered prisoner of war camps, whereas the navy remained intact.

The head of the Vichy state was Marshal Henri Philippe Pétain (1856–1951), by 1940 an old man and a hero of World War I. His supporters would be known as Pétainists. For at least part of the war Pétain's prime minister was Pierre Laval (1883–1945). Together those two names would become symbols of French collaboration with Nazi Germany. Some of the French, however, refused to accept defeat. Among those, General Charles De Gaulle (1890–1970) emerged as leader of the Free French forces, and he too escaped to London.

In the years before 1940, France had been a haven for refugees from all over Europe. Many Communists and other supporters of the Spanish Republic had fled to France in 1939 when their side lost the civil war in Spain. Jews from other parts of Europe had taken refuge in France as their homelands fell prey to German aggression. Now all of these people came into the hands of the Germans and their new French partners.

Among the many foreigners residing in France in 1940 were a young boy named Saul Friedländer and his parents. Friedländer was born in Prague in 1933. He and his parents, middle-class, secular Jews, had left Czechoslovakia in 1938, even as German troops were moving in. France seemed a safe destination, and it was hard enough to move that far, leaving behind property, career, and relatives. It would prove difficult, and for Friedländer's parents eventually impossible, to remain safe in a society where one was a stranger, without money, friends, or adequate language skills. For the Friedländers the collapse of France in 1940 was not primarily a national humiliation; it was a personal catastrophe that eventually put the parents in the clutches of the Nazis and left the son an orphan.

The Battle of Britain

With the fall of France, most textbooks will tell you that Great Britain stood alone against Germany. Indeed, Britain was the only European power

A Gypsy woman with a group of children in the Rivesaltes internment camp in 1942. Located in the French Pyrenees Mountains, Rivesaltes was used in the late 1930s for refugees from the Spanish Civil War. In 1941 and 1942 thousands of Gypsies and foreign-born Jews rounded up in France were interned there.

both to declare war on Germany in 1939 and to stand firm until 1945. Neither the Soviet Union nor the United States would enter the war against Germany until 1941.

The British, however, were not entirely alone. The Dominions—Australia, New Zealand, Canada and, after considerable internal debate, South Africa—joined in declarations of war against Germany. The British-controlled government of India also did so, although without consulting the Indian political parties or, for that matter, the Indian public. Rather than joining the other Dominions, the Irish Free State proclaimed its neutrality.

Support of the Allied cause by countries all over the world was significant, both to the outcome of the war and after the fact, to the national pride of citizens of the nations concerned. People in the Dominions would bear a substantial burden in the war, and if the British Isles were to have fallen to the Germans, there would still have been the possibility of continuing the war effort. In fact, the British leadership planned to do so from Canada and moved large parts of Britain's gold reserves to Canada in case they would be needed to finance the war.

Within Europe Britain became the last refuge for many people fleeing Nazi Germany. The governments-in-exile—Polish, Norwegian, Dutch—were surrounded by communities of people forced to flee their homelands. Czech and French opponents of Germany also gathered in Britain, as did those Jews from the continent who could make it in. Among the people who had arrived before war began in 1939 were some ten thousand Jewish children from Germany, Austria, Czechoslovakia, and Poland. A special program organized by private citizens, known as the Kindertransport, brought them to Great Britain. Forced to leave their families behind on the continent, most of them never saw their parents again.

Two veterans of the Kindertransports were Ilona and Kurt Penner, children of a Polish Jewish father and a Hungarian Jewish mother. Born in Berlin in 1928, the twins were sent to England in March 1939, where they were placed separately. Their parents, owners of a dry goods store, managed to leave Germany in 1940, although they initially only got as far as France. Fortunately they were able to secure passage to the United States in 1941. Kurt joined them there that year; Ilona, two years later.

Now, more than sixty years later, the children of the Kindertransports are adults, many of them grandparents. One girl who came to England from Vienna became known as an adult as Ruth Morley, an Academy Award–nominated costume designer who worked on such well-known American movies as *Tootsie, The Miracle Worker,* and *Taxi Driver.* Morley's daughter, a filmmaker named Melissa Hacker, included some of her mother's experiences in a documentary film titled *My Knees Were Jumping: Remembering the Kindertransports.*

By May 1940, with the fall of France, Hitler saw the British as Germany's main enemy in Europe. He proceeded with plans for an invasion, while British prime minister Winston Churchill rallied the British population against the Germans. One of Churchill's most famous speeches included the following challenge: "The Battle of Britain is about to begin. Upon this battle depends the survival of Christian civilization. . . . If we fail then . . . all we have known and cared for will sink into the abyss of a new Dark Age." After the evacuation of Dunkirk, Churchill's rousing words helped strengthen and inspire British determination:

> Even though large tracts of Europe and many old and famous states have fallen or may fall into the grip of the Gestapo and all the odious apparatus of Nazi rule,

we shall not flag or fail. We shall go on to the end. We shall fight in France, we shall fight on the seas and oceans, we shall fight with growing confidence and growing strength in the air, we shall defend our island, whatever the cost may be. We shall fight on the beaches, we shall fight on the landing grounds, we shall fight in the fields and in the streets, we shall fight in the hills; we shall never surrender; and even if, which I do not for a moment believe, this island or a large part of it were submerged and starving, then our Empire beyond the seas, armed and guarded by the British Fleet, would carry on the struggle, until, in God's good time, the new world, with all its power and might, steps forth to the rescue and the liberation of the old. (Sachse, 314–15)

The German plan for landings in Britain had the code name Operation Sea-Lion. German planners were convinced that successful crossing of the English Channel and establishment of beachheads on the English coast depended on control of the skies, and Göring assured Hitler that the Luftwaffe could destroy the Royal Air Force (RAF).

In August 1940 the Luftwaffe began massive attacks on British air and naval installations. Every day for the next two months hundreds of planes fought in the skies over Britain. The Germans, however, could not gain the mastery they expected. On 15 September 1940, the RAF shot down sixty aircraft, and two days later, Hitler postponed the invasion "until further notice." He hoped among other things that invasion and defeat of the Soviet Union—both of which were already planned—would isolate and weaken Britain so that the Germans could come back later for an easy victory. Those two months—August and September 1940—became known as the Battle of Britain. Throughout 1941, the Germans turned to bombing British cities, industrial centers, and ports. Air raids became a nightly event, with the inhabitants of such cities as London, Coventry, and Plymouth seeking safety in subways, cellars, and homemade bomb shelters. German bombing took a heavy toll on civilian lives and property, but British morale remained firm. Meanwhile German air raids spurred the Allies to develop radar technology that would play a crucial role winning the war in the air.

Events on the Periphery of German Warfare

Some European countries remained neutral throughout World War II, most notably Spain, Portugal, Switzerland, Sweden, and Turkey. The neutrals would play different roles during the war. Some provided escape routes for victims of German persecution. For example, in October 1943 the small Jewish community of Denmark was smuggled out to safety in neutral Sweden. Others, such as Switzerland, turned many refugees away. Among those sent back at the border were the young Saul Friedländer's parents. In despair they ended up back in France, and eventually they were sent to Auschwitz and killed there.

Some of the neutrals profited considerably from the war. Swiss banks grew rich on stolen gold sent there by German authorities and on deposits from European Jews desperate to protect some assets from the German predators. The Swedes delivered massive amounts of iron ore to Germany. Turkey offered refuge to some European Jews but charged special taxes intended to transfer wealth from the refugees to native Turks. After the war Turkey also provided an escape route to the Middle East for many Nazi criminals. Neutral or not, no nation in Europe would be untouched by the war.

In 1940 Germany entered into the Three-Power Pact with Italy and Japan. Later that arrangement would be consolidated into a formal military alliance, although coordination among the three powers was minimal. For the time being the three states committed themselves to aid one another against their enemies.

Later in 1941, Hungary, Romania, Slovakia, Finland, Bulgaria, and Croatia would join the pact. Why were these less powerful nations interested in allying themselves with Germany and Italy? A look at a map suggests an answer. None of these countries shared a border with either Germany or Italy. All hoped to expand with German or Italian help at the expense of their neighbors. They operated on a common assumption: "the enemies of my enemies are my friends." By the end of World War II, that notion would prove disastrously false.

Soviet Assault on the Baltic States and Finland

As evident in the division of Poland in September 1939, Germany was not the only belligerent power in Europe. Under the leadership of Josef Stalin, the Soviet Union had its own expansionist program, linked to the goal of crushing all threats to internal security.

After seizing eastern Poland, Stalin turned his attention to the three tiny Baltic states, Estonia, Latvia, and Lithuania. By October 1939 massive Soviet threats had compelled all three to accept Soviet military bases with tens of thousands of Red Army troops. In June 1940, as the victorious Wehrmacht marched into defeated Paris, Stalin grabbed the opportunity to transform those "bases" into a full-scale invasion and occupation of the Baltic states.

Along with Red Army tanks came the Stalinist system of terror, presided over by the NKVD (People's Commissariat for Internal Affairs) and its political police, known after 1941 as the NKGB (People's Commissariat for State Security) or simply KGB. Soviet authorities organized a wave of purges and deportations of local nationalists of all ages. Hundreds of thousands of people simply vanished—into Soviet torture chambers, prisons, and labor camps in Siberia. In Latvia alone, 2 percent of the population "disappeared" as NKVD operatives sought to destroy the possibility of any national resistance. For the next year, Soviet interrogators and guards and local collaborators followed Stalin's injunction to "beat, beat, and again beat."

Likewise in June 1940, Stalin took advantage of the situation in western Europe to seize the province of Bessarabia in northern Romania. There too NKVD rule and ruthless state terror followed, with the same deadly consequences as in the Baltic states.

By the time the Germans launched their own invasion of these regions in mid-1941, the people of the Baltic states and northern Romania had been brutalized by deprivation, abuse, and violence. Small wonder that many of them in turn would seek revenge and scapegoats for their suffering by throwing their lot in with the Nazis. It can be tempting to set up competitions in evil between Hitler and Stalin. Who was worse? Who caused more murder and misery? This brief survey of the events of 1940, however, reminds us of an even more terrible reality; Nazism and Stalinism coexisted in time and place, and for many Europeans the horrors of one vicious system served to increase the destructive force of the other.

Already in November 1939 the Soviets had invaded Finland, another neighbor to the west. The gigantic attack was intended to overwhelm the 3.5 million Finns in rapid "blitzkrieg" style. Instead the Finns mounted a resourceful, heroic resistance and held out until March 1940, when they were forced to sign a peace treaty and cede territories to the Soviet Union. In that conflict, known as the Winter War, Stalin again took advantage of British and French inability to aid the targets of his aggression and used the protective cover of German assaults elsewhere in Europe to pick up spoils of his own. At the same time, at least in the short run, Hitler and the Germans benefited from anything that further disrupted the stability of Europe and distracted attention from their own activities.

WAR AND ITS IMPACT
INSIDE NAZI GERMANY

War had many repercussions inside Germany too. For one thing, German military successes brought floods of luxury goods into the hands of Germans back home. Men sent furs and jewels to their wives; German museums and galleries acquired costly art treasures; the finest wines, chocolate, cheeses, pâtés, and other delicacies ended up on German tables. The wealthier the nation conquered, the richer the spoils of war.

In the words of the historian Robert Gellately, war also "revolutionized the revolution" in Nazi Germany. War allowed German authorities to step up the pace of change at home and crack down hard on dissenters. For example, restrictions on public meetings and control over the press tightened considerably after 1939. Numbers of arrests continued to climb: for spreading so-called malicious rumors critical of the government or the Nazi Party, for violating state monopolies on information, for maintaining illegal organizations, and for engaging in other activities considered subversive. The population of the ever-expanding network of concentration camps and their satellites grew accordingly.

War exported Nazi policies such as persecution of Jews and applied Nazi practices such as divide and conquer in new territories. Already between 1933 and 1939 Hitler's regime had built on the principle that nothing succeeds like success. In wartime that notion again proved extremely powerful.

The prewar triumphs of Hitler's rule—for example, the annexation of Austria and the seizure of the Sudetenland in 1938—had helped to bring some reluctant Germans in line. Germany's spectacular military successes in 1939 and 1940 turned out to be even more effective. German patriots of all kinds, including many who consistently had voted against Hitler, rejoiced with him at the destruction of Poland and the victory over France. To German nationalists these successes seemed to vindicate old desires for revenge and to legitimate German aggression.

The family of Alfons Heck, an eager member of the Hitler Youth, illustrates this particular effect of Germany's war. Before 1939 Heck's father, a committed Socialist, and his grandmother, a devout Catholic, had both opposed Adolf Hitler. They also disapproved openly of Heck's enthusiastic involvement in the Hitler Youth. Nevertheless both were thrilled with the German conquest of France in 1940. Living as they did near the border with France they were particularly aware of Germany's long enmity with its neighbor to the west. By mid-May 1940, Heck's father and grandmother had stopped complaining about Hitler's government and joined Alfons as supporters of the German war effort.

War brutalized life in ways that did not alter the goals of the German leaders but did transform what it was possible for them to achieve. War provided a cover for mass murder; remember Hitler's false dating of his order to murder the handicapped to 1 September 1939 and his repeated claim that he had given his speech "predicting" annihilation of the European Jews not in January 1939 but in September of that year. War also made possible the training of large numbers of experienced killers, beginning in Poland in 1939.

War trapped the victims of Nazism inside Europe, making them ever more vulnerable. After September 1939 it became extremely difficult for Jews to leave Europe. By 1941 it was practically impossible. The German police regulation of September 1941 that required all people defined as Jews to wear the identifying Star of David simply reinforced the obvious: Jews were now open targets.

War enabled Nazi propagandists to present attacks on innocent civilians of all ages as if they were defensive measures necessary to protect the German nation from its foes. For all these reasons, war was a necessary ingredient in what would develop into genocide—the deliberate effort at total annihilation of identifiable groups of people.

ASSAULT ON THE BALKANS—
YUGOSLAVIA AND GREECE

In 1941, the Germans again turned east, first to the Balkans in southeastern Europe. Mussolini had gotten in over his head when he sent his Italian forces in to conquer Greece in 1940. Now he needed the Germans to bail him out.

The German attack on the Balkans was also linked to preparation for an assault on the Soviet Union. Hitler and his generals considered it necessary to control the Balkan states in order to secure their southeastern flank and safeguard access to Romanian oil. With Romania, Bulgaria, and Hungary already bound to Germany through diplomatic arrangements, only Yugoslavia and Greece remained to be brought into the Nazi sphere.

On 6 April 1941 the Luftwaffe launched an air raid on Belgrade. German forces surrounded the Yugoslav army, which capitulated on 17 April. Italian, Hungarian, and Bulgarian troops invaded Yugoslavia in aid of the Germans, and the Yugoslavian king fled to Britain, where he too formed a government-in-exile.

Things did not go as smoothly for the Germans in Yugoslavia as the previous description suggests. The German offensive faced tough resistance that in turn forced delay of Hitler's long-awaited invasion of the Soviet Union. Yugoslav partisans used the rugged terrain to their advantage and benefited from the effective, ruthless leadership of Tito (Josip Broz, 1892–1980). Aid from the British in the form of supplies and intelligence helped too.

In Yugoslavia the German forces stooped to new depths of organized brutality that may have surpassed even their behavior in Poland. Here too they relied on familiar techniques of divide and conquer. Part of the country (Croatia, Bosnia, and Herzegovina) became an independent Croatian state under Ante Pavelic (1889–1959) and his fascist Ustasha movement. The Germans used their ally Pavelic to carry out their will. At the same time they gave him and his henchmen license to do what they wanted against enemies of their own, which meant above all the Serbs.

Meanwhile the Germans annexed some northern parts of Yugoslavia to the German Reich and set up a military government in Serbia. Everywhere, they encouraged thugs to attack Jews, Gypsies, Communists, liberals, and anti-German nationalists of any kind.

The Germans' brutal occupation policies ensured a steady flow of people into the partisan groups. In particular the practice of reprisals roused hatred. For every one German whom Yugoslav partisans attacked or killed, German authorities ordered a certain number of Yugoslavs shot. Sometimes the ratio was fifty to one; sometimes it was one hundred or even two hundred to one. The victims seized included people of all ages, female as well as male. Germans used reprisals—often based only on fear or suspicion of partisan actions—as an excuse to massacre hundreds of thousands of Yugoslavs.

In Yugoslavia it was generally the regular German military, not some special SS units, who carried out mass shootings of civilians. Although soldiers were not forced to participate in these killings, there were always enough volunteers for such duties. Some of them even took photographs of their exploits to send home to their girlfriends and wives.

Often the Germans took their first victims from among the local Jewish and Gypsy populations, but they also took hostage and shot many Serbs. There were Croats, Bosnian Muslims, and people with mixed backgrounds among those shot in reprisals too. Some of the most damning evidence of atrocities committed by the Wehrmacht—the regular German military—during World War II comes out of Yugoslavia.

Already in 1940, Hitler's Italian ally, Mussolini, had launched his own military campaign against Greece, but the Italian offensive bogged down until the spring of 1941, when the Germans took over. In April and May 1941 German forces overran Greece. Here too the Germans brutally assaulted civilians as well as the military. In so-called special actions, often in retaliation for resistance or partisan activity, they wiped out entire villages and towns.

The body of a Jewish doctor hangs on an electric pole in front of a bank in Sabac, Yugoslavia, in August 1941. The building has been painted with antisemitic graffiti showing a rich banker, presumably a Jew, holding a money bag in one hand and in the other pulling the strings behind Franklin Roosevelt, Winston Churchill, and Josef Stalin.

On orders from above, German soldiers tried to spare Greece's artistic treasures. Hitler had always been fascinated by Greek and Roman art. He held the notion that the best artistic achievements had been made by "Aryans" who later migrated north and brought their superior creativity to Germany. According to Hitler, the Greeks of his own time were a lesser people unworthy of their country's glorious past. In Greece, as elsewhere, Hitler adjusted reality to fit his view of the world.

German police pose near the bodies of recently murdered Serbian civilians in
1941 in Yugoslavia. Many Germans took photographs like this one
and sent them home to their families.

GERMAN ASSAULT ON THE SOVIET UNION

On 22 June 1941 German troops invaded the Soviet Union. The invasion was
given the code name Operation Barbarossa. With this step Hitler's forces
crossed the final line to what he called a "war of annihilation."

War in the Soviet Union was extremely bloody. An estimated 27 million
Soviet citizens were killed, the majority of them civilians. Carnage on this scale
was no mere replay of Napoleon's failed invasion of Russia 129 years earlier.
The German assault on the Soviet Union was not a war of soldier against soldier or army against army. It was a war whose goal was total destruction of the
Soviet Union, seizure of its land, colonization, enslavement, and murder of its
people, in short, establishment of the Nazi new order in Europe.

By mid-1941 German forces were ready to wage a war of annihilation.
Trained in conquest in Poland, flushed with successes in the west, and brutalized by war on partisans and civilians in the Balkans, they were no longer likely
to protest at atrocities as some had in 1939. From day one German operations
in the Soviet Union would be characterized by a level of ruthlessness that has
led the historian Omer Bartov to speak of the "barbarization of warfare."

You may have heard people say that Germany would have won the war if Hitler had not made the mistake of attacking the Soviet Union. Given Hitler's worldview this claim makes little sense. For Hitler the whole point of the war was to conquer land and resources to support his purportedly superior "Aryan race." The Lebensraum—living space—he sought could only be found in the east. He was interested not in some limited European empire but in world domination. Hitler had always planned on war with the Soviet Union; it was only a question of when. Recently some writers have contended that Hitler's assault on the Soviet Union was purely defensive. According to them, Stalin was poised to attack Germany, so Hitler ordered a preemptive strike. This theory simply does not hold. Neither the German nor the Russian archival records support such a notion. Hitler made his intentions against the Soviet Union very clear, not only in *Mein Kampf* and in his second, untitled book, written in 1929 and never published, but in numerous conversations and speeches. Most significantly, German military planners had worked out the details of an offensive against the Soviet Union long before June 1941. Failure to defeat Britain and partisan opposition in Yugoslavia were among the factors that had led to a series of postponements. Operation Barbarossa was no defensive reaction.

Of course it is certainly possible that Stalin had his own violent plans for eastern and central Europe, but such schemes do not alter the fact of Hitler's aggression. Unfortunately there is no reason why two opponents cannot both be scoundrels.

What about the Hitler–Stalin nonaggression pact of 1939? Like all of Hitler's diplomatic agreements it was made to be broken. The deal had served Nazi goals well; it enabled rapid defeat of Poland in 1939, freed up German forces to concentrate in the west in 1940, and bought almost two years of time to prepare for war with the Soviet Union. It seems highly unlikely that Hitler or his generals even gave it a thought in June 1941.

The First Victims—Caught between Stalin and Hitler

It is important to note that the Germans invaded the Soviet Union, not just Russia. The Soviet Union was a multinational empire that included many republics in addition to Russia. In fact some of the worst devastation of World War II occurred not in Russia but in Ukraine, Belorussia, and the Baltic states of Latvia, Estonia, and Lithuania.

In June 1941, before the Germans reached Russia, they first entered territories that the Soviets had seized after the German attack on Poland in 1939. As a consequence, people in places such as Latvia and the eastern Polish city of

Lvov—after the war part of western Ukraine and called L'viv—experienced two rounds of invasion in less than two years. In September 1939 Stalin's armies moved in; Hitler's troops arrived in 1941.

Some people in such areas had greeted the Soviets in 1939 as bearers of Communism and protectors from Nazism. By 1941 almost all had become disillusioned. That year some people in eastern Europe welcomed the German invasion, expecting Hitler's forces to crush Communism and grant them independence. For example, many Ukrainian nationalists hoped the Nazis would let them set up their own state. They too would be disappointed. Very quickly most eastern Europeans learned that they could expect only terror and destruction from a war fought not for them but on top of them.

An Account from Lvov

One person who experienced Soviet takeover in the fall of 1939 and then the German invasion in 1941 was Nelly Toll. Born in 1935, Nelly was just a little girl in 1939. Her family was among the 110,000 Jews in Lvov, home to Poland's third-largest Jewish community, after Warsaw and Lodz. About 1 million Jews lived in the surrounding region, called eastern Galicia.

Under Soviet rule more Jews streamed into the city to escape the Germans, but Soviet control brought its own hardships. Nelly Toll's father had to go into hiding to avoid being sent to a labor camp in Siberia. As the wealthy owner of a dry goods store he was considered an enemy of Communism. Soviet officials seized much of the Tolls' property and took over their spacious apartment. Nelly remembers her family's relationship with the Russian officers as a mixture of fear, friendliness, and contempt for people she and her relatives considered somewhat less civilized than themselves.

When the Germans came to Lvov in 1941 even some Jews there thought they might be an improvement over the Soviets. Nelly's grandfather, for example, at first regarded German takeover in 1941 as a good thing. In his view the Germans were more cultured and intelligent than the Russians. He was wrong. The Germans proved at least as barbaric.

In Lvov some of the local people saw arrival of the Germans as a chance to take revenge for all they had suffered under the Soviets. In particular Ukrainians in the region wanted to seize the chance to get back at the Russians as well as their Polish neighbors. Most of the Soviets had fled before the advancing Germans. So angry residents of Lvov attacked their Jewish neighbors as convenient scapegoats instead. They accused Jews of collaborating with the Soviets to oppress them. No doubt there had been Jews who supported the

Soviet regime, but there had certainly also been gentile Poles and Ukrainians who had done the same.

As usual German authorities encouraged ethnic strife and rewarded pogroms. They urged local Ukrainians to take out their grievances against the Polish majority, in particular against those elements the Germans targeted too, intellectuals, Catholic priests, and other community leaders. They gave gentile Poles and Ukrainians license to terrorize Jews and steal their possessions.

In June 1941 Ukrainians in Lvov arrested some Jews on the charge that they had committed atrocities against Ukrainians during the Soviet occupation. Many of those Jews were executed in prisons and nearby forests. Others were taken to prison cells already stained with Jewish blood, forced to clean them, and then shot. Pogroms raged in the city throughout July 1941, and thousands of Jews were killed. On one occasion little Nelly Toll watched from the balcony with her cousins as German soldiers beat an old Jewish man. A crowd gathered to laugh and clap.

A local Jewish dignitary named Rabbi Levin appealed for help to Metropolitan Sheptitsky, the head of the local Ukrainian Catholic church. Sheptitsky called on Ukrainians to stop murdering Jews, but without effect. He then invited the rabbi to take refuge in his personal residence, but Rabbi Levin thought his place was with his people, so he left the metropolitan's residence to go home. He never made it. Instead rioters seized him and dragged him to prison, where he was murdered.

Nelly Toll was luckier than Rabbi Levin. She lived through 1941, although children threw stones at her in the street, her mother was beaten black and blue by a Ukrainian policeman, and the family was forced into a ghetto. Eventually Nelly's mother sent her to hide with a Christian family. When that place proved too risky she returned to the ghetto to learn that her brother, aunt, and little cousins had all been taken away by the Gestapo and put on a train. None of them returned.

In 1943, after more close calls and a failed attempt to escape to Hungary, Nelly and her mother went into hiding. They ended up with a Polish Catholic couple who sheltered them in exchange for money. The woman was kind and thoughtful but not her husband. He was violent, paranoid, and antisemitic, abusive to his wife yet overattentive to Nelly's mother. It was a very difficult situation. Somehow both Nelly and her mother survived the war, but they never saw Nelly's father again. Nelly Toll immigrated to the United States in 1951, where she became an artist and a counselor.

Hitler expected the campaign against the Soviet Union to be easy for the Germans. In this regard he and his military planners were caught in their own ethnic and racial stereotypes. They thought of Slavs as stupid and incompetent and believed that the Communist Soviet Union was in the grip of Jews, whom they viewed as cowardly and perfidious. Such attitudes caused the German leaders to make some severe miscalculations.

The German invasion did not turn out as planned. The Soviets were better equipped than German planners had thought; the Germans themselves were overextended and unprepared for winter. Contrary to what many German accounts claim, the winter of 1941 was neither unusually early nor extraordinarily harsh; it was more or less a typical Russian winter. Nor, as the historian Gerhard Weinberg has pointed out, did it snow only on the Germans; the Soviets faced the same winter conditions. Hitler and his generals, however, had anticipated quick victory, another "lightning war" that of course they would win. They had not thought it necessary to prepare for winter.

Crossing the Line to Annihilation

From the beginning of war with the Soviet Union, the German leadership advocated unprecedented, ruthless measures. In instructions to the military and the SS, Hitler, Himmler, and Heydrich made it clear that no mercy was to be shown Germany's enemies, whether they were Jews, Communists, or resistors. High-ranking officers passed the message down to their men.

With the invasion of the Soviet Union the Nazi leadership would move to full implementation of their ideas of race and space on a massive scale. Their warfare reached new depths of brutality, especially against civilians but also against Soviet prisoners of war. Most noticeably they crossed the line from persecution and killing of Jews to a systematic attempt at total destruction.

Yet in many ways 1941 was not a radical break with earlier Nazi practices. All of the pieces were already in place. Hitler had spelled out the quest for Lebensraum in *Mein Kampf*. The Germans had begun to grab territory in Europe even before the war. They had assaulted civilians on a wide scale in Poland since 1939; they had used their enemies as slave labor, forcibly relocated enormous numbers of people, and started to slaughter Jews, Gypsies, and people deemed handicapped even before June 1941. All of these terrible developments culminated in the Soviet Union in 1941 and the years to follow.

Perhaps the most glaring sign of Germany's brutal style of warfare in 1941 was the use of special murder squads. German authorities dispatched mobile killing units to follow the regular military into Soviet territory. The main units, known as the Einsatzgruppen—"special action groups"—included between five hundred and one thousand men each, many of them well educated, lawyers, theologians, and other professionals. The Einsatzgruppen worked together with more numerous German units known as the Order Police. Both the Einsatzgruppen and the Order Police cooperated with the German military.

The task of the mobile killing units was straightforward. They had explicit instructions from Heydrich to kill Jews, prominent Communists, and anyone suspected of sabotage or anti-German activity. Officially their goal was to combat Bolshevism and prevent guerrilla warfare. In fact, during the summer of 1941, they began to interpret their primary job as slaughter of all Jews, including women, children, and old people. The Einsatzgruppen and Order Police also murdered Gypsies and inmates of mental hospitals, although they seem to have been less systematic against those target populations.

Members of the mobile killing units tried to involve local people in their work. Many non-German auxiliaries—Ukrainians, Latvians, ethnic Germans from eastern Europe, Belorussians, and others—helped in their grisly task. Threats, bribes, massive amounts of alcohol, and promises of privileges for recruits and their families all helped the Germans find willing henchmen.

The Einsatzgruppen and Order Police attempted to stir up pogroms wherever they went. In some cases locals did take spontaneous action against Jews, but the mobile killing groups were less successful in this regard than they had hoped. Local individuals sometimes launched spontaneous attacks on Jews and took the initiative to steal their property, but generally the impetus and organization for systematic killing came from the Germans.

Many of the actions of the mobile killing units more or less followed the same pattern. First they rounded up the Jews in a given area using various ruses to deceive them and relying on local collaborators for denunciations. The Germans ordered large pits dug in some convenient area—a local cemetery, nearby forest, or easily accessible field. Often they forced the prisoners themselves to dig what would be their own graves. At gunpoint they made the victims undress. Then they shot them by groups directly into the graves. In this manner the mobile killing units and their accomplices killed around a million people even before construction of killing centers for gassing had begun.

Of course, such mass killings in the open air could hardly be kept secret. Eyewitnesses of all kinds saw these shootings—German soldiers and workers, ethnic Germans who lived nearby, Russian, Polish, or Ukrainian families from the region, and others. Some of those observers gave detailed, chilling accounts of what they saw. For example, a German builder named Hermann Graebe watched while mobile killing squads shot scores of people of all ages near

Dubno in Ukraine. He was surprised to be allowed to stay, but he noticed three uniformed postal workers looking on as well.

Elsewhere in Ukraine a fifteen-year-old Mennonite boy and his friends saw the slaughter of a group of Gypsies at a local cemetery. Later someone came around the village to distribute clothes taken from the murdered people. According to the eyewitness's account, no one in that particular Mennonite (and ethnic German) community wanted anything to do with booty won in such a way.

Most of our information about the mass shootings comes from the perpetrators themselves or from onlookers. Few victims lived to tell about their experiences. One of the exceptions is a man named Zvi Michalowsky, whose account appears in a book by Yaffa Eliach called *Hasidic Tales of the Holocaust*.

In 1941 on Rosh Hashanah, the Jewish new year, Germans and their local helpers murdered the Jews in a Lithuanian town called Eisysky. Michalowsky, a teenaged boy at the time, was among those forced to strip and wait at the edge of a grave for a bullet. A split second before the Germans fired, Zvi threw himself back into the pit. Miraculously he avoided serious injury.

German troops shoot a small group of Poles in Lithuania in 1941 or 1942 as Lithuanian auxiliaries and others, including a young man taking a photograph, look on.

For the rest of that day Zvi lay in the mass grave, feeling the bodies pile up on top of him. Only long after the shooting had stopped did he dare to climb out. He ran, naked and covered with blood, to the nearest house, but when he knocked, the terrified Polish Christians who lived there refused to let him in. Finally he approached an old woman. He told her he was Jesus Christ come down from the cross, and she opened the door to him. Zvi Michalowsky went on to found a Jewish resistance group in the woods of Lithuania. He survived the war.

Probably the biggest slaughter carried out by the Einsatzgruppen and their helpers was the massacre at Babi Yar. In just two days in September 1941, German mobile killing units and local collaborators shot more than thirty thousand Jews and an unknown number of other people at Babi Yar, a ravine on the outskirts of the Ukrainian city of Kiev. That act, just months after the invasion of the Soviet Union, destroyed the thriving Jewish community in Kiev and its surrounding area.

Germans continued to use Babi Yar as a killing field throughout the occupation of Ukraine. Some estimates of the total number of people killed there are as high as one hundred thousand. The majority were Jews, although others targeted by the German occupiers were murdered at Babi Yar as well. That massacre has become emblematic of the vicious brutality of Nazi Germans in the Soviet Union generally and particularly in Ukraine.

In Soviet times state authorities put up a monument to the victims of Babi Yar. The plaque dedicates the memorial to the more than one hundred thousand Soviet citizens killed there. Nowhere does it mention that most of those dead were murdered solely because they were Jews. Here the official act of remembering also became a way of forgetting.

The exact number of people killed by the mobile units cannot be known, although German records have allowed experts in the field to come to an estimate approaching 2 million total victims. Most were Jews—some 1.3 million—and there may have been as many as 250,000 Gypsies. The Einsatzgruppen and Order Police followed the regular military and in many cases even relied on them for provisions, security, and intelligence. They could not have carried out such an enormous number of killings without the knowledge and cooperation of the Wehrmacht. How did the military respond?

At first it seems there might have been some misgivings. One incident illustrates the forms such doubts might have taken. In mid-August 1941, German authorities in the Ukrainian town of Belaya Tserkov, more than two hundred miles east of Lvov, ordered local Jews to report for registration. Over the next few days, SS and German soldiers scoured the area for Jews, slaughtering hundreds of men and women.

In the summer of 1941 some of the killers still seemed unclear as to whether their task included murder of Jewish women and children as well as men. Perhaps for this reason, the shooters at Belaya Tserkov did not initially kill all the children. Instead they dumped about ninety of them and a handful of women in a school.

German soldiers in a field hospital nearby heard babies crying in the night. Uncertain how to respond, they appealed to their military chaplains. The two German clergy, a Protestant pastor and a Catholic priest, went to see for themselves. They were appalled. It was hot, but the children were crammed into a small space without water, food, or adult care. Some of the mothers were locked in an adjoining room, from which they could see the misery of their children without being able to get to them.

The chaplains appealed to the local military commander, an elderly Austrian, to take pity on the children. Their effort failed, one of them later reported, because the man was a convinced antisemite. Together the chaplains convinced another German officer to intervene. He got Army High Command to agree to postpone shooting of the children, but SS representatives and military officers on the spot prevailed, pointing to instructions from General Field Marshal Walter von Reichenau, commander of Army Group South, that they were to show no mercy.

On 21 August 1941, the children were taken from the school and killed. It is unclear whether it was Germans or Ukrainian volunteers who did the job.

Killings of civilians did not end in the summer or fall of 1941 but continued throughout the war. Presumably German soldiers and the military chaplains who ministered to them got used to the routine. The comfort of knowing they were backed by orders from above must have helped too.

One of the most widely circulated of such orders came in October 1941 from German Field Marshal Walter von Reichenau. Reichenau admitted that there was "uncertainty" among the German troops as to the current situation in the east. However, he told his men, given the nature of this war and the need to destroy what he called the "Jewish-Bolshevist system" completely, it was necessary to break the conventional rules of war, to show no mercy to those defined as Germany's enemies, above all the people Reichenau labeled "Jewish subhumans."

It is certainly not common practice for military superiors to justify themselves and their decisions to their men. Reichenau, however, did just that. His order implies that there was some uneasiness in the ranks about military

German troops stand at the edge of a trench used as a mass grave for the bodies of Jews and Gypsies killed by the 750th Infantry Regiment in October 1941 in the Macva region of Yugoslavia. A German soldier sent this photograph to a woman friend in spring 1945.

involvement in slaughter of civilians. We can assume that those reservations were overcome. After all, the killings continued with the necessary military support. Perhaps German soldiers accepted the official justifications offered to them, that such excesses were a necessary part of the German struggle against partisans, or later on, that they were some kind of revenge for Allied bombings of German cities.

Of course neither of those rationalizations actually makes sense. How could a baby be responsible for a partisan attack on German rail lines? What could an old Jewish woman more than a thousand miles away who spoke nothing but Yiddish possibly have to do with British planes dropping bombs on Hamburg or Cologne? Nevertheless these nonsensical explanations may have helped men live with themselves once they were already involved in killing. Many of their motivations for killing in the first place were undramatic. Their comrades were doing it, and they did not want to stand out; they considered it part of their job; they had gotten used to it.

What we do know is that Germans were not forced to be killers. Those who refused to participate were given other assignments or transferred. To this day no one has ever found a single example of a German who was executed for refusing to take part in the killing of Jews or other civilians. Defense attorneys of Germans accused of war crimes during World War II have looked hard for such a case because it would support the claim that their clients were forced to kill. The Nazi system, however, did not work that way. There were enough willing perpetrators. For the most part coercive violence could be reserved for those deemed enemies.

Romania and the Killing Fields in Transnistria

Brutalization, it seems, is contagious; violence tends to breed more of the same. This point is evident if we look briefly at Romania, one of Germany's World War II allies, in 1941. The Romanian army took an active part in the German offensive against the southern Soviet Union. In the areas conquered, German and Romanian armies cooperated with the Einsatzgruppen in massacring Jews and Gypsies.

The case of the Jews in the Ukrainian city of Odessa provides an example. In the fall of 1941, several days after German and Romanian forces occupied Odessa, an explosion rocked Romanian army headquarters there. In retaliation, Romanian leader Ion Antonescu ordered the execution of two hundred "Communists" for every Romanian officer killed and one hundred for each soldier. Most of the victims selected were Jews. Einsatzgruppen killers worked together with German and Romanian military, Ukrainian auxiliary police, and recruits from the local ethnic German population to slaughter some thirty-five thousand Jews. In February 1942, Odessa was proclaimed "Judenrein"—"cleansed of Jews."

Beginning in 1941, persecution of Jews also exploded within Romania. The Romanian government introduced laws restricting Jews in all kinds of ways, and pogroms resulted in the death of well over a thousand Romanian Jews. Antisemitism was not new to Romania, but the war and German leadership gave antisemites license to act on their hatreds in dramatic, large-scale ways.

In the fall of 1941, Romanian authorities began moving Jews out of Romania and forcing them east across the Dniester River and then the Bug River into an area of intense Einsatzgruppen operations. First 50,000 and then another 120,000 Romanian Jews were driven into the hands of the Germans and their accomplices in Transnistria in the occupied Ukraine.

Among those deported in this way was a young boy named Aharon Appelfeld. Separated from his father, he ended up in a makeshift Transnistrian camp. Somehow he escaped, dodged the killing fields of the Einsatzgruppen, and evaded the reach of local collaborators. Just nine years old in 1941, he survived for four years working as a shepherd, hiding in the woods, stealing, begging, and taking refuge with people who helped him. After the war Appelfeld moved to Israel. He is the author of many acclaimed works of fiction dealing with themes from the Holocaust.

Many Romanian Gypsies shared the fate of their Jewish compatriots. A woman named Drina Radu survived deportation to Transnistria as a girl of about ten. She remembers crossing the Dniester River into the part of Ukraine occupied by Romania. Everyone rushed to get on the first boatloads, she told the journalist Isabel Fonseca, not because they were eager to reach the other side but because, in her words, "the boats were made of paper." Hastily constructed from cheap, porous material, they became waterlogged and sank after three or four trips. That detail reveals the deadly cynicism of the Romanians in charge. Why go to any effort or expense to protect the lives of people they knew were slated for death anyway? Between 1941 and 1944, approximately thirty-six thousand Roma were killed in Transnistria.

For the Romanian Jews and Gypsies murdered in the killing fields of Transnistria, there was nothing ambiguous about their government's plan for them. It was deadly, but there were ways in which the Romanian situation was complex too. For one thing, German authorities did not welcome Romanian initiatives, such as the expulsion of almost two hundred thousand Jews into territories the Germans held. The German masterminds of mass killing preferred to retain control themselves. Accordingly Antonescu was told to stop striking out on his own and to wait for Germans to take the lead.

Romanian gentiles continued to have their own ideas about how to solve what they considered their "Jewish problem." The Romanian government set up an office to look after Jewish affairs. It tolerated the existence of Jewish mutual-aid activities and allowed them to try to help the Jewish expellees. Leaders of the Jewish community maintained relations with some heads of state and in some incidents even managed to mitigate anti-Jewish measures. There were prominent Romanians—including the queen—who approached the Germans on behalf of Romanian Jews. Those efforts were rejected.

In wartime Romania, traditional antisemitism and widespread persecution of Jews were the norm. Nevertheless the Romanian leadership, for all its viciousness, did not show the same single-minded and systematic dedication to eradication of the Jews that the Nazi Germans introduced in the countries they controlled. Traditional Jewish means of self-preservation—mutual aid, intercession with rulers, evasion, and bribery—continued to have some effect in Romania. For all the horrors of 1941 and the years to follow, a higher percentage of Jews in Romania would survive the war than would be the case in Poland or the Netherlands.

German Treatment of Soviet POWs

Hitler's war of annihilation against the Soviet Union included killing of prisoners of war on a massive scale. Of the millions of non-Jews killed in German camps, by far the largest group of dead was Soviet POWs. Their brutal treatment violated every standard of warfare.

Statistics only begin to tell the story. Initial German successes in the summer and fall of 1941 brought an enormous numbers of POWs into German hands. In total, between 22 June 1941 and the end of the war, Germans took approximately 5.7 million Red Army soldiers prisoner. As of January 1945, about 930,000 Soviet POWs remained in Wehrmacht prison camps. About 1 million had been released as helpers of the German military. Another estimated half million had escaped or been liberated by the Red Army. That still leaves 3.3 million—57 percent—unaccounted for. They were dead.

Such a staggering death rate was neither an accident nor an automatic result of war. It was deliberate policy. German treatment of Soviet POWs differed wildly from German handling of POWs from Britain and the United States. Of the 231,000 British and American prisoners held by the Germans, only about 8,300—3.6 percent—died before the end of the war.

Death came in various ways to the more than 3 million Soviet POWs who died in German hands. In the early stages of the conflict the Germans shot many of the prisoners they took. They had made few provisions to accommodate their captives; they simply disposed of them. Eventually they erected some makeshift camps, but the lack of proper food, clothing, and shelter took a terrible toll. By the end of 1941, epidemics—especially typhoid and dysentery—emerged as the big killers. In October 1941 alone, as many as 4,600 Soviet

POWs died per day. Death rates fell off somewhat in 1942 as German authorities decided POWs could be a useful source of wartime labor. In 1943 and 1944, however, they soared again, due above all to hunger.

Starvation of Soviet POWs was directly tied to the Nazi policy of making sure there was plenty of food for the German homefront. No doubt Hitler and others remembered the food riots of the First World War, a war they believed Germany had lost because of its weak homefront. This time they intended to keep food supplies—and morale—up, even if it meant starvation of what one bureaucrat called "umpteen million people."

German authorities viewed Soviet POWs as a particular threat, regarding them not only as Slavic subhumans but as part of the "Bolshevik menace," linked in their minds to some imaginary Jewish conspiracy. They spared no violence against the Soviet prisoners. In the camp of Gross-Rosen, in Germany, the commandant had sixty-five thousand Soviet inmates killed within six months by feeding them a soup made only of grass, water, and salt. In Flossenbürg, SS men burned Soviet POWs alive. In Majdanek, they shot them into trenches. In Mauthausen, in Austria, so many POWs were killed that people living near the camp complained about pollution of their water supply, for days the rivers and streams of the area ran red with blood.

The notorious German camps of Auschwitz, near Krakow, and Majdanek, by Lublin, were originally built to shelter Soviet POWs and to exploit their labor for the industrial complexes Himmler planned there. In 1941 some fifteen thousand Soviet POWs were taken to those camps; by January 1942, only a few hundred remained alive. In early 1942, Himmler filled those sites with 150,000 German Jews and transformed the camps into killing centers. In this way camps constructed for Soviet POWs became part of the machinery for destruction of Jews.

It was when dealing with Soviet POWs at Auschwitz that camp commandant Rudolf Hoess and his assistants experimented with the means of killing that have become the symbol of Nazi genocide: Zyklon B. In early September 1941, six hundred Soviet prisoners selected for execution by the SS arrived at Auschwitz. In order to avoid the cumbersome task of shooting so many people, Hoess and his men decided to gas them with the pesticide Zyklon B, also known as hydrogen cyanide. While they were at it they included another 250 inmates who had been designated unfit for work.

The T-4 killers had already experimented with gassing as a way to murder people considered handicapped. Those lessons were subsequently applied first to Soviet POWs and then to Jews.

THE WANNSEE CONFERENCE—
STREAMLINING THE KILLING OPERATIONS

By the end of 1941, the German leadership concluded that mass shootings were not the most efficient way to carry out their so-called Final Solution. Their concerns were not about the victims but rather about the perpetrators, who found it physically and psychologically difficult to shoot people all day long at close range.

Led by Heydrich, top German officials met in early 1942 to coordinate and streamline their efforts to annihilate the Jews. This meeting was called the Wannsee Conference because it took place in a villa in Wannsee, a suburb of Berlin.

At the conference were representatives from all of the offices and agencies in the German government, military, and Nazi Party who had a direct hand in the killing process. High officials from the Foreign Office were on hand as were representatives of the SS, Einsatzgruppen, Nazi Party headquarters, Justice Ministry, Hans Frank in the General Government in Poland, and others. Heydrich himself chaired the meeting. Eichmann, who would later be in charge of transporting Jews to the killing centers, produced the official report.

Wannsee focused on Jews as the top priority of Nazi destruction. Eichmann's report makes it clear that all 11 million Jews in Europe were targeted for murder. The list even included Jews in Sweden, Ireland, and England, places not in German hands in 1942.

The Wannsee Conference marked another step in the killing process. Mass murder was already under way when the conference met, but at Wannsee the SS asserted its leadership in the annihilation of the Jews. Heydrich needed the cooperation of the other agencies and offices represented, but he made it clear who called the shots. Of course, by their very presence those other bureaucrats, party functionaries, and military men demonstrated that they understood what was going on and endorsed it. The line to genocide was not one Hitler would cross alone.

Participants at the Wannsee Conference also discussed methods of killing. Killing centers with gas chambers emerged as their means of choice. Instead of bringing the killers to their victims, it was decided that the victims should be transported to their killers. Accordingly, construction of new killing centers began within months. Meanwhile, existing camps such as Auschwitz were ordered expanded and equipped with gassing facilities. At the same time, the methods of killing already introduced continued, that is, shootings, starvation, death by overwork, abuse, and disease. It was remarkable how quickly things could move forward once the line to annihilation had been crossed.

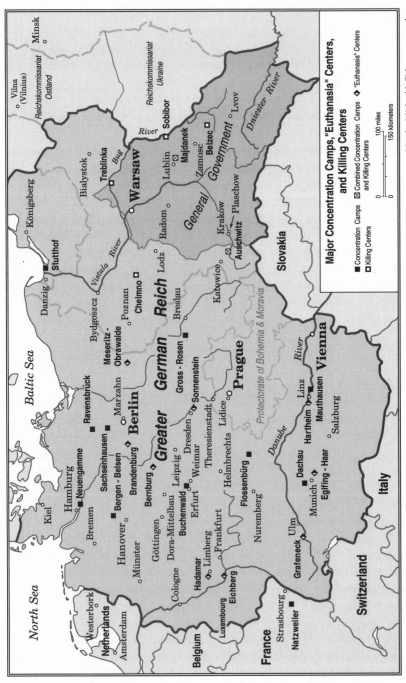

Major Concentration Camps, "Euthanasia" Centers, and Killing Centers

■ Concentration Camps ⊠ Combined Concentration Camps and Killing Centers ◆ "Euthanasia" Centers
□ Killing Centers

0   100 miles
0   150 kilometers

Map by Michael J. Fisher, cartographer

North Sea

Baltic Sea

Minsk ○

Reichskommissariat Ostland

Vilna ○
(Vilnius)

Königsberg ○

Bialystok ○

Treblinka □

Warsaw

Sobibor □

Bug River

Lublin ○
Majdanek ⊠

Reichskommissariat Ukraine

Lvov ○

Dniester River

General Government

Zamosc ⊠
Belzec □

Danzig ○   Stutthof ■

Vistula River

Bydgoszcz ○
Meseritz ○
Obrawalde ◆

Poznan ○
Chelmno □

Lodz ○

Greater German Reich

Radom ○

Breslau ○

Krakow ○
Auschwitz ⊠
Plaschow ○

Katowice ○

Ravensbrück ■

Marzahn ◆

Berlin
Brandenburg ◆

Sachsenhausen ■

Bernburg ◆

Gross - Rosen ■

Sonnenstein ◆

Prague

Protectorate of Bohemia & Moravia

Slovakia

Kiel ○

Hamburg ○
Neuengamme ■

Bremen ○

Bergen - Belsen ■

Hanover ○

Leipzig ○
Dresden ○

Dora-Mittelbau ○

Buchenwald ■
Weimar ○
Erfurt ○

Theresienstadt ○
Lidice ○

Helmbrechts ○

Flossenbürg ■

Göttingen ○

Münster ○

Cologne ○

Hadamar ◆

Limberg ○

Frankfurt ○

Nuremberg ○

Eichberg ◆

Luxembourg ○

Belgium

France

Strasbourg ○
Natzweiler ■

Grafeneck ◆

Ulm ○

Munich ○
Dachau ■
Egifing - Haar ◆

Danube

Linz ○
Hartheim ◆

Mauthausen ■

Vienna

Salzburg ○

River

Switzerland

Italy

Netherlands
Westerbork ○
Amsterdam ○

7

THE PEAK YEARS OF KILLING: 1942 AND 1943

When it comes to human suffering, each year of a war tends to be worse than the year before. The passage of time adds further material deprivation, more wounded, and more dead to the accumulated misery of the people involved.

This depressing observation certainly holds true for the Second World War. By the end of 1942 the Germans were heading into their fourth year of war. At least in the short term their victories insulated them from much of the bereavement and hardship that war brings. The same was not true for the people they conquered. The devastation of Poland—economically, politically, socially—became ever more terrible as the Poles endured year after year of defeat and occupation. The Nazi German hand may have been less heavy on western Europe, but there too—in occupied Denmark, Norway, the Netherlands, Belgium, France, and elsewhere—adversity and demoralization continued to build. Meanwhile, in the Balkans and the Soviet territories overrun in 1941, German occupation practices produced an ever-escalating reign of terror.

It was not just the normal dynamic of war that served to multiply human suffering as World War II continued. The Nazi principles of spatial expansion and "racial purification" meant that more and more killing was itself a direct goal of the German war effort. The more Hitler's empire extended its reach and consolidated its hold on subject lands and peoples, the more its forces sought to destroy those it deemed enemies—Jews above all, but also Slavs and others defined as unwanted inferiors. For this reason, 1942 and 1943—the years when German power in Europe reached its height—were also the peak years of killing.

This chapter examines both sides of the space and race equation during those two years. What did German military conquest mean for the people of Europe? How did Nazi Germans and their accomplices carry out this most deadly stage of their program to annihilate Jews? Who resisted them?

GERMAN MILITARY POWER AT ITS HEIGHT

One point is so obvious it is often not stated: Hitler and the Nazis planned to win the war. War, Hitler believed, would not merely defeat the enemy militarily; it would create a "new order."

General Plan East, Germanization, and the Nazi "New Order"

German planners developed in detail the implications of their notion of Lebensraum—living space—in an important memorandum called "General Plan East." Drafted in 1941, that document presented the Nazi vision for eastern Europe. One of its primary authors was a young historian named Theodor Schieder. After the war Schieder pursued a successful academic career in West Germany. Only after his death, half a century after the war had ended, would his students and many people who admired his scholarship realize the use to which he had put his training and skills during the war.

General Plan East called for Germans and ethnic Germans to settle vast areas of eastern Europe, where they would produce food and babies for the "Aryan master race." To make such settlements possible, the plan demanded expulsion of those currently living there. Those tens of millions of people, most of them Slavs, were to be forced into less desirable areas, allowed to die of starvation and disease, or turned into slaves for the German empire. According to General Plan East, Jews were to disappear altogether.

Like so much Nazi writing, General Plan East was full of euphemisms. Instead of spelling out the goal as to kill people or make sure they died of starvation, overwork, or disease, the document talked about "reducing" or "removing" certain populations. Nevertheless its intentions were obvious. It also made clear that German policies toward different population groups were closely connected. Settlement of Germans and ethnic Germans in the east; expulsion, enslavement, and decimation of Slavs; and murder of Jews were all parts of the same plan.

General Plan East envisioned "Germanization" of an enormous territory that stretched eastward from the old German Reich all the way to the Ural Mountains. Someday, according to the plan, 500 to 600 million people would live there: "Aryan" Germans and their slaves.

German population planners realized that even a massively increased birthrate could not produce enough children to achieve the rate of population growth they wanted. As a result, they proposed taking "racially valuable" children away from supposedly inferior parents in order to "Germanize" them. In other words, they intended to transform some of the children of non-Germans into members of the "Aryan race." So-called racial experts estimated that about 50 percent of Czech children were suitable for "Germanization." They thought as many as 75 percent of the children in some parts of western Belorussia might be acceptable, but under no conditions were Jewish children to be "Germanized."

Schemes of Germanization remind us just how artificial Nazi notions of blood and race were. The case of two Polish women provides an illustration. Although the parents of Johanna and Danuta W. were "pure Polish," the sisters both applied for Germanization. No doubt they hoped to get the benefits that being classified as German rather than Polish would bring.

In 1944 SS racial authorities in one city approved Johanna's application, and she became officially recognized as an ethnic German. A similar office elsewhere rejected Danuta. Meanwhile both women went to Germany to work as housemaids.

Danuta became pregnant by an SS man. When her baby was born he received ethnic German status, but his mother was still classified as a Pole. The only reason German authorities gave for rejecting Danuta was that "she did not look so good."

Danuta's status caused practical problems because the sisters lived together. Under the terms of Nazi racial law, ethnic Germans such as Johanna were to have no social contact with Poles like Danuta. Nor was Danuta's own child permitted to interact with his mother. The postwar fates of Johanna, Danuta, and her son are unknown.

Slave Labor

During 1942 and 1943 Germans enslaved millions of people, women as well as men, from the Soviet Union and elsewhere in eastern Europe. Some were forced to labor in the occupied areas; millions of others were sent to Germany to work in factories, on farms, and in private homes.

Hitler and other planners considered slave labor a way to keep the German homefront happy. They did not want to introduce measures that might have been unpopular with many Germans; for example, recruiting large numbers of German women into factory work or curtailing supplies of food and consumer goods. After all, Hitler and others like him still believed that discontent at home had led to German defeat in the last war. So they brought in millions of people they considered disposable and used them to make waging a war of annihilation as comfortable as possible for the German people.

The German occupiers also seized agricultural produce in the areas they controlled, causing famine and starvation among the people left behind. They took over whatever industrial production had not been evacuated by the Soviet Army as it had fled in 1941. In the name of fighting partisans, German forces burned entire villages, often along with many of the people who lived in them. Public hangings, torture, rape, and sexual slavery were all common occurrences in the occupied east.

German Reactions

Some German authorities worried that such brutality was counterproductive because it sparked opposition that could have been avoided. As one high-ranking German official observed, many of the Soviet people had suffered terribly under Stalin. It would not have taken much to persuade them that their lives under German rule would be better than they could expect with the return of Communism. The extreme viciousness of German occupation, however, convinced the vast majority of Soviets that even Stalin was preferable to Hitler.

Hitler and propaganda minister Goebbels paid lip service to the need to soften up in order to prevent an explosion of opposition in the east, but German policies did not change. To the contrary, reprisals against guerrilla activity kept increasing in their ferocity. Meanwhile the Germans defined partisan activity, or "banditry," as they preferred to call it, more and more broadly.

SS leader Himmler summed up dominant German views in a speech to top SS men in October 1943:

> We must be honest, decent, loyal, and comradely to members of our own blood and to nobody else. What happens to a Russian or to a Czech does not interest me in the slightest. What the nations can offer in the way of good blood of our type we will take, if necessary by kidnapping their children and raising them here with us. . . . Whether 10,000 Russian females fall down from exhaustion

while digging an anti-tank ditch interests me only in so far as the anti-tank ditch for Germany is finished. We shall never be rough and heartless when it is not necessary, that is clear. We Germans, who are the only people in the world who have a decent attitude towards animals, will also assume a decent attitude towards these human animals. But it is a crime against our own blood to worry about them and give them ideals, thus causing our sons and grandsons to have a more difficult time with them. [Noakes and Pridham 3:919–920]

The comparisons Himmler drew between subject peoples and animals were telling. In his mind Russians and Czechs merited nothing more than the self-interested care one would show a beast of burden.

Hitler and many top Nazis rejected Christianity. They considered it an offshoot of Judaism that encouraged weakness and humility instead of aggression. In wartime, however, they realized that it was counterproductive to deprive Germans of the comfort of religion. Accordingly they allowed Christian military chaplains—Roman Catholic as well as Protestant—to minister to the men of the Wehrmacht. Accounts from these German clergy give another perspective on conditions in the east.

One Catholic chaplain buried 120 German soldiers in the first five months of 1942. In a report to superiors he admitted that the "long duration of the war and the many dead have brought a certain indifference to death." If the Germans had become numb toward their own casualties, how much less must they have cared about anyone else?

Christian clergy also heard confessions of terrible crimes. For example, a German Catholic priest stationed in Ukraine met a wounded soldier who confided to him about his past. The man had taken part in a mass shooting of Jews near Sevastopol in the Crimea. According to the priest, the soldier was ruined by his experience. He described the Jews, lined up, naked—women, children, and men. Although he had manned one of the machine guns he insisted he had only shot in the air. What should he have done, he asked the priest?

We do not know what the priest answered, but it seems evident that at least some Germans could not tolerate conditions in the east. Desertions and self-mutilations were not uncommon, although military authorities punished them severely, often with death. Nervous breakdowns generally led to transfers to less trying duties.

Not only military men but German civilians too were drawn into the war of annihilation. In Poland, for example, German employees of a bank found themselves assigned to guard the street between a Jewish ghetto and the train station as SS and Gestapo cleared out Jews and sent them on trains to be killed.

Some people accepted such tasks, eager to win promotions or prove their hardness. Others sought transfers to places where it was easier to shut out the realities of the war, back home in Germany, perhaps, or in western Europe.

When it came to his top military leaders, Hitler used bribery to make sure that their consciences did not protest too loudly. Every month, on orders from the führer, German generals received special tax-free supplements of between 2,000 and 4,000 Reich Marks. They had their pick of the finest estates in Poland and elsewhere, stolen, of course, from the original owners. On special birthdays—when a general turned fifty, for example—he received a bonus of as much as 250,000 Reich Marks. Of course cooperation and good behavior increased the amount.

Such sums made the German generals fabulously wealthy. In contrast, German infantry who cleared mines during the war—an extremely dangerous job—received supplements to their regular incomes of only one mark per day.

Military Developments and Nonmilitary Repercussions

Discussions of the Holocaust often pay little attention to the war itself, but without war and German victories there would have been no genocide of the European Jews. The vast majority of Jews murdered by Nazi Germans— about 95 percent—came from outside Germany. Without military conquests the perpetrators would never have got those victims in their hands.

Yet even during the war itself many people on the Allied side did not see the links between the German war effort and mass murder. Soviet, British, and American military planners tended to take a fairly narrow view of events. Their goal was to win the war, whatever that meant; their objectives were military ones. It is probably fair to say that they devoted little thought to what seemed bizarre, nonmilitary "sideshows" on the part of the Germans, such as attacks on handicapped people, Gypsies, and Jews.

Nevertheless military decisions and developments in 1942 and 1943 had repercussions far beyond the military sphere. We will look at just three examples: Stalingrad, North Africa, and Italy.

THE BATTLE OF STALINGRAD

From 1941 to 1943 most of the combat in Europe occurred between German and Soviet forces on Germany's eastern front. In 1941 the Red Army had checked the Germans and their Axis partners, but by mid-1942 the Germans took the offensive again.

The new German offensive had two prongs. One entered the Caucasus region with an eye to the oil fields there. The other moved toward the city of Stalingrad—modern Volgograd—on the lower Volga River. What is now known as the Battle of Stalingrad began in the late summer and fall of 1942 as the advancing Germans were blocked by the defending Red Army.

Hitler instructed the German 6th Army under General (later Field Marshal) Friederich von Paulus to take Stalingrad. In September the 6th Army and the 4th Panzer Army advanced into the outskirts; by mid-November they had captured much of the city.

Fighting was extraordinarily fierce. The Soviets, ordered by Stalin to defend the city with everything they had, contested every inch. Losses on both sides were staggering. Between 21 August and 16 October 1942, the German 6th Army alone suffered some forty thousand casualties. In late November, a Soviet offensive cut off the 6th Army, parts of another German army, and two Romanian armies in the Stalingrad area. The Red Army surrounded them. German attempts to relieve their forces in December failed, and the Soviets demanded capitulation.

Already earlier, some of Hitler's generals had advised a withdrawal, but he and others were determined to hold on. The territory had been won at such a high cost, and Stalingrad was an important hub of Soviet transport. Hitler did agree to retrenchment in the Caucasus, so it is not the case that he never authorized retreats. With Stalingrad, however, Hitler did not give in.

On 31 January 1943, the German southern contingent under Paulus capitulated. A few days later the northern contingent followed. The Soviets took ninety thousand German prisoners of war; there were hundreds of thousands dead on both sides.

Even after the Battle of Stalingrad, the outcome of the war was far from a foregone conclusion. Just a month later, in late February 1943, the Germans mounted a successful counteroffensive at the southern part of their eastern front. Still, at least in hindsight, Stalingrad appeared to have been an important military and symbolic turning point.

Back home Goebbels's propaganda machine presented Stalingrad as a strategic retreat, but few were fooled. The Red Army victory at Stalingrad marked a visible departure from the way the war had gone so far for Germany. At least some Germans were scared. SS reports indicate that the Nazi Party began to lose support. Many Germans had lost family members at Stalingrad; they wanted the war to end as soon as possible.

Discontent for the most part did not translate into open opposition to the regime. Instead the German public became more cynical and withdrawn. Distracted by increasing Allied air raids on their cities, Germans at home busied themselves with the practical matters of staying alive and keeping their families together. The regime did make some concessions to try to boost public spirits; it eased restrictions on the churches and slackened its campaign against cigarette smoking.

Nazi SS reports also indicate that many Germans knew quite a lot about the atrocities their country was committing in the east. In 1943, when mass graves of Polish officers shot by the Soviets were found at Katyn, there was little reaction within Germany. The Soviets would soon find plenty of mass graves of murdered Jews, some muttered, so it was better not to draw too much attention to similar crimes on the other side.

In the meantime, the German leadership cracked down tighter on its critics at home. Beginning in early 1943, offenses such as "defeatism" were often punished by death. For example, the sister of Erich Maria Remarque, author of the World War I classic *All Quiet on the Western Front,* was condemned to death for remarking that Hitler should resign. German authorities also introduced draconian measures against accused deserters and traitors in the military, an estimated fifteen thousand of whom they had shot over the course of the war, mostly in its later stages.

Still, being defined as "Aryan" continued to offer considerable protection for Germans throughout the war. An important illustration involves a group of German gentile women in Berlin who were married to German Jewish men. In early 1943, in preparation for Hitler's upcoming birthday, Goebbels planned to remove the last Jews from the city and send them east to be killed. Most of Germany's Jews had already been deported and killed, beginning in late 1941. Many of those who remained were married to non-Jews.

German officials had long been uncertain as to how to proceed against German Jews married to "Aryans." Participants at the Wannsee Conference in early 1942 had debated the issue without reaching a decision. On the one hand, Nazi principles of racial purity left no room for exceptions. According to that logic, any Jew left alive represented the possible pollution of generations of "Aryan blood."

On the other hand, however, practical considerations made it dangerous to strike against Jews married to "Aryan" Germans or to attack the "half-Jewish" offspring of such unions. Obviously any "mixed" families had a "pure Aryan" side, which meant lots of relatives who would be antagonized by the deportation and murder of their husband, uncle, son-in-law, niece, granddaughter, or so forth. During wartime the Nazi regime was reluctant to risk stirring up discontent among its own public and its fighting men.

Outside Germany of course the matter was easy. German officials hardly cared if they alienated Polish or Ukrainian gentiles or mistakenly included some of them among the people they defined as Jews. Inside Germany the situation demanded much more delicacy.

By early 1943 Nazi planners decided the remaining Berlin Jews had to go. Police arrested most of the men at the factories where they worked and locked them in a building on the Rosenstrasse—German for "Street of Roses." From there they were to be deported and killed.

In a spontaneous show of disobedience, the gentile wives of those German Jewish men gathered in the Rosenstrasse to protest the arrest of their husbands and demand their release. Sympathizers joined them until there were several thousand people milling about. Hitler and Goebbels were furious, but they did not dare order police or military to open fire on a crowd of Germans. Instead they allowed the men to be released. Many of the internees of the Rosenstrasse survived the war. The historian Nathan Stoltzfus recounts these events in his book *Resistance of the Heart*.

Meanwhile the Nazi regime's air of invincibility was challenged from outside Germany too. In 1942, at German insistence, Romanian and Hungarian troops had also been included in the advance on Stalingrad. Improperly armed and trained, those satellite forces were crushed in the Red Army offensives. Small wonder that by 1943 the leadership of those countries began looking for ways to get out of the war. Suddenly partnership with Germany seemed more a liability than an advantage.

After Stalingrad, Romanian and Hungarian leaders also became less willing to turn over the Jews among their populations to the Germans to be killed. It was not that those authorities suddenly became humanitarian. Rather they recognized that, should they need to negotiate with the Allies, Jews might be useful bargaining chips. Perhaps, they reasoned, they could barter Jewish lives for things they needed. Thus the German setback at Stalingrad might have had the unanticipated effect of prolonging and maybe even saving the lives of some Romanian and Hungarian Jews. On the whole, however, Stalingrad left the situation of Jews in Europe even more catastrophic than it had been before.

The Battle of Stalingrad is often described as the beginning of the end for Nazi Germany, but it signaled no change in the assault on the Jews. To the contrary, Stalingrad occurred right in the peak of the killing process, and genocide continued unabated.

Meanwhile, the guards, SS men, and German bureaucrats who were attached to the program for killing Jews found a new reason to step up their efforts. For them it was clearly preferable to be in the camps and offices overseeing mass murder of unarmed people than to face the Red Army on the eastern front. The chances of living through the war seemed quite good for Germans engaged in the slaughter of defenseless civilians. The odds were much lower for those assigned to fight armed opponents.

Even after Stalingrad the Germans had substantial military resources and a solid eastern front. Germany still held Poland and the killing centers built there—places such as Treblinka and Auschwitz. From that base of power the Nazi leadership would launch the effort in late 1943 to destroy the last remnants of the Jewish communities in central Poland.

People often wonder why Nazi Germans wasted manpower and other resources slaughtering innocent Jewish civilians when there was a war to be won. According to Nazi logic, however, murder of the Jews was just as much part of the war effort as were offensives against the Soviet Union. To the proponents of race and space, it was as urgent to use trains to transport Jews to killing centers as it was to move German troops from place to place. Military setbacks in 1943 did not slow down the killing operations; if anything, they speeded them up.

In the fall of 1943, the Germans launched a new offensive against the remaining Jews of Poland. Its code name was Harvest Festival. Within just a few days in November 1943, Germans and their accomplices massacred forty-two thousand Jews in the Lublin area. The Harvest Festival relied heavily on mass shootings. In special "Jew Hunts," the German Order Police and Einsatzgruppen worked with local collaborators to locate and kill as many Jews as they could.

By the end of 1943, only a few thousand Jews remained alive in German-occupied eastern Europe. Many of those were in hiding or fighting in partisan units. German officials kept some alive in the Lodz ghetto for economic reasons, and a few survived in work camps.

In the case of Stalingrad, a military setback for the Germans did not improve the immediate situation of European Jews or, for that matter, of other civilians under the German yoke. However, it may have helped to break down the myth of the invincible Germans and to encourage resistance.

NORTH AFRICA

The years 1942 and 1943 also brought German setbacks in North Africa. In this case too, military developments had enormous nonmilitary results.

Africa had been the focus of Fascist Italian ambitions ever since the 1920s when Mussolini's forces invaded Ethiopia. By 1940, the Italians requested German help against the British and their Allies in Africa. The following year saw formation of the German Africa Corps under the popular General Erwin Rommel (1891–1944), the "Desert Fox."

In late October and early November 1942, the British 8th Army under Bernard L. Montgomery (1887–1976) defeated Rommel's German–Italian forces at El Alamein. At the same time, the American and British "Operation Torch" landed 106,000 Allied forces in Morocco and Algeria under the command of General Dwight D. Eisenhower. Soon Allied troops had pushed the Axis back into Tunisia and a small part of Libya.

The Germans managed to halt the initial Anglo–American advance and reinforce their position. By March 1943, however, Rommel was unable to supply his troops. He flew to Hitler's headquarters to request an evacuation, but Hitler refused. In May 1943 Tunis, the last Axis outpost in Africa, fell to the Allies, who took more than 230,000 soldiers prisoner. About half of them were German.

The reverberations of military action in North Africa were felt all over the world. Already in 1942 Hitler had blamed his Vichy French collaborators in North Africa for capitulating to the Allies, and in November of that year, he ordered German occupation of Vichy France. From then on Germans would administer the territory directly, as they did the rest of France. There would be no more concessions to French independence.

Developments in North Africa also generated a chain reaction that affected the Soviet Union. Thanks to massive reinforcements in November 1942, the Germans held their bridgehead in Tunisia until May 1943. As a result, the Allies had to mount a campaign to crush those remaining Axis forces in North Africa. In turn it became impossible for the Allies to undertake the long-awaited invasion of northwestern Europe in 1943.

Stalin nonetheless continued to call for the western Allies to invade northwestern Europe as soon as possible. Since 1941 the Soviet Union had borne the brunt of German power, and Stalin and the Red Army were desperate for relief.

The western Allies could not liberate Tunisia and make the switch to operations in northwestern Europe during the same year. Instead British and American planners decided for landings in Sicily, then on the Italian mainland for 1943, and postponed invasion of France until 1944.

In the meantime, during 1943 and 1944, Germans in Soviet territories slaughtered millions of people: Red Army soldiers, Soviet civilians, and Jews from all over Europe. Military developments in North Africa, worked out by both sides with little regard to the impact on Soviet civilians, Jews, or Italians, had enormous—and unforeseen—consequences for all those groups of people.

In 1942 and 1943, the territory that today is the state of Israel was still part of the British mandate of Palestine. Arabs as well as some Jews lived in the area. During meetings with Arab leaders, most notably the Grand Mufti of Jerusalem, Hitler had promised that German forces would drive the British out of Palestine, occupy the territory, and slaughter the Jews there. Thanks to Allied victories in North Africa, the Germans never occupied the British mandate of Palestine, so the Jews there remained alive. Allied military planners probably gave no thought to the fate of the world's Jews as they made their moves in North Africa. Nevertheless their triumphs there in 1942 and 1943 made possible the eventual establishment of a Jewish state in Israel by saving the lives of those Jews already in the area.

ITALY

Military developments in North Africa also affected Italy, Germany's longest-standing alliance partner. The loss of North Africa completed Italy's disillusionment with the Axis. German demands, German arrogance, and German contempt for Italian officials and the Italian armed forces had also led to growing discontent.

In July 1943, Allied forces landed on Sicily. Soon they were advancing northward through the Italian peninsula. Committed Italian Fascists and their German backers retreated to the north of Naples, around the top of the ankle on the Italian boot.

After more than twenty-one years, Benito Mussolini's regime collapsed. In July 1943 the Italian king assumed supreme command, dismissed Mussolini from office, and had him arrested. A new Italian government under Marshal Badoglio dissolved the Fascist Party and surrendered to the Allies. Badoglio's government then fled to southern Italy and abandoned most of the country, as well as the Italian-occupied portions of France, Yugoslavia, Albania, and Greece, to the Germans.

The Germans took severe countermeasures. German troops occupied Rome and disarmed Italian soldiers, discharged them from service, or placed them in POW camps. By December 1943, the Germans had interned 725,000 Italian soldiers and had sent 615,000 Italian men to Germany as forced laborers.

Badoglio's government declared war on Germany. Meanwhile the Germans managed to free Mussolini by using a special paratroop unit and install him in a puppet state in northern Italy. Not until the end of April 1945 did the German forces in Italy capitulate. That month Italian partisans shot Mussolini and his mistress as they tried to flee to Switzerland.

Events in Italy had devastating effects for civilians in Yugoslavia, Albania, Greece, and France. In those countries the Germans had divided occupation duties with their Italian allies. The Italians tended to be fairly mild as occupiers, especially when it came to genocide of Jews. Neither the Italian military nor diplomatic officials would cooperate with the Germans in what they considered a barbaric procedure unworthy of any civilized society.

As a result, many Jews from German-occupied areas had fled into the Italian zones. When the Germans took over in 1943, those refuges disappeared. Already in the spring, Nazi Germans had begun to destroy the ancient Sephardic Jewish communities in Greece and Yugoslavia, deporting their members to Auschwitz to be killed. Now, with the Italians out of the way, the job could be completed. They even sent boats to take the last old Jewish men from remote Greek islands.

In Italy itself, Jews had been fairly safe until 1943. In the late 1930s, under German pressure, Mussolini had introduced legislation limiting Jews' activities. In contrast to the leadership in Slovakia and Vichy France—partners who cooperated eagerly with German plans for the Jews—Italians had refused to turn over their Jews for killing.

Beginning in 1943, Germans came in to Italy and took the Jews out themselves. Most of the Italian Jews murdered in the Holocaust died in 1944 or early 1945.

Primo Levi, an Italian survivor of the Holocaust, produced some of the most insightful reflections on that event ever written. Born in Turin in 1919, Levi was arrested with his Italian partisan group in December 1943. When his German captors discovered he was Jewish, they sent him to Auschwitz.

Levi survived, but almost all of the inmates he knew in the camp did not. His closest friend in Auschwitz was another Italian named Alberto. Levi and Alberto shared what little food they received or "organized" for themselves. They encouraged each other to muster the energy and will to try to stay alive, both physically and in some deeper, moral way that meant retaining an awareness of themselves as human beings.

Thanks to Levi's prewar training as a chemist, he got a job in the camp that protected him from some of the harshest conditions there. Somehow he lived through the war. Alberto, however, did not. He too was a resourceful, intelligent young man full of the desire to survive. In early 1945, as the Red Army advanced from the east, the Germans evacuated the camp at Auschwitz.

Guards marched Alberto, along with most other inmates, out of the camp to the west. Levi, sick in the infirmary at the time, was left behind with others too weak to walk. Who could have known that what seemed the chance for life—leaving the camp at last—would be Alberto's death, whereas Levi, abandoned by the guards as almost dead, would survive?

In his writings about the Holocaust, Levi described the camp as above all a place of dehumanization. The English translation of Levi's memoir is called *Survival in Auschwitz,* but he originally titled the book "Se questo è un uomo" (If this is a man). For Levi, to be human meant more than merely to eat and breathe. It meant having an identity, relationships with others, ties to a past and a future, and a sense of decency and dignity.

The camp took all that away. Physical abuses heaped on the prisoners—starvation, beatings, exposure—together with the many humiliations and indignities they suffered attacked their sense of humanity. In the camp, prisoners lost their names and became numbers. Emaciated, sick, shorn, and forced to wear rags, they looked nothing like their former selves. Brutality and deprivation turned them against one another; pain and despair made them forget the values and ideals they had cherished. It was this destruction of people's humanity that Levi considered the most terrible crime of the Holocaust.

After the war Levi did everything he could to share his insights and to warn against dehumanization and brutality in the postwar world. Already in Auschwitz he had nightmares that people "outside" would not listen to his story. Toward the end of his life he expressed frustration that the world refused to learn from the past. Primo Levi died in 1987 when he fell down the stairs in his home. Many people believe he committed suicide.

THE HOLOCAUST AT ITS PEAK

The Killing Centers

By the time of the Wannsee Conference in January 1942, Nazi Germans and their helpers were already engaged in mass killing of Jews from all over Europe. Since late 1939 they had been starving Jews to death in the ghettos of Poland. Mobile murder squads followed the regular military into Soviet territory in June 1941 and began immediately to concentrate their slaughter on Jewish civilians. In September 1941 German police introduced a regulation forcing all Jews in Germany to wear an identifying Star of David. A month later they began deporting Jews from Germany and elsewhere in central and western Europe to the east for killing. One killing center, at Chelmno, near Lodz, started operations in December 1941.

Although it may have seemed impossible, for European Jews 1942 and 1943 went even beyond the horrors of the years before. At the beginning of 1942, even after three years of war, ghettoization, torture, and forced labor, 75 percent of the Jews who would be murdered in the Holocaust were still alive. By the beginning of 1943, 75 percent of the approximately 6 million who would be killed were already dead.

In December 1941 the SS opened its first killing center at Chelmno, called Kulmhof by the Germans. Located just forty miles from Lodz, the Chelmno facility used specially equipped gas vans to kill Jews and also Gypsies. Guards loaded their victims into the cargo compartment and sealed the doors. As the van drove, pipes brought the diesel exhaust directly into the back so that the people there were asphyxiated. T-4 killers had developed this technique, which they used first against people deemed handicapped. Within months of the Wannsee Conference of January 1942, five more killing centers

A woman selected for "deportation" bids farewell to her son through the fence of the central prison in the Lodz ghetto. In September 1942, along with fifteen thousand other Jews deemed unsuitable for work—children, the elderly, and the infirm—she was sent to the killing center at Chelmno to be gassed.

were in operation, all of them, like Chelmno, in territories that had once been part of Poland. Contrary to popular notions, German mass killing of Jews was not some perfectly coordinated, "clean" enterprise. Like the entire Nazi regime it was characterized by confusion and rivalry, which only served to exacerbate the horror.

CHELMNO

The killing center at Chelmno was located in the incorporated territory, that is, the part of Poland annexed to the Reich and earmarked for Germanization. Chelmno was a small village on a railway branch line. An unoccupied castle proved useful as headquarters for the killing process.

Trains brought Jews, mostly from the surrounding area, to Chelmno, and then trucks drove them to the courtyard of the castle. There an SS man addressed them. They were to be sent to Germany, he told them, but first they had to take a shower. Ordered to strip, they were handed towels and soap and pushed through a corridor labeled "washroom" into the vans.

About ninety people were forced into a van at once. The vans drove slowly for a few miles into the forest. There personnel opened the doors and dumped the bodies. Guards shot anyone who was still alive.

The Germans kept a few Jews around to unload the corpses and bury the bodies. Known as the Sonderkommando—"special unit"—this small group of men handled twelve to thirteen vans—about one thousand bodies—each day. Jews were also assigned to sort the clothing left behind and clean out the vans. The more lucrative task of extracting any gold teeth went to the Nazis' Ukrainian helpers.

Most members of the Jewish Sonderkommando did not hold that position for long. As additional shipments of Jews arrived the German guards selected new workers and killed the old ones. Some of the Jewish workers tried to escape, and a few succeeded. The Germans responded to those attempts by chaining the legs of Sonderkommando members.

By the spring and summer of 1942, the area around Chelmno was filled with the stench of rotting bodies. German officials ordered ovens brought in so that the mass graves could be opened and the bodies exhumed and burned. Of course they delegated this gruesome job to members of the Jewish Sonderkommando.

One Jewish man assigned to the task found the bodies of his wife and two children in a mass grave. He begged the SS guards to shoot him. When they refused, he tried to commit suicide. This time his comrades stopped him. Eventually he escaped. One of very few survivors of the killing center at Chelmno, that man later served as a central witness at the postwar Chelmno trial.

Rumors about the killing center at Chelmno soon spread. Jews in the region struggled to know how to react, but their options were extremely limited. In December 1941, German authorities demanded that Rumkowski, head of the Jewish Council at Lodz, hand over twenty thousand members of his community for "special treatment." Aware that selection most likely meant death, Rumkowski and his committee tried to fill their list with outsiders and people considered asocial. Among those early victims were the remainder of some five thousand Gypsies who had been sent to Lodz from the Reich. Located in a separate part of the ghetto, many had already died from hunger and disease. Now those left would be murdered in Chelmno.

By mid-1942, the German district commander reported to Himmler that in the next two to three months, the "special treatment" of some one hundred thousand Jews from the area would be complete. Given the "success" of the project, he suggested a similar program for Poles with tuberculosis.

From December 1941 to the end of 1942, Germans and their henchmen

A young Jewish woman in the Lodz ghetto writes her last letter before boarding a train to the killing center at Chelmno.

killed about 145,000 people, most of them Jews, in Chelmno. About five thousand Gypsies from the ghetto in Lodz were murdered in the gas vans at Chelmno as well. In late 1942 the SS closed the killing center until 1944, when it was reactivated briefly. Its job in the area had been completed.

BELZEC

Only one inmate of the killing center at Belzec survived the war. Located near the Polish city of Lublin, Belzec began operations in March 1942. German governor Hans Frank of the General Government in Poland had boasted that Jews in his territory would be the first victims of the so-called Final Solution. To that end, after the Wannsee Conference, the labor camp at Belzec was outfitted as a killing center.

Belzec had a fixed installation for gassing that used diesel fumes. On 1 April 1942, the first night of the Jewish holiday of Passover, the SS brought more than fifteen thousand Jews from the city of Lvov to Belzec to be killed. By the time the camp was dismantled in the spring of 1943, some six hundred thousand Jews had been murdered there, along with perhaps several thousand Gypsies.

We have an early account of a gassing at Belzec from an unusual source: an SS man named Kurt Gerstein. Gerstein was a Nazi Party member and devout Protestant. He had served a brief term in a concentration camp himself for criticizing the anti-Christian attitudes of the SS. Nevertheless, thanks to family connections, he was able to have his name cleared and join the SS.

Gerstein was an engineer with some training in sanitation and medical matters. Accordingly he received a post as SS chief disinfection officer. Early in 1942, a deputy of Eichmann's assigned Gerstein to transport Zyklon B to a secret place. The destination was Belzec.

At Belzec the commandant, Dr. Christian Wirth, invited Gerstein to witness the killing of Jews using diesel fumes. That day the diesel motor broke down. About eight hundred Jews were forced to wait naked for nearly three hours until the gassing began. The killing itself took thirty-two minutes; Gerstein timed it with his stopwatch.

Horrified by what he had seen, Gerstein decided to try to use his position to stop the killings. He destroyed some of the Zyklon B he was supposed to deliver to Auschwitz, and he tried to get the word out about German mass murder of Jews in Poland. When he met a Swedish diplomat on a train, Gerstein blurted out the whole story. He went to the papal nuncio—the Vatican's representative—in Berlin to pass the news to the pope. Gerstein's efforts met with little response.

At the end of the war, Gerstein was captured by the French. Arrested and charged with war crimes, he died in prison, either by his own hand or as a victim of foul play. Only half a century later, due to efforts by his family, did he gain a reputation as a hero.

Gerstein's story is instructive. A lone individual who tried to sabotage a murderous process from within, he ended up caught in the system himself and destroyed. Gerstein did not have the public backing within Germany that allowed someone like Bishop von Galen to protest the killing of the handicapped with some effect. Nor would or could the foreigners he told about what he knew grasp what must have seemed to them the ravings of a madman.

SOBIBOR

The camp at Sobibor was constructed solely for the purpose of killing. Its first commandant was an Austrian named Franz Stangl, a policeman trained in the T-4 program.

Sobibor was one of the Operation Reinhard camps, named after Reinhard Heydrich, Himmler's deputy and the driving force at the Wannsee Conference. Mass slaughter of Jews began there in April 1942. Sobibor functioned as a killing center until October 1943.

At Sobibor, Germans and their accomplices murdered 250,000 Jews from eastern Poland, the occupied Soviet Union, and other European countries. Many Dutch Jews, for example, were killed in Sobibor. Trains brought the victims right into the camp. Guards selected some Jews as workers in the killing process, and the rest they gassed immediately.

In October 1943 Sobibor was the site of an uprising by its Jewish workers, who staged a mass escape. Most were recaptured, but some survived the war. The Germans closed the camp shortly after the revolt. It is not clear whether the revolt hastened the camp's closure, but by the time Sobibor stopped operations, most of the Jews in the territories from which it had drawn its victims were already dead.

TREBLINKA

Another Operation Reinhard camp built solely as a killing center, Treblinka began operations in July 1942. Just eighty miles from Warsaw, it became the grave of a staggering number of Polish Jews. Its first victims were some three hundred thousand Jews from Warsaw, but Gypsies from the Warsaw ghetto and Jews from all over central Poland, Germany, Austria, Czechoslovakia, and Greece were killed there. In all close to a million Jews were murdered at Treblinka.

Treblinka too had its Sonderkommando, more than eight hundred Jews who worked in the camp. They included craftspeople employed by the SS as well as men assigned to work in the gas chambers, cutting hair and burying and burning bodies. In August 1943 Jewish workers at Treblinka revolted, after which German authorities gradually shut the camp down.

A number of Nazi high-ranking officials visited Treblinka. Eichmann, for example, paid a call. He described the fake railway station that greeted arrivals to Treblinka as looking "just like Germany." Camp organizers intended the facade to create a semblance of normalcy so that people would not suspect they were about to be killed. Eichmann also saw guards chase Jews into the gas chambers through a path between barbed wire fences that the Germans in charge of the camp called the "hose," the "funnel," or the "way to heaven."

Treblinka was far from perfectly organized. Often corpses littered the train tracks both inside and outside the compound. Eventually the commandant of Sobibor, Franz Stangl, was transferred to Treblinka to clean the place up. Even Stangl's "improvements"—increased efficiency and a beautification scheme that included planting flower beds—could not conceal the unbearable smell that surrounded the place. Fields came right up to the security fence, so that Polish farmers who lived nearby could see much of what happened inside. No one in the area could be unaware of the massive killing operations at Treblinka.

MAJDANEK

Majdanek combined a labor camp with a killing center. Just a mile from the city of Lublin, the camp, modeled after Dachau in Germany, was built in the winter of 1940–1941 for prisoners of war. In fact, the Jewish POWs from the Polish army who were its first inmates did much of the construction.

In July 1941 the Germans brought Soviet POWs to Majdanek. Over time they added many Polish gentiles, especially political prisoners. They built gas chambers in 1942, but death vans and shooting were also widely used at Majdanek. All of Majdanek's inmates were subjected to terrible abuses, and many were worked to death. Most of the Soviet POWs died from torture and starvation. The SS men in Majdanek were known as sadists who enjoyed killing children in front of their mothers and forcing the prisoners to engage in deadly "sports."

At Majdanek, gassing, for the most part, was reserved for Jews. Guards brought most transports of Jews straight to the gas chambers. Those kept alive to work had a precarious existence.

In late 1942 Eichmann visited Majdanek. Guards forced the inmates to spend the entire day on parade. Eichmann looked at them and said, "Get rid of the whole lot." In Nazi eyes, the lives of the inmates at Majdanek were worth less than nothing. In just one day, 3 November 1943, guards at Majdanek mowed down some seventeen thousand prisoners with machine gun fire and forced the few left alive to conceal the evidence. In all, two hundred thousand people were killed in the camp. About 75,000 were gentiles; the other 125,000 were Jews.

AUSCHWITZ-BIRKENAU

Auschwitz-Birkenau was the last camp established as a killing center, but it functioned the longest in that capacity. Like Belzec and Majdanek, Auschwitz started as a labor camp. Many of the early inmates were political prisoners from Poland. Facilities for mass killing were added later as were a number of factories using slave labor drawn from the camp; the chemical company IG Farben had a plant there as did the Buna artificial rubber works.

In the summer of 1941—before the Wannsee Conference—Himmler decided to transform the camp at Auschwitz into a killing center. He assigned a man named Rudolf Hoess, trained at Dachau, to the task. Auschwitz seemed an ideal location to Himmler. It was near the small Polish town of Oswiecim and convenient to rail lines yet securely distant from the front. The prisoners already on hand provided a ready source of manpower.

Germans conducted some early trial gassings at Auschwitz. In September 1941 they killed nine hundred Soviet POWs using Zyklon B. By March 1942 Jews were being sent there from the surrounding area to be gassed. The killing center was known as Auschwitz II or Birkenau. Eventually Birkenau would be the destination of Jews rounded up for killing from Slovakia, France, and then all over Europe. An estimated 6,400 Gypsies would be gassed at Birkenau too.

The killing procedure at Auschwitz-Birkenau was similar to that elsewhere. Often German officials met the transports of Jews right at the ramp as they came off the trains. There they made their "selections"—the decision as to who would go immediately to the gas and who would be kept alive in the camp for a time as laborers.

Many survivors remember selections conducted by Dr. Josef Mengele. Mengele was a scientist and SS doctor who had his own special projects that involved experiments with dwarfs, twins, and others. Mengele's abusive experiments killed the vast majority of his subjects. With a wave of the hand, Mengele and his counterparts sorted those deemed useful for work from those considered fit only for killing. Children, women with children, pregnant women, older men and women, the sick, and the weak were sent to one side and then on to the gas. Others were admitted into the camp.

The officials who presided over the killing process developed a series of tricks and deceits to keep their victims calm. Often SS men addressed those selected for gassing in polite, helpful tones as they entered the gas chambers. "You have been on a journey, and you are dirty," the SS informed their victims. "You will take a shower." Sometimes they even handed out soap and towels before cramming the people in the "Shower Room." Hoess was proud of arrangements at his camp; he had a sense that he had perfected procedures.

Auschwitz-Birkenau represented another refinement to the Nazi system of killing. From early in the process German officials had worried about conflicts between German economic interests and the goal of annihilating Jews. In Auschwitz, those two aims were combined. The SS found they could make money by essentially renting out slave laborers to manufacturers and industrialists. Employers need not worry about keeping their workers alive; there were always more where they came from.

Bizarre as it may seem, some Germans made a rather pleasant life for themselves at the killing centers. Ambitious Nazi doctors had an endless supply of disposable human subjects on whom to conduct experiments. Commandants and other high-ranking administrators often brought their wives and children to be near them. They had access to every luxury and of course to free labor. Hoess's wife supposedly said about Auschwitz, "Here I want to live until the end of my days." Himmler authorized fish farms, gardens, brothels, and even zoos on the sites for the employees' enjoyment. As for the guards, assignment to a killing center was certainly preferable to being sent to the front. The killing centers marked the culmination of the killing process. They were not separate from the Nazi German war for race and space but were an integral part of it. In all, an estimated 3 million Jews were murdered in the six killing centers outlined here. The number of Gypsies killed with them is even harder to pin down, but it was certainly in the tens of thousands. Approximately twenty thousand Roma died in Auschwitz-Birkenau alone—two thirds of them from starvation, disease, experimentation, beatings, and shootings; the rest in the gas chambers.

GENDER AND GENOCIDE

Women's and men's experiences in the Holocaust converged and diverged in significant ways, summed up in the scholar Myrna Goldenberg's phrase "different horrors, same hell." Jewish men were more likely to be killed in labor camps in Poland in 1939 and 1940, but more women were among the groups "selected" from the ghettos in 1941 and 1942 for transport to killing centers. In places like Auschwitz, men had a better chance of being chosen for work; SS authorities regularly consigned women, particularly if pregnant or with small children, directly to the gas.

Accounts by Jewish women in Auschwitz and other Nazi camps often emphasize the physical transformation that their bodies underwent. Isabella Leitner, a survivor from Hungary, described her feelings in Auschwitz in May 1944:

> Our heads are shaved. We look like neither boys nor girls. We haven't menstruated for a long time. We have diarrhea. No, not diarrhea—typhus. Summer and winter we have but one type of clothing. Its name is "rag." Not an inch of it without a hole. Our shoulders are exposed. The rain is pouring on our skeletal bodies. The lice are having an orgy in our armpits, their favorite spots. Their bloodsucking, the irritation, their busy scurrying give the illusion of warmth. We're hot at least under our armpits, while our bodies are shivering. (Rittner and Roth, 67)

Secrecy, Denial, Disbelief

German authorities tried to keep the operation of the killing centers secret, just as they had attempted to conceal the murder of people deemed handicapped and the mass shootings of Jews and others in 1941, but in no case was secrecy really possible. The killing operations were simply too big and involved far too many people to keep them quiet.

Local populations watched full trains pull in and saw them depart empty. The air for miles around was thick with the ashes of burning bodies and heavy with the stench of death. Civilians of all kinds came from Germany and elsewhere for jobs in the camps. There were guards, of course, but also architects and engineers, suppliers, telephone operators, and secretaries. What did the German and Polish women think whose job it was to type up lists of the dead and prepare statistics of the numbers of people killed?

Presumably perpetrators, bystanders, and onlookers found ways to live with their knowledge of the killing centers. One individual's account illustrates some of the forms denial and rationalization could take. Teresa Stangl was married to Franz Stangl, commandant first of Sobibor and then of Treblinka. A devout Catholic, she had initially opposed her husband's involvement with the Nazi Party. According to Mrs. Stangl, she had never really understood his position in the T-4 program; she claimed she did not know the nature of the programs he administered.

Later Teresa Stangl moved to Sobibor to be near her husband. From their house near the camp she could not see the activities inside. One day a drunken coworker of her husband's called on her. He told her the details of Franz's job.

Horrified Mrs. Stangl confronted her husband. He denied any direct connection with killing and assured his wife that he was just responsible for routine administration. Nevertheless she found herself unable to have sexual relations with him for some time. Eventually she moved away, and they continued their marriage from a distance.

Despite her misgivings Mrs. Stangl stood by her husband. He loved her and would have done anything for her, she said. Once, she admitted in an interview that he would have chosen her over his work if she had given him an ultimatum, but later she insisted that she could have done nothing.

What of the Jews? What could Jews in Europe know in 1942 and 1943 of the killing centers? The answer is complicated by geography. Clearly Jews farther away—in Greece, for example—might have access to very little reliable information, but even Polish Jews, at least in the early stages of the killing centers' operation, could have problems grasping the reality of genocide. The word "genocide" did not even exist until after World War II.

Perhaps one account can illustrate. Piotrków Trybunalski, in the incorporated territories, was home to about 11,400 Jews, some 22 percent of the overall population. Since October 1939 the Jews of Piotrków had been confined to a ghetto.

In the spring of 1942, two young Jewish men escaped from Chelmno. They arrived in Piotrków and revealed the truth about German gassings of Jews. Most people refused to believe their ears. Why, during wartime, when it was well known that Germany had a serious shortage of labor, would the Germans try to slaughter every Polish Jew?

The leaders of the community met. Desperate to reassure themselves, they decided that the excesses the two young men had witnessed must be regional aberrations. Everyone knew that the SS commander Odilo Globocnik in Lublin was exceptionally vicious. Surely nothing so terrible could happen in their district.

Were the Jewish leaders of Piotrków naive? Maybe, but perhaps that innocence is to their credit. Who could imagine mass gassings as part of systematic annihilation of Jews? Such a thing had never happened. Nazi planners in turn manipulated and exploited that inability to believe the worst.

Hope, even false hope, had some advantages over despair. One of the chroniclers of the Warsaw ghetto wrote, "It is good that we console ourselves, for even if these are false hopes, they keep us from collapsing." For the most part those Jews who grasped German intentions toward them could do nothing anyway. In the summer of 1942, Adam Czerniaków was head of the Jewish Council in Warsaw. When the Germans ordered him to hand over the children of the ghetto, he knew that they would be killed. Powerless to stop the slaughter, Czerniaków took the only way out still left to him: he committed suicide.

Jews in Hiding

Not all of the Jews targeted in the Holocaust ended up in killing centers. Many Jews fled, taking refuge where they could. Others hid, and still others "passed" as gentiles. An estimated 80,000 to 120,000 Jews were hidden in Poland; maybe half of those survived the war.

Many of the Jews in hiding were children. It was easier to persuade non-Jews to have pity on children than on adults, who took up more space, ate more, and were harder to explain. It tended to be more difficult to find hiding places for Jewish boys than for girls. In Europe very few Christian parents had their sons circumcised. So Jewish boys had their religion marked on their bodies in a visible way. It was not uncommon for police or local collaborators hunting for Jews to demand that men or boys pull down their pants so that they could see if they had been circumcised.

The decision to put a child into hiding was agonizing for parents. Whom could one trust? When was hiding the best option? Was it not better to stay together no matter what? How could one leave a child one might never see again?

Only as adults have many of the people hidden as Jewish children during the war recounted their experiences publicly. Here are two of their stories.

Henny. Henny was the daughter of Lithuanian Jews from Kovno. When she was just a year and a half old she and her parents were forced to move into the ghetto. For more than two years Henny's parents hid her in a small room that had been a walk-in pantry, but when she developed whooping cough it became too risky to keep her there. So they arranged for a Lithuanian Christian family outside the ghetto to take her in.

Henny's mother also arranged a hiding place for her two-year-old niece,

Shoshana, after Germans shot the little girl's father. She made contact with a Lithuanian priest who got false papers for Shoshana and placed her in a convent. Later the nuns passed her on to a family of pig farmers. Miraculously, Shoshana, Henny, and Henny's parents all survived the war.

Rudy. Rudy was a little boy in the Netherlands. He survived the war in about twenty different hiding places, most of them in rural Holland. He remembers spending three days with a Jewish family in the woods while Germans searched the area. He heard German vehicles and dogs at night, but he stayed hidden under branches and leaves, and they did not find him. Later two young women hid him with a group of ten other children. Several times a local Dutch policeman warned them of an impending raid. Once, they stayed in a cave for two days until it was safe to return. Eventually the group had to be split up. Only after the war, as adults, did some of them find one another again.

Concentration Camps: Microcosms of the Third Reich

Killing centers were just one part of the vast network of German camps that had been expanding since 1933. Those who passed through the killing centers were overwhelmingly Jewish, although Gypsies were murdered there as well. Other kinds of camps included a much wider range of inmates. The years 1942 and 1943 were also a time when the Germans incarcerated huge numbers of people from all over Europe. A closer look at the concentration camps belongs in this discussion of the peak years of killing.

The total number of Nazi German camps of various kinds is not known, but it must be in the thousands. An estimated 18 million people passed through the camps; some 11 million died there. Many of those who survived bore deep scars, physical and psychological.

In crucial ways Nazi concentration camps were microcosms of the Third Reich. The camps reflected the nature of Nazism, and the Nazi system would have been impossible without the camps. German practices inside the camps echoed methods used elsewhere. The principle of divide and conquer was evident, for example, as was promotion of rivalry among German authorities with the end result of increasing brutality toward the victims.

NATURE OF THE CONCENTRATION CAMPS

Political prisoners, such as Communists, Jehovah's Witnesses, homosexual men, common criminals, so-called asocials, and critics of the regime, all served terms that in some cases proved fatal. Representatives of all those groups were still found in large numbers in the German camps during the war.

German conquests brought influxes of new kinds of prisoners too. German police arrested Polish and French Communists and Socialists as well as members of resistance groups from all over Europe. These inmates were not gassed, but they were beaten, starved, used for experiments, and forced to do backbreaking labor. Some of them survived only a few weeks. Others lived for months, and a few made it longer, often because they managed to wrangle some kind of privileged position in the camp.

Camps often used for political prisoners included Gross-Rosen, Stutthof, Bergen-Belsen, Flossenbürg, and Ravensbrück for women, but there were many others. Even these names often encompassed a vast network of satellite facilities; Buchenwald, for example, included some 134 satellite camps.

Another type of mass-detention facilities was the labor camps. Most of their inmates were non-Jewish women and men from conquered nations. German authorities used them for work connected to military requirements, in factories, mines, quarries, and production of armaments. One example was Dora-Mittelbau, a camp in north-central Germany not far from the city of Göttingen. In its extensive underground facility slave laborers built V-2 rockets.

The German state viewed slave workers as a renewable resource; their lives had no value. Death tolls in such camps were astronomical. Toward the end of the war, as more Jews were kept alive for labor, they died in even greater numbers than the rest of the prisoners. Camp organizers quartered the Jews separately, gave them less food, and treated them even more harshly than they did the gentile inmates.

Like the killing centers, concentration camps specialized in brutality, with an eye to comfort and ease for the staff. Buchenwald had a zoo; many had gardens and brothels staffed by sex slaves from the occupied territories. Sometimes camp authorities also assigned German "asocial" women—lesbians, Communists, and criminals—to brothels. Clients included staff and especially privileged male prisoners.

All of the big camps, even places such as Dora-Mittelbau, had orchestras. Often they included Gypsies, popular as musicians in Europe, or trained classical musicians. There was no shortage of candidates; Europe in the 1940s was a very musical place. Orchestras performed to entertain the guards, to send the prisoners off to work, and sometimes during executions in the camps. They played well-known marches, arias, folk songs, and even Christmas carols.

The cynicism of those behind the camp system is evident in other ways

too. A sign over the gate of Auschwitz read "Arbeit macht frei"—"work liber-
ates." Buchenwald, built in 1937, had its own slogan: "Jedem das Seine"—"to
each his own."

German authorities recruited for high-ranking positions at the camps
from within the German police. They hired unskilled or semiskilled workers
to be guards at the lower levels. At Ravensbrück, for example, women guards
were recruited through ads that promised job security, a responsible position,
and wages higher than many nonskilled positions. Successful candidates underwent only a very short training course.

Outside of Germany, SS men took the top positions in the camps. Often
they had been trained at German camps such as Dachau. Lowlier guards commonly came from subject populations; for example, ethnic Germans from eastern Europe, Ukrainians, Latvians, Croatians.

Jobs in the camps gave individuals a chance to enrich themselves at the
expense of the inmates. They also provided an opportunity to lord it over one's
local enemies. For example, the Germans hired Croatians to guard Serbs,
Yugoslavian Gypsies, and Jews; they often used Ukrainians against Poles.
Working conditions that tolerated and even encouraged drunkenness, rape,
and brutality appealed especially to sadists and thugs.

Women occupied almost all of the same positions that men did, at least at
the lower levels. Generally women prisoners had women guards. There were
also female SS units, usually assigned to communication duties and housekeep-
ing for SS men at the front. It was no secret that these women, chosen on the
basis of their supposedly valuable "blood," were expected to help German SS
men resist the temptation of sexual liaisons with "non-Aryans" by making
themselves available.

About two thousand female guards assisted the SS at the Ravensbrück
camp for women. Some women, like some men, were notorious for cruelty.
Most infamous were Irma Griese, a guard at Auschwitz, and the "Bitch of
Buchenwald," Ilse Koch, wife of Commander Karl Koch. Koch, though not
herself a guard, was active and visible in the camp. After the war, wild rumors
circulated about her sexual deviancy and fondness for lampshades and other
household decorations made of tattooed human flesh. Some of the most horrific stories about Ilse Koch were never proven, but what seems clear is that to
prisoners and outside observers alike, the involvement of women in Nazi brutality seemed even more shocking than the behavior of men.

German authorities in the camps also appointed some prisoners to supervise and control other inmates. Such prisoner functionaries became known as

kapos. Often the leaders of labor gangs, kapos had access to some power and privilege. At the same time they remained answerable to camp authorities.

The use of kapos encouraged development of elaborate hierarchies of power within the camps. Such divisions, of course, benefited the Nazis, who needed to invest less time and energy to control prisoners who were at odds with one another. By rewarding kapos for brutality against fellow prisoners, German officials continued to undermine solidarity. Every kapo realized that he or she could be replaced at a moment's notice. There were plenty of prisoners eager to increase their chances to survive by accepting positions of privilege within the camp.

To reinforce divisions among prisoners, camp officials introduced a system of colored badges to identify the various groups. Criminals wore a green triangle; Communists received red. Gypsies and "asocials" were marked with a black badge, and Jehovah's Witnesses with purple. A pink triangle designated homosexual men. A yellow triangle—or more often two triangles together to form a six-pointed star—identified Jews.

Camp authorities recruited most kapos from the green and red triangles, the two groups at the top of the hierarchy. Kapos from the other groups were not unknown, but it was hard for people to assert authority over those considered above them. Jews, marked as they were for death, invariably occupied the bottom of the hierarchy. Often the other prisoners ostracized and tormented homosexual men in particularly vicious ways. Nevertheless, in a few cases Jews and homosexuals too served as kapos or in similar positions.

The perpetrators devised special humiliations for members of each of their victim groups, and even the same treatment was experienced in different ways by people whose own values and taboos set them apart from one another. German aggressors often launched attacks on Jews on the Jewish holidays. Camp officials frequently put tough, homophobic kapos in charge of gay prisoners. Nakedness of adults in front of their own children was particularly taboo among Roma, so orders to strip carried extra humiliation for members of that group.

Many accounts from the camps stress the importance of support from other prisoners. German officials tried to divide and conquer their prey. They set people against one another by forcing competition for absurdly small prizes—an extra crust of bread, a button, a piece of string.

Some of the most powerful stories of the camps explain how inmates countered such efforts to isolate them. Primo Levi, an Italian Jew, tells how he reminded himself and a coworker of their humanity by reciting lines from Dante's *Divine Comedy*: "Think of your breed; for brutish ignorance / Your mettle was not made; you were made men, / To follow after knowledge and excellence." Sara Nomberg-Przytyk, a Jewish Communist woman from Poland, attributes her survival to an anonymous woman in the next train car who sacrificed her own blanket so that Sara would not freeze to death.

THE ROMA/GYPSIES

Almost every memoir of the concentration camps mentions Gypsies. For Gypsies, like Jews, 1942 and 1943 were the peak years of killing. As German forces consolidated their hold on subject territories, they located more and more groups of Roma. In all, German perpetrators and their accomplices killed an estimated one-quarter to half a million Roma, including many children. Thousands of others were sterilized.

Nazi ideology considered Gypsies impure and unworthy to live. One of the absurdities of the situation was that according to Nazi terminology, Gypsies were in fact more "Aryan" than the Nordic Germans. Gypsies originated in India, home of the original Aryan tribe, whose name was appropriated by

A group of Roma, awaiting instructions from their German captors, sit in an open area near the fence in the Belzec camp in late 1941 or 1942.

European racists for their own purposes. The Romani language even bears some similarity to Indian languages.

SS leader Himmler was fascinated by Gypsies. He set up an office within the German Ministry of Health called the Racial Hygiene and Population Research Center. Its main task was to study the approximately thirty thousand German Gypsies, draw up genealogies of them, and identify those considered "pure." Information it gathered made it possible to locate Gypsies and kill them.

Initially Himmler wanted to preserve some "pure Gypsies" in a kind of reservation or zoo, where they could be examined by future German scientists. "Experts" estimated that between 3 and 4 percent of the Gypsies would fall into that category. Later Himmler abandoned that idea. The German government provided generous funding for research on the Roma, and many scientists got involved in the project, especially social scientists such as anthropologists.

As we have seen earlier, Gypsies shared many of the experiences of Jews in the Holocaust. Classified, dispossessed, deported, forced into ghettos, shot into mass graves, and gassed, they too were marked for annihilation, but Nazi authorities never devoted the same fanatical energy to killing Gypsies as they did to eradication of Jews. They seemed to regard Gypsies as a nuisance rather than part of some diabolical, international conspiracy. Either way, however, Roma were targeted for murder.

The experience of Nazi persecution highlighted just how isolated Gypsies were within Europe. Church leaders in Germany protested the killing of people deemed handicapped in 1941. In the 1943 Rosenstrasse protest, the gentile wives of German Jewish men forced cancellation of plans to deport their husbands to the east to be killed. In Poland, the Netherlands, Ukraine, Yugoslavia, and elsewhere, non-Jews risked their lives to hide Jewish children and adults, sometimes for years. Who protested on behalf of the Roma? Who beyond their own circles sheltered Gypsy children from death? There may have been some people who did so, but their stories are not well known.

HOMOSEXUALS—THE "MEN WITH THE PINK TRIANGLE"

Hitler's regime had harassed and persecuted homosexuals since its early years in power. Between 1933 and 1945 German courts convicted fifty thousand men on charges related to homosexuality. The year 1942 brought a record number of arrests, mostly of Germans. Nazi ideology regarded homosexuals, particularly men, as a threat to "Aryan racial health" because they refused to take part in producing children for the fatherland. In wartime, especially in 1942 and 1943, as German casualties began to climb, the German leadership took that offense very seriously. German police arrested thousands of men accused of homosexual activity. Between five and seven thousand of these men perished in World War II, perhaps half of them in concentration camps.

Like every group targeted by Nazi Germany, homosexuals had experiences unique to them. For one thing, Nazi theorists were confused as to whether homosexuality was biological or acquired. So German officials vacillated between treating gay men as if they were racial enemies or handling them as candidates for reeducation. In 1933 Himmler had estimated there were between 1 and 4 million homosexually inclined men in Germany, but even the homophobic Himmler never mounted a systematic effort to wipe out homosexuality as such. Instead police made arrests on the basis of denunciations and raids.

By 1942 many concentration camps had homosexual inmates. Sachsenhausen and Buchenwald housed the largest numbers, in separate "queer blocks." Gay men, like Jews and Gypsies, fell near the bottom of the camp hierarchy. Viewed even by many fellow prisoners as the scum of humanity, they suffered severely from torture, beating, and medical experimentation. Perhaps their isolation from other prisoners explains the extremely high death rate among gay inmates in Nazi camps; it was about 60 percent as compared to 41 percent for political prisoners and 35 percent for Jehovah's Witnesses.

As the war went on and German demands for labor increased, officials allowed some of the homosexuals in Sachsenhausen to be released as civilian laborers, but there were strings attached. In order to be pronounced "cured," a candidate for rehabilitation had to perform "properly" with a prostitute from the camp brothel. If he failed but agreed to castration, he might still be released for heavy labor. Some gay men also won release by volunteering for special penal units sent to the very worst areas of the front. Few of those individuals survived.

Harry Pauli, an actor from Berlin, was one of the rare exceptions. Sentenced on grounds of homosexual activity to twenty months' imprisonment, he served eight months before being drafted into the Wehrmacht. Ridiculed and abused by the other men, he tried to desert but was caught. His punishment was a year with the penal battalion Dirlewanger. Thanks to a nonfatal wound, he witnessed the end of the war from a military hospital in Prague.

In significant ways persecution of homosexual men in Nazi camps continued what went on outside. After liberation of the camps in 1945, occupation authorities arrested again some gay men, reconvicted them, and sent them back to prison. Homosexual activity remained a criminal act in West Germany until the 1960s. Illegality and social stigma account for the silence that shrouded the treatment of gay men in Nazi Germany until the 1970s and 1980s.

RESISTANCE

All over Europe people resisted Nazism in many ways. There were individual acts of defiance and heroism; there was sabotage and rescue of people targeted for killing. The Communist Party organized resistance groups, often with backing from the Soviet Union. The British Special Operations Executive supported nationalist guerrilla movements from France to Yugoslavia and Greece.

Any discussion of resistance has to define the term. Does opposition have to be effective to count as resistance? Does it need to be organized? Armed? Unmixed with collaboration or opportunism? I define "resistance" as any actions taken with the intent of thwarting Nazi German goals in the war, actions that carried with them risk of punishment. Under this definition, resistance could be individual or group, armed or unarmed. Whether we talk about intelligence as resistance, Jewish resistance, or resistance within Germany, all discussion of resistance serves to counter some popular misconceptions about World War II.

The Spread of Information as Resistance

Resistance can take many forms. Many anti–Nazi organizations took enormous risks to collect and transmit information that would undermine the German war effort. One of the most remarkable examples of intelligence as resistance involved a member of the Polish underground named Jan Karski.

Born in 1914 Karski made a career before the war in the Polish Foreign Service. He joined the Polish army in 1939 and was taken prisoner of war by the Soviets. Karski escaped and became part of the Polish underground. In the fall of 1942, Karski was charged with a mission to London. He was to carry a report to the Polish government-in-exile that described the situation in German-occupied Poland.

Leaders of two Jewish organizations learned of Karski's impending trip to London and asked if he would also carry a report for them. Karski agreed. The Jews of Poland were being exterminated, the Jewish leaders told Karski. Eventually Hitler would lose the war, they said, but he would win his war

Stjepan Filipovic, commander of a partisan detachment, calls on the people of Serbia to fight just before his execution in May 1942. Such shows of defiance often had a profound impact on those who saw them.

against Polish Jewry. The Jewish leaders asked Karski to tell the highest circles of the Allied governments that Hitler planned to kill every Jew regardless of the outcome of the war. Polish Jews and even Polish gentiles were helpless to stop the destruction. Only the Allied governments could save the Jews.

Before they sent him off with their message, the Jewish leaders wanted Karski to see for himself what they meant. They smuggled him into the Jewish ghetto in Warsaw and then into the killing center at Belzec. Karski was devastated by what he saw. After an hour in Belzec disguised as a guard he broke down and had to be taken out, vomiting blood. Karski became one of the first

Willem Arondeus (left) and friends dancing at a garden party. During the war, Arondeus led a Dutch gay resistance group that bombed the Amsterdam Population Registry offices in an effort to destroy government records on Jews and others hunted by the Nazis. Arondeus was executed in 1943.

eyewitnesses to present to the West the whole truth about the fate of the Jews in occupied Poland.

Karski delivered his reports as promised. He met with British, American, and Polish representatives; he spoke directly with Prime Minister Churchill in Britain and President Roosevelt in the United States and sought out journalists and other opinion leaders.

All of Karski's perseverance and heroism did not get the results he so desperately wanted. People simply did not comprehend. After U.S. Supreme Court justice Felix Frankfurter listened to Karski's report, he responded that he could not believe it. Frankfurter did not mean he thought Karski was lying; he simply could not grasp the enormity of what he had heard. Karski found no effective help for the Jews of Poland from any nation, government, or church. Only a few courageous individuals like himself were willing to act. Karski survived the war and moved to Washington, D.C., where he taught political science for many years. He died in 2000.

Jan Karski's experience highlights the issue of Allied knowledge of Nazi crimes. What did the British or the Americans know and when? By late 1942, when Karski prepared his report, at least some people within the Allied leadership had access to a great deal of information about German atrocities. Already in 1941 British codebreakers were reading German dispatches, including those from the Soviet Union describing Einsatzgruppen murders of Jews and other civilians. Reports from eyewitnesses and individuals who had managed to escape from Nazi prisons and camps reached world leaders through all kinds of channels, and every government had its own sources of intelligence. The press offered considerable detail for the reading public—in the United States, Canada, Switzerland, and elsewhere—so that it is not possible to speak of mass murder as if it were a Nazi secret.

Nevertheless a number of factors prevented the Allies from broadcasting their knowledge of slaughter of European Jews and other people. Most importantly there was a war to be won, a war whose outcome was by no means clear in 1942 or even 1943. In particular military leaders in the United States and Britain emphasized the need to stay focused and avoid being distracted by "sideshows." No doubt some individuals were indifferent to the fate of Europe's Jews or even had antisemitic notions of their own. Nevertheless it is probably fair to assume that many people simply could not grasp the unprecedented nature of this war of annihilation, and even those who could tended to be preoccupied with their own issues and struggles.

Jewish Resistance

Jewish resistance of various kinds was much more widespread than many people used to assume. All across German-occupied Europe, Jews and other opponents of Nazism took to the woods, often forming partisan units to combat the Germans.

The existence of Jewish partisans was precarious at best. They lived from hand to mouth, stealing when necessary, arranging secretly for deliveries of food, and spending hours and even days in holes in the ground when danger threatened. Afraid that the presence of Jews nearby would jeopardize their own security, gentiles often denounced or killed their Jewish counterparts. Nevertheless, as German police records for 1943 indicate, Jews in the woods of eastern Europe managed to acquire explosives and weapons and to perform acts of sabotage against the Nazi system. In some cases, young Jewish men and women even married in the woods and gave birth to children there.

In Lithuania in early 1942, about ten thousand Jewish men and women were fighting as partisans. At least thirty different Jewish partisan groups existed in the General Government alone. Jews also revolted in such major ghettos as Warsaw and Bialystok. In general, the groups that banded together were desperate, pitifully small, and barely armed. Their chances of success were minimal, but still they defied Nazi power.

Even in the camps, under the most adverse conditions, resistance in many

A partisan fighter, Sara Ginaite, at the liberation of Vilna in August 1944. A Jewish major in the Red Army took the photograph. He was surprised to see a Jewish woman standing guard.

forms occurred. Numerous survivors' memoirs tell the story of the beautiful dancer in Auschwitz who seized a gun from an SS man and shot him. Both Sobibor and Treblinka had revolts in 1943. In October 1944, Jewish prisoners at Auschwitz-Birkenau blew up the camp's fourth crematorium. Starved, abandoned by the world, and robbed of their property, the Jews were in a weak position to offer resistance to the Germans. Nevertheless, like others they did resist—violently, passively, spiritually, physically, and emotionally—throughout the entire process of the "Final Solution."

The Jewish ghetto in Warsaw must have been one of the last places the Germans expected an uprising in the spring of 1943. By then 80 percent of the population of the Warsaw ghetto was already gone, most of them murdered at Treblinka in the summer of 1942.

Initially the Warsaw Jewish rebels had little support even within their own community. The Jewish Fighting Organization had fewer than five hundred fighters. Armed only with gasoline bombs, hand grenades, pistols, one or two submachine guns, and about ten rifles, they must have seemed unlikely to accomplish anything other than rapid mass suicide. Yet this ragtag band managed to mount the largest armed resistance organized by any targets of Nazi mass murder during the Second World War. What happened?

In January 1943 German SS planned to liquidate what was left of the Warsaw ghetto. To their surprise they met with organized resistance from ghetto Jews. Unwilling to risk casualties they gave up the attempt a few days later.

Four months later, on 19 April 1943, the Germans returned much better prepared. More than two thousand men came with armored vehicles, artillery, flame throwers, heavy-caliber machine guns, and even aircraft. For their part Warsaw Jews had prepared an elaborate system of bunkers and underground passages. Determined to make a stand they held off the Germans for four weeks.

The SS burned down buildings, dynamited, and smoked out the Jews' bunkers until they won the upper hand. The Jewish fighters' tenacity was astounding, especially because the ghetto was sealed off and it was almost impossible to get weapons or supplies. The Nazis crushed the uprising at a huge cost in human lives, almost all of them Jewish. The SS commander reported sixteen German dead; the actual number may have been slightly higher.

Small pockets of Jewish resistance continued for weeks, but in the end, more than fifty-six thousand Jews surrendered. The Germans shot many on the spot and transported the others to killing centers and labor camps. Thousands of Jewish dead remained buried in the rubble.

The Warsaw ghetto uprising marked the first large-scale urban revolt against German occupation in Europe. It did not save Jewish lives. To the contrary, it may have led the Germans to use more force more quickly in the future when they set out to liquidate ghettos. Given their intention to kill the Jews anyway, however, it could hardly have worsened the Jews' situation. Certainly its moral and symbolic importance as an assertion of life cannot be underestimated.

Resistance within Germany

Examples of resistance within Germany are few although so-called Aryan Germans were certainly in the strongest position to oppose the Nazi regime. The early years of Hitler's rule had paralyzed organizations that might have been the focal point for resistance activities. Members of the Communist Party, for example, had been dispersed, although they managed to retain some links to one another and preserve some pockets of resistance. The time to oppose Nazism had been in the first phases of its rule in Germany. By 1942 and 1943 the stakes were much higher. Only in 1944, once Germany was clearly losing the war, would more opponents of the regime be emboldened to acts of resistance.

Still there were some important incidents earlier on. In the winter of 1942 a handful of Catholic students at the University of Munich formed an organization they called the White Rose. The key figures were a brother and sister, Hans and Sophie Scholl. Both had been enthusiastic Nazis as children, but as students they broke from those ideas. Hans's tour of duty as a medical orderly on the eastern front gave him firsthand exposure to the horrors of Nazi German warfare.

Under the name "the White Rose," the Scholls and their associates printed a series of leaflets decrying the crimes of Nazism. The last issue, in February 1943, was called "The Spirit Lives!" In it they protested the moral destruction of German youth. Nazism, they wrote, had turned German young people into godless, shameless, unscrupulous murderers.

Police caught Hans and Sophie Scholl along with three of their friends, including one professor. They were interrogated and tried for spreading malicious and defeatist rumors against the state. Sophie, a twenty-two-year-old philosophy student at the time, addressed the court as guards led her away: "What we have written is in all your minds, but you lack the courage to say it aloud."

Hans and Sophie Scholl were executed in February 1943. Their university remained silent; there was neither protest nor any show of solidarity from administrators, faculty, or students on behalf of the members of their community. After the war the University of Munich named its main quadrangle after the Scholl siblings.

Obstacles to Resistance

There were enormous barriers to resistance, especially for members of groups targeted for persecution and death, in German-controlled Europe. One of the most significant was the Nazi policy of exacting reprisals. As we have seen, the Germans made entire communities suffer for acts of resistance on a scale massively out of proportion to the supposed offense.

In June 1942 members of the Czech underground, with support from the British Special Operations Executive, assassinated Reinhard Heydrich. The Germans responded with total destruction of the town of Lidice, near Prague. They murdered all 199 men there as well as many of the women and children. Those remaining were removed for Germanization.

In 1943 a group of Jewish fighters from Vilna escaped from the ghetto to join partisans in the forest. Somehow they got their hands on a few weapons and attacked some Germans outside the city. In retaliation, the Gestapo seized the entire family of each Jewish fugitive or everyone who lived with him or her. They also arrested the leaders of all of the Jewish work parties in the vicinity, together with their families. All of those people were shot.

The policy of reprisals was a major deterrent. It probably explains why revolts in the Jewish ghettos often occurred only after the rebels were certain that death was planned for them and those close to them anyway.

Divisions within communities could present another obstacle to resistance. What would be the prospects? What were the best tactics? Were some would-be heroes risking increased horror for other people?

After years of war and occupation few people had the prerequisites for resistance. Overwhelmed by events, isolated, exhausted, and hungry, they could not hope for much success when it came to stopping Nazi Germany. Given those conditions we should perhaps be surprised at how much rather than how little resistance there was in German-occupied Europe.

The topic of resistance easily lends itself to manipulation and stereotypes. For decades the insistence of the postwar French governments that they were the heirs of the heroic French resistance made it impossible to face the realities of French collaboration. Old stereotypes of Jewish passivity in turn blinded many scholars and other observers to the abundant evidence of Jewish resistance.

It is tempting to offer resistance as a sort of antidote to the depressing subject of World War II and the Holocaust, but some caution is in order. For one thing, a focus on heroism—those "lights in the darkness" who dared to defy the Nazi juggernaut—can serve both to encourage us with the possibilities for resistance and to remind us of just how many people participated in the crimes of the Third Reich or stood by silently.

It is also important to keep in mind that resistance arguably did not change the course of the war. It was military might that defeated Nazi Germany; with very few exceptions it was the Red Army and the western Allies that liberated occupied territories from German control.

Nevertheless resistance had a crucial impact. To other conquered peoples it sent a message that they were not alone and that the Germans were not invincible. Resistance also left a positive legacy for a postwar world in which so many people had been compromised by collaboration and opportunism or paralyzed by death and misery.

A CASE STUDY: THADDEUS STABHOLZ

Thaddeus Stabholz experienced many of the events that have been addressed in this chapter. "Teddy" Stabholz grew up in a middle-class, assimilated Jewish family in Poland. He was a young medical student in Warsaw when World War II began. Months after the Germans defeated Poland, they forced Teddy, his father, his grandmother, and the rest of his relatives to move into the Warsaw ghetto. Teddy's mother had died in 1938 of cancer; in 1941 his father was killed by the Germans.

Teddy was left alone "like a homeless dog," he wrote later. With his fiancée, Fredzia, he survived as best he could on the food they could scrounge. Teddy cared for his grandmother too, until January 1943, when Germans beat her to death in the street. By that time, many of the Jews—especially the old, very young, and sick—had already been taken out of the ghetto and sent to the gas chambers at the killing center of Treblinka.

In early 1943 some of the young Jews left in the Warsaw ghetto organized an uprising against the Germans. Teddy and Fredzia were among them. They fought desperately with whatever weapons they had, but they were no match for the SS firepower. The Germans burned the ghetto, killed most of the peo-

*Dr. Bigula Vajs, a Jewish member of the resistance, attending
to a sick child in Yugoslavia during the war.*

ple in it, and sent the remaining few to Treblinka. There Fredzia was murdered, but Teddy, for some reason, was sent on to Majdanek, a labor camp as well as a killing center. He remained a prisoner of the Germans in various camps for two more years.

Through extraordinary luck—if one can speak of good fortune in the context of genocide—Teddy Stabholz survived. Guards selected him to be killed at Majdanek but at the last minute pulled him out of the group and made him a medic. At Auschwitz-Birkenau he was starved, beaten, and forced to carry enormous loads of water and cement for miles. He almost died of pneumonia. For a time he even had a "job" delousing the body hair of fellow prisoners with Zyklon B, the same insecticide used in the gas chambers. Stabholz managed to win the favor of some senior prisoners and guards by "operating" on the corns and calluses on their feet. In the summer of 1944, he witnessed the murder of all of the Gypsies in Auschwitz.

Stabholz endured excruciating work, plagues of typhus and lice, and transfers to camps farther from the front lines. At one point he resigned himself to death, but a vision of his father and mother encouraged him and revived his will to live.

In April 1945 American troops fighting their way through southern Germany found Stabholz and some fellow prisoners who had escaped from the SS and hidden in the woods. After spending time in a displaced persons camp in Germany, Teddy came to the United States. He graduated from medical school and started a practice in Ohio. Dr. Stabholz's memoir of the Holocaust is called *Seven Hells*.

8

DEATH THROES AND KILLING
FRENZIES, 1944–1945

I f the Germans were to lose the war, Hitler once said, they would bring down with them "a world in flames." Hitler kept that promise. The last stage of the war in Europe, from 1944 until May 1945, brought German retreat, defeat, and collapse, but the Nazi Empire remained bloody and destructive until its very end.

At the beginning of 1944, many Germans still expected to win the war. By the end of the year, few persisted in that hope. Germany was under assault—from the air, from the Red Army in the east, and after D-Day in June, from the Allies in the west. Even internally there were some signs of weakening, but it still took until May 1945 for total collapse.

The death throes of the Third Reich were deadly themselves—far less for the privileged elite of the regime than for its victims. Even as defeat became ever more certain, killing went on in many settings. The Allies, both eastern and western, had to fight hard and suffer many casualties to advance. When a plot to assassinate Hitler and stage a coup failed in July 1944, the Nazi regime responded with a vicious crackdown on its own population.

Well into 1945, Nazi programs of mass murder continued in the ever-shrinking territories that Germany controlled. Most of the Gypsies in Auschwitz were gassed in 1944. The murder of almost four hundred thousand Hungarian Jews took place that summer too. Throughout the last year of the war, the Germans kept opening new labor camps. As they abandoned killing centers and camps in areas lost to Allied advances, guards sent the inmates still left alive on murderous treks known as death marches.

None of that killing halted the disintegration of German power, but it ensured that the defeat of Nazism was accompanied by the maximum amount of carnage. This chapter will survey developments in the last stage of the war. How did the Nazi Reich, the Holocaust, and the war in Europe end?

ATTACKS ON THE NAZI REGIME

The Soviet Advance

From late 1943, the Soviets remained on the offensive against Germany. The Red Army made rapid advances in 1944. On the third anniversary of Operation Barbarossa—in June 1944—the Soviets launched a massive offensive against the German Army Group Center.

By the end of 1944, odds on Germany's eastern front were heavily in favor of the Soviets. Against the total German strength of between 2 and 3.5 million men loomed 6 million Red Army soldiers. A German disadvantage of one German to every five Soviets was common; in some places the odds were closer to one to thirty or forty.

Still the Soviets fought at a tremendous cost. Even at the end of 1944, the Germans were still killing or wounding four Soviets for every casualty of their own. The huge Soviet advantage in replacements—and the need to send in wave after wave of those troops—itself implied the staggering death toll that the fighting took on the Red Army.

Allied Bombing and Conditions in Germany

Air raids on Germany by the Royal Air Force and the U.S. air force peaked between January 1944 and January 1945. In the words of U.S. President Franklin Roosevelt, "Fortress Europe" had no roof. American planes alone made some 755,000 sorties that year and dropped 1.4 million tons of bombs on Germany and German-controlled territories. Much of that aerial bombing was inaccurate, so that planes often dropped their loads indiscriminately in and around major German cities. Allied bombing may have killed as many as five hundred thousand German civilians.

Attacks from the air hit the petroleum and chemical industries hard. By September the Germans could supply only 10 percent of their needs in aviation fuel. By early 1945, the flow of fuel and ammunition to the German fronts had almost stopped.

Nevertheless the German war machine demonstrated remarkable resilience to the assault from the air. Electric power stations continued to function, and German war production rallied during the last stage of the war. Manufacturing of fighter planes reached its wartime peak in September 1944. In December of that year German factories set new records for production of tanks and assault guns. German total military output in 1944 was more than five times the country's 1939 level.

Such achievements were largely the organizational work of Albert Speer (1905–1981), Hitler's minister of armaments and war production from 1942. A trained architect and a friend and confidante of Hitler, Speer also indulged the führer's passion for designing giant buildings for the Nazi world of the future. The Allies captured Speer at the end of the war and brought him to trial for his role in German crimes against foreign labor. He served twenty years in prison. Speer published memoirs and a diary. Unlike almost all of his Nazi counterparts, it appears that by the end of his life Speer was repentant toward the victims of the Third Reich and regretted his role in German crimes.

The real key to German wartime production was the massive use of slave labor. In 1939 there were about three hundred thousand forced laborers in Germany. By 1944 that number had skyrocketed to 7.5 million. It was above all these non-Germans—from Russia, Ukraine, Belorussia, Poland, France, the Netherlands, Italy, Hungary, and elsewhere—who bore the tremendously high human cost involved in outfitting the German war machine.

The impact of the attack from the air on the morale of German civilians is hard to gauge. Certainly air raids alone did not destroy German support of Hitler's regime, although it is possible that the destruction of German cities made it easier for Germans to recognize defeat and surrender at the end of the war. Much easier to measure was the physical impact of the bombing. Allied raids destroyed between 4.5 and 5 million habitations, so that Germans experienced an incredible shortage of housing in the last stages of the war. Production of consumer goods fell dramatically at the same time.

By 1944 the German economy was in serious trouble. Hitler's insistence on protecting the homefront from the costs of war meant deficit financing on a huge scale. The idea, of course, was that the vanquished would pay for the war. As long as the Germans were victorious they supported themselves through theft and plunder. Once the tide of the war turned, however, they were left with the hollowness of their own economy. Printing large amounts of money sparked inflation. Rapidly rising prices, in conjunction with stringent wage and price controls, led—as that particular combination always does—to the emergence of an active black market. In the German case, even before the war was over cigarettes began to overtake the official currency as the preferred medium of exchange.

D-Day—Allied Invasion from the West

On 6 June 1944, in a massive action with the code name Operation Overlord, the western Allies landed in Normandy in northwestern France. D-Day, as it became known, was the greatest amphibious assault ever. The numbers alone are staggering. More than 4,000 Allied ships landed 176,000 troops after 10,000 aircraft dropped 10,000 tons of explosives on the German defenders of the French coast.

By the end of July, after hard fighting and heavy casualties, Allied forces broke out of the beachheads and began to drive the Germans eastward. In August 1944 the Allies liberated Paris. The next month the western Allies under General Dwight Eisenhower crossed the German border. Germany's new "wonder weapons"—the V-1 and V-2 rockets—were deadly enough for those targeted, but they were no match for the onslaught of Soviet, British, and American artillery and tanks during 1944.

In the wake of D-Day and the Soviet offensive of June 1944, Hitler named Goebbels the Reich plenipotentiary for total war. Together the führer and his loyal associate painted a gruesome picture for the Germans of what lay in store if they were defeated. Germans could expect only the harshest of treatment from the vengeful Allies, they warned. Their scare tactics assumed widespread knowledge of the atrocities that Germans had committed throughout the preceding years, especially in the east. It was as if Hitler and Goebbels were taunting the German public with its complicity—we Germans are all in this together, they insisted, and all of us will have to pay the price if we surrender.

Meanwhile Hitler and Goebbels instructed the German press to keep blaming the Jews for the war. U.S. President Roosevelt held out to Europeans the promise of the four freedoms: freedom of speech, freedom of worship, freedom from want, and freedom from fear. Hitler, for his part, threatened the German public with his own version of what Allied victory would mean: "Jewish poison, Bolshevik slaughter, capitalist exploitation, and Anglo-American Imperialism."

It was not love for his people that motivated Hitler's raving but an obsessive fixation on his own goals of race and space. "I will shed no tears for the German people," he had once said in contemplating what defeat would mean. According to Hitler's logic, any people that allowed itself to be conquered proved its own unworthiness to wear the mantle of the master race.

Marion Kaufmann (center), a Jewish girl from Berlin, with the Gypsy family that hid her for a month in the Netherlands in late 1944, after the area had been liberated by the Canadians only to be reoccupied by the Germans. Marion had fled Germany with her mother in 1942. They were separated, and Marion spent the war in a series of hiding places. She and her mother were reunited in 1945.

The Plot of 20 July 1944

Not internal dissension but military defeat eventually brought down the Nazi regime. Nevertheless there was one important attack from within Germany during the last year of the war: the plot of 20 July 1944.

The plot was the work of a fairly disparate network of opponents of Hitler's regime. The conspirators included high-ranking military men who resented the way Hitler was conducting the war effort. Some of them hoped to overthrow his government and then join up with the western Allies against the Communist Soviet Union. Others more loosely involved in the plan had moral and humanitarian motivations. Appalled by German crimes against civilians in the east, such people saw no option but overthrow of the dictator if Germany's soul was to be saved.

Typical of the humanistic side of the opposition to Hitler was Count Helmuth James von Moltke (1907–1945), a lawyer and devoted Christian who, from 1939 to 1944, was a war administration counselor in the international law section of the German Armed Forces Supreme Command. Moltke organized a group of anti-Nazi friends and likeminded individuals who met during the war to make plans for a new, democratic Germany. Moltke, who struggled with issues of violence, did not support assassination, but he did urge military leaders to overthrow Hitler. Arrested already in January 1944, Moltke was hanged in Berlin-Plötzensee a year later.

Anti-Communists, conservatives, liberals, monarchists, and dedicated Christians all numbered among those who hoped to see Hitler assassinated or at least removed in July 1944. Although their visions for a reorganized Germany differed, they all saw the need to replace Hitler's rule with a government that would seek peace with the Allies and introduce reforms at home.

The plan for 20 July 1944 itself was straightforward. A high-ranking General Staff officer named Colonel Claus Schenck von Stauffenberg (1907–1944) would plant a bomb at a meeting in the "Wolf's Lair," Hitler's East Prussian headquarters. The death of Hitler would then give the signal for a coup d'état in Berlin.

The plan failed. Stauffenberg set the bomb in his briefcase, placed it under the table around which the meeting was taking place, and then left the building. As he drove toward Berlin he heard the explosion and assumed Hitler had been killed. In fact only part of the explosives went off, and Hitler was barely injured. Instead of a successful coup the conspirators experienced the führer's terrible revenge.

Stauffenberg was captured and shot by firing squad on the evening of 20 July 1944. He went to his death shouting, "Long live Germany!" Others accused of participation in the plot were hauled before the so-called People's Court, publicly humiliated, and sent to prison. Hitler had many of them killed, some immediately, others only after some months. The assassination attempt provided an excuse for a general crackdown within Germany on anyone suspected of opposition.

A WORLD IN FLAMES

The Volkssturm

In September 1944, Hitler ordered full deployment of Germany's resources against the enemy through creation of a Volkssturm—a "people's storm." The Volkssturm was to mobilize all men between the ages of fifteen and sixty, adding a total of 1.5 million men under arms. Not just intended for local defense, Volkssturm units were to close gaps in the regular Wehrmacht and engage the enemy in combat.

Some of the Volkssturm boys and men fought valiantly and desperately against the Red Army and the western Allies. Some Volkssturm units were well organized and fairly well equipped. Others were thrown together; thirteen-year-old boys stood on bridges expecting to take on men in tanks, and men in their sixties took up arms to try to hold their villages. Some units took appalling losses of life; others collapsed in the face of the Allied advance.

By early 1945 even Nazi true believers had to see that the war was lost. The German army was falling apart. Increasing numbers of men deserted, although military authorities continued to shoot those they caught and in many cases to arrest members of their families. Special courts-martial were set up with the intent of frightening the German troops into reckless resistance. Propaganda announced the existence of the Werewolf organization to continue Nazi efforts behind enemy lines. None of these measures slowed the Allied advance, but they did reveal for anyone who had not yet noticed the heartless ruthlessness of National Socialism.

On 19 March 1945, Hitler gave what became known as the Nero Order. He instructed Germans fleeing before the advancing Allies to destroy everything they left behind and leave nothing for the enemy. The Nero Order called for the destruction of all installations serving military purposes, transportation, communication, industry, and supply. At the same time Hitler ordered the defense of German cities under threat of the death penalty for anyone disobeying his orders. When Speer suggested that the Germans too would starve if such measures were implemented, Hitler showed no concern.

The Warsaw Uprising

The unraveling of German power emboldened the regime's opponents in occupied Europe. Once again, as in 1943, the city of Warsaw was the site of a major revolt. By August 1944 the Red Army was approaching Warsaw from the east. Leaders of the Polish Home Army decided to try to liberate the city from the Germans themselves. The Home Army was the non-Communist wing of the Polish resistance linked to traditional Polish nationalists and the Polish government-in-exile. Drawing on an armed force of about twenty-five thousand people, Home Army leaders launched a large-scale uprising.

Instead of continuing their advance into Warsaw, Red Army units stopped on the east bank of the Vistula River and waited. Perhaps they did not want to risk confrontation with the Germans massing on Warsaw, or perhaps Stalin preferred to let German forces wipe out the anti-Communist elements inside the city to clear the way for his own takeover. Whatever the reason, the Soviets abandoned the Polish insurgents.

German forces outnumbered and vastly outgunned the struggling Poles. Throwing everything they had into the effort, the Germans crushed the revolt by 2 October 1944. In the process they killed some 170,000 people in Warsaw.

By the fall of 1944 the Germans' overall position was weak. Nevertheless they still had the might to wreak terrible destruction, especially on civilians. Soon after the Warsaw Uprising began, Hitler ordered the city leveled. German forces carried out the command. Unlike Moscow and Leningrad, which the Germans never conquered, or Paris, which they spared, Warsaw was flattened. It was an act of revenge unique even in the gory history of World War II, but typical of the killing frenzies of the last stage of Hitler's war.

Germany's Allies and the Jews of Hungary

The year 1944 also brought dramatic changes within those countries that had been partners in the German war effort. In mid-August Finland signed an armistice with the Soviet Union and withdrew from the war.

German leaders had never succeeded in convincing Finnish authorities to hand over the small community of Jews in their country. There had even been a few Finnish Jewish soldiers fighting alongside the Wehrmacht against the Soviet Union. The history of World War II and the Holocaust is full of such strange twists.

For some time already the authoritarian regimes in Romania and Hungary had been eager to get out of the war. By August 1944 the Red Army blocked German access to Romania, making it impossible for the Germans to get their hands on Romanian oil. By the fall of 1944 the Soviets occupied Romania and Bulgaria and were moving toward Hungary and Yugoslavia. Both Romania and Bulgaria signed armistices with the Soviet Union and declared war on Germany.

In March 1944 the Germans took steps to prevent Hungary from capitulating. That month German forces occupied Hungary, their ally, to keep control of the territory and safeguard access to its resources. In October 1944, when the Hungarian leader Admiral Miklos Horthy was caught trying to cut a deal with the Soviets, Hitler had him overthrown. The Germans installed a Hungarian Fascist regime dependent on their support.

Until the spring of 1944 the Jews of Hungary had managed to stay out of German hands. In March 1944, however, when German forces moved into Hungary, they brought with them experts like Adolf Eichmann who were intent on making sure that Hungarian Jews too would be annihilated.

In the summer of 1944, Germans and Hungarian collaborators worked together to deport a large proportion of Hungary's Jewish population to Auschwitz-Birkenau. In hindsight it is clear that the war was lost for the Germans. Nevertheless, they continued to pursue their goal of racial purification in those areas still in their control. Between 15 May and 9 July 1944, German and Hungarian police crammed some 437,000 Hungarian Jews into 147 transports and sent them north to Auschwitz. As usual, Roma from Hungary shared that fate.

One of those Gypsies was fifteen-year-old Karoly Lendvai, who came from a town near Budapest. Rounded up by Hungarian police, he and his family walked forty miles to an internment camp, where they stayed for two weeks. Decades later Lendvai remembers his hunger and the pits overflowing with corpses as typhus raged among the prisoners. Among his most vivid memories is the double-barreled curse a Hungarian guard shouted at him: "Rot, you Jew-Gypsy!"

Because of Germany's acute shortage of labor, German officials decided to postpone the killing of some of the Hungarian Jews until they had been exploited as slave workers. In 1944 Hitler allowed Himmler and Speer to bring some Jews into Germany to add to the labor force needed for military production. Under those terms, about one hundred thousand Hungarian Jews slated for killing were brought to German labor camps. There they were used to excavate underground bunkers and make armaments. Conditions were terrible, but they had at least a chance to live, something denied to their more than three hundred thousand relatives and friends sent directly to the gas at Auschwitz.

Why did the Germans persist in the slaughter of the Hungarian Jews? Some scholars have suggested that such determination even in the face of impending defeat showed just how deeply committed many Germans were to the project of annihilating the Jews. Many German functionaries, however, showed similar dedication in the last stages of the war in their efforts against other victim groups, for example, Polish gentiles, Slavic slave laborers, Soviet POWs, and homosexual men.

At least some of these last-minute brutalities were motivated by the common drive of self-preservation. By 1944 and 1945 the prospect of the front looked worse all the time. Many German guards, police, and officials of various kinds who were involved in attacks on civilians worked feverishly to prove how crucial their jobs were—jobs they could do in relative safety. Even in Nazi Germany, cowards were probably more common than fanatics.

Some Hungarian Jews survived within Hungary, thanks to rescue efforts on the part of many people, including foreign diplomats and international Jewish groups. The most famous rescuer in Hungary was Rauol Wallenberg. Wallenberg was a Swedish businessman and diplomat who rescued as many as one hundred thousand Hungarian Jews from deportation. Using money raised largely from the Jewish community in the United States, Wallenberg set up safe houses under the jurisdiction of the Swedish embassy, issued Swedish passports, bribed German and Hungarian officials, and even rescued some Jews from transports slated for Auschwitz.

At the end of the war Wallenberg wound up in Soviet hands. His fate is unknown, but it seems likely that he was sent to Siberia as a suspected spy and perished there.

Elie Wiesel is no doubt the best-known Jewish survivor from Hungary. His book *Night* is probably the single most widely read personal account of the Holocaust. It recounts the experiences of Wiesel, at the time an adolescent boy, in the hell of Auschwitz in the deadly last months of the war.

Another Hungarian survivor is Judith Magyar Isaacson, who recorded her experiences in *Seed of Sarah*. Like Wiesel just a teenager in 1944, Judith Magyar landed in Auschwitz with her mother and a young aunt. Somehow the three women managed to stay together. Once, Judith faced down an SS man who tried to send her to one side of a selection, her mother to another. He let her go with her mother. Camp functionaries offered Judith a position as kapo, but she refused.

Judith, her mother, and her aunt were among the Hungarian Jews taken out of Auschwitz and sent as slave laborers to Germany. Beaten, half-starved, and terrified of rape, Judith lived through the final stages of the war. Later she married an American soldier and moved to Maine, where she taught mathematics and served as dean of students at Bates College until she retired.

Auschwitz at the End of the War

The killing center of Auschwitz reached new records of destruction in the final phase of the war. In the summer of 1944, as the transports from Hungary poured in, camp functionaries murdered as many as twelve thousand Jews per day.

There was one large operation against Gypsies that summer too, in which the entire Gypsy "family camp" was wiped out in one night. Of the twenty-three thousand Gypsies sent to Auschwitz, almost twenty thousand died there. By 2 August 1944 more than thirteen thousand were already dead. That night on orders from Berlin, the remaining six thousand Roma in the camp were gassed. Camp leaders had decided they needed space for the incoming Hungarian Jews. German military setbacks, however severe, did not save the lives of those thousands of Gypsies any more than they spared the Jews of Hungary.

The last year of the war also saw several important incidents of armed resistance within German camps and killing centers. In mid-May 1944, when SS and camp workers first tried to liquidate the Gypsy camp at Auschwitz-Birkenau, they encountered violent resistance. Roma inside the camp improvised weapons as best they could or fought with their bare hands. That defiance may have helped postpone killing of all the Gypsies in Auschwitz until early August 1944.

The most dramatic example of resistance within Auschwitz came in October 1944. Jewish Sonderkommando prisoners blew up and destroyed Crematorium IV. Some of the necessary explosives were provided by a young Polish Jewish woman named Roza Robota. Assigned to work in an ammunition factory, Robota, along with some other women, began to smuggle small amounts of explosives to the Sonderkommando. The SS arrested and tortured her, but she refused to divulge any information. Robota was hanged in January 1945, shortly before the arrival of the Red Army.

THE DEATH MARCHES

Beginning in the fall of 1944, as the Germans lost control of much of the territory they had occupied, they began to evacuate many of the camps and killing centers. At the same time, they opened new labor camps in areas still safe from Allied advance. On orders from Himmler, camp officials began to empty the camps of prisoners. They sent the inmates, under guard, marching in columns toward places farther from the ever-advancing front. Throughout late 1944 and early 1945, these trails of half-dead prisoners made their way through the

Polish, German, and Czech countrysides. Because of the awful numbers killed and dying along the way, these treks have come to be known as death marches.

A few examples give some idea of this new form of torture and killing. In the late fall of 1944, Germans sent about a thousand Jewish women, many of them Hungarian, from Auschwitz to Gross-Rosen. There the women were forced to dig antitank ditches, in the snow, with little or nothing to eat, and often without shoes.

In early January 1945, as the front advanced, that camp too was evacuated. Guards forced the remaining 970 women to begin a new march. In eight or nine days they had covered only about sixty miles. One hundred and fifty of the women died along the way. Perhaps 20 succumbed to starvation; guards shot another 130.

They were soon evacuated again from their next destination, with about a thousand additional prisoners. The group was divided into two, with half of the women being marched toward Helmbrechts in Bavaria, a satellite of Flossenbürg. In the middle of winter the women walked about three hundred miles. After five weeks, 621 of them arrived at the camp. A few hundred and around 230 had remained at various camps along the way. Between 200 and 250 of the prisoners did not survive that march. Many were shot by guards.

The camp at Helmbrechts was quite new. Established in the summer of 1944, it housed women prisoners set to work for an armaments firm. As always, they suffered brutal beatings and deadly privation.

In April 1945 Helmbrechts too was emptied. German guards forced some eleven hundred women on yet another death march to nowhere. The group was about half Jewish and half gentile. Guards refused food and water and forbade inhabitants of the surrounding area to help the prisoners. By many accounts Jewish women received even worse treatment than the others. Another 175 to 275 of the Jewish women died during this stage of the march, just weeks before the war ended. Every one of them would have died had they not been rescued by American forces.

On 15 April 1945, the same day that British troops reached the concentration camp of Bergen-Belsen, SS and camp guards forced seventeen thousand women and forty thousand men to march westward from the concentration camps of Ravensbrück and Sachsenhausen into territories still in German hands. Hundreds of women died of exhaustion on the march from Ravensbrück. Retreating guards and SS men shot hundreds of others. Some were killed by Allied bombs. Having made it so long, thousands died by the roadside just days away from the end of the war. Death marches continued right up until German surrender on 8 May 1945. In all, an estimated 250,000 to 375,000 people died in such forced marches.

FINAL COLLAPSE

On the military front too, Hitler's Germans exacted a high price from their enemies. At the end of December, Hungary finally completed the reversal of its allegiances. Declaration of war on Germany was followed a month later by an armistice with Moscow.

The Germans came back with a final onslaught in the west. The Ardennes Offensive, called the Battle of the Bulge by the Allies, began in December 1944. That grandiose effort failed, but only after it had cost many lives on both sides.

By early March 1945 the German front in the west had collapsed. U.S. and British forces were advancing in the north, center, and south. German authorities responded by lowering the age for the draft to include boys born in 1929.

In the last months things unraveled quickly. March brought a partisan offensive by Tito's forces against German troops in Yugoslavia. By April the Red Army was in Vienna, and German forces in Italy capitulated at the end of that month. In early May, Czechs revolted against German occupation in Prague. In this climate, even the death of U.S. President Roosevelt on 12 April 1945 did not weaken the Allies' demand for Germany's unconditional surrender.

Finally, in the last stage of the war, many Germans came to feel something of the reality of the conflict their leadership had inflicted on Europe. More Germans died in bombings, expulsions, and the collapse of the military fronts in the last six months of war than in the previous four years together. Approximately 160,000 German soldiers died in 1940–1941. In 1944 that number increased almost fourfold to some 600,000. The all-or-nothing mentality of Hitler's Social Darwinism made all lives cheap, including those of the German people.

If you look at textbooks on Nazi Germany you will notice that many of them label the last days of the Third Reich the "Götterdämmerung," or "twilight of the gods." The reference is to the end of the ring cycle, a group of operas by Richard Wagner. Hitler loved those operas, and the massive, tragic cataclysm at the end fit his own obsession with heroic death. That morbid fascination came to the fore in the last months of Hitler's regime.

In his poem "The Wasteland" (1922), T. S. Eliot wrote the following lines: "This is the way the world ends, not with a bang but a whimper." Eliot's description could be applied to the Third Reich, which ended with both an explosion of death and destruction and a whimper of cowardice and defeat.

In a small way, Hitler reaped what he had sown with the principle of divide and conquer when it came to the behavior of his inner circle in the last days. Whimpering treachery turned out to be more characteristic of Hitler's henchmen than that iron loyalty they had loved to espouse. Everyone, it turns out, seemed to have a plan as to how to salvage the Reich—and of course, save his own neck. In February 1945, Goebbels suggested that Hitler should remain head of state but appoint a new chancellor and foreign minister. Goebbels's preferred candidate for the job: himself, obviously. In deference to Himmler's control of the SS empire, Goebbels proposed Himmler for minister of war.

Himmler himself had toyed for a long time already with the idea of a separate peace with Britain. He used his contacts to test the waters, but they were icy cold. Efforts on the part of Luftwaffe commander Göring and German foreign minister Ribbentrop to negotiate a separate peace with the western powers also failed.

Hitler was determined to continue the fight, but on 22 April 1945, two days after his birthday, he fell into depression. Hitler realized that the war was lost, and he knew he could not negotiate a peace himself. Göring, he decided, was the man for the job.

When Göring heard about Hitler's remarks he decided it meant he was to take over. Outraged by that presumption, Hitler denounced Göring as a traitor, dismissed him from his many posts, and had him arrested by the SS. Göring would eventually be captured and brought to trial at Nuremberg, where he committed suicide before his scheduled execution.

Just days after he dismissed Göring, Hitler got word of Himmler's treachery. Furious, he ordered the arrest of the SS leader as well, but Himmler slipped through his hands. Himmler too would manage to kill himself before the Allies could exact justice. In the last days of April, Hitler swung briefly from depression into a kind of manic activity. He ordered a massive counterattack to drive the Soviets back from Berlin. He announced that the western Allies would soon be at war with the Soviet Union and that Germany would be saved. Nothing came of any of these notions.

On 29 April 1945, holed up in his bunker in Berlin, Hitler dictated one final document: his last will and political testament. In it he admonished Germans "punctiliously to observe the racial laws" and to fight on against "the poisoner of all the nations of the world, international Jewry." True to form he blamed the entire course of the lost war on "international Jewry and its helpers." Consistent to the end, Hitler described annihilation of the Jews of Europe as his greatest achievement.

That same day Hitler married Eva Braun. On 30 April the "first soldier of the German Reich" deserted by committing suicide in his bunker. Dead beside him by their own hands were his new wife, the loyal Goebbels, and Goebbels's wife and six children. Hitler's war would end as it had started—with a lie. His chosen successor, Admiral Karl Dönitz, reported by radio to the nation that its führer had sustained "heroic death in battle." Two days later, the city of Berlin surrendered to the Soviets. Hitler's successors signed documents of unconditional surrender on 8 May 1945.

The reality of how Nazi rule ended sweeps away the myth of order that has grown up around Hitler's regime. There was neither order nor glory to his demise. No heroic struggle marked his death, only cowardice, the ruin of his own people, and lies.

The Nazi revolution had promised a new awakening. Instead it brought destruction and death far beyond the borders of Germany. Of the 55 million who died in what is often called "Hitler's war," some 4.3 million were Germans. Another million Germans were reported missing. An estimated 27 million Soviet citizens were dead, as well as millions of Poles, over a million and a half Yugoslavs, and scores of other people from all over Europe. Close to 6 million Jews were murdered, and Jewish civilization was almost eradicated from Europe. The list could go on and on, and the world continues to feel the effects of hatreds sown for the Nazi goals of racial purification and territorial expansion.

Conclusion

THE LEGACIES OF ATROCITY

This book ends in May 1945, but the legacies of Nazism, World War II, and the Holocaust extend much further. Perhaps one account can begin to illustrate some of the personal and political repercussions of the history described in the previous eight chapters. Like many stories that end in death, the details can only be pieced together in a fragmentary way, but they are nonetheless significant.

This account begins in the mid-1930s in the Soviet Union. Frightened by manifestations of antisemitism under Stalin, a young Russian Jew whom we will call N. decided to leave his home and move west. He settled in France, where he built a life for himself until the Germans invaded in 1940, and his existence again became precarious.

For a while N. succeeded in evading the Nazi dragnet, but sometime in 1942 or 1943 German or French police rounded him up, along with many other foreign Jews living in France, and sent him east to a Nazi camp. Against terrible odds, N. survived more than a year as a prisoner and slave of Nazi Germany. In mid-April 1945, when British troops arrived at the concentration camp Bergen-Belsen, N. was one of the inmates liberated.

Under the terms of an Allied agreement, N., a citizen of the Soviet Union, was turned over to Soviet authorities. Instead of relief from years of torment at Nazi German hands, he soon found himself again on a deportation transport, this time to Siberia. Suspicious of the loyalty of Soviet citizens who had spent years outside the country, Stalin had tens of thousands of people like N.—Jews, POWs, forced laborers—sent directly from their "liberation" to labor camps and prisons in remote regions, where they toiled in massive indus-trialization projects.

N. did not survive this second round of abuse. N.'s son, who lived through the war in France and later moved to New York, spent years trying to trace his father through the Red Cross and other international organizations. Decades after the war ended, he received the news he had long feared: his father had died in Siberia.

The fate of N. highlights several facts about the end of the Holocaust and World War II. The arrival of Allied forces and the collapse of Nazi Germany were not miracles that could undo or even stop the spirals of violence and misery unleashed by years of brutality. Although in hindsight it is easy to speak of liberation, for many individuals and groups of people, the end of the war meant continued and even new forms of misery. The defeat and total collapse of Hitler's Germany unleashed a movement of people within Europe, some of it voluntary, much of it coerced. Wartime atrocities created urgent demands for justice, even as the enormity of the crimes committed and the overwhelming death and destruction made any kind of restitution painfully inadequate and often impossible. Whether they had been victims, perpetrators, or bystanders in Nazi barbarity—and many Europeans had reason to count themselves in more than one of those categories—people faced the challenge of building lives for themselves and what was left of their families and communities with scarce resources and restricted freedom, and in a climate of distrust and grief.

As Allied troops moved into German-held territory in the last stages of the war, they encountered shocking scenes. The Soviets were the first to reach the major killing centers. Even they, many of whom had experienced and witnessed Nazi German brutality firsthand, were stunned by the horror of places like Auschwitz-Birkenau. Soldiers from the United States and Great Britain who fought their way into Germany from the west were even less prepared for what they found: mass graves, abandoned camps, boxcars full of corpses, and emaciated, dying prisoners.

On 15 April 1945, the first British tanks entered the concentration camp of Bergen-Belsen. Terrorized and enfeebled, inmates of the camp could not believe they were free. And in fact, freedom did not come easily. After initial contact, the British tanks moved on. For the next forty-eight hours, the camp was only nominally under British control. Hungarian soldiers whom the Germans had stationed there as guards remained in command. In two days they shot more than eighty Jews and non-Jews for such offenses as taking potato peels from the kitchen. Even after British troops entered Belsen in force, for more than two weeks three hundred inmates continued to die daily of typhus and starvation. Horror on the scale of the Holocaust did not simply disappear with the arrival of the Allied liberators.

The images captured on film by photographers and journalists who accompanied and followed Allied forces horrified people back home, just as the sights themselves stunned and sickened the soldiers who saw them first-hand. Decades later those images continue to haunt us and to shape the way we perceive and present atrocities in our own time. The questions they raise remain pressing even though they have almost become clichés: How could human beings do such things to other people? How can we go on living in a world where crimes and suffering of such magnitude are possible?

For those who survived, the end of World War II brought the realization of all that had been destroyed. Alone, without family or friends, often far from what had been their homes, many survivors, particularly Jews, had nowhere to go. Separated from their parents for years, some Jewish children no longer knew their birth names or even that they came from Jewish families. Many Jews had seen their gentile neighbors turn against them, denouncing them to Nazi officials and stealing their possessions. Could they now simply go back as if nothing had happened? In Poland, Ukraine, Hungary, and elsewhere, Jewish survivors who returned home to search for family members or reclaim their property were often met with violent hostility from the new "owners." Some Jews were attacked and beaten; some were killed.

Non-Jewish victims of Nazism faced their own problems as they discovered that true liberation was impossible in hostile surroundings. Gypsies who had managed to live through the Nazi assault were no more welcome in many places after May 1945 than they had been before or during the war. Few non-Gypsies realized or cared that Nazi Germany had singled out the Roma for particular abuse. Only decades after the war would Gypsies gradually begin to be acknowledged legally and unofficially as victims of Nazism. In some places—for example, in the western zones of occupied Germany—homosexual men were released from Nazi prisons and concentration camps only to be arrested again and incarcerated under old or new laws that criminalized homosexuality. Jehovah's Witnesses, thousands of whom endured imprisonment in Hitler's Germany, faced renewed persecution, especially under Communism, such as in the eastern zone of Germany, subsequently East Germany. Looking back at Nazism and the Holocaust, we often vow "never again," but for the Jews hounded out of Polish cities and towns by pogroms in 1945 and 1946, the Jehovah's Witnesses sitting in Communist jails in the 1950s, and the Gypsies crippled and left homeless by arson attacks in Romania in the 1990s, a more apt slogan might have been "Still?"

World War II sparked the movement of the largest number of people in the shortest period of time that the world had ever known. Refugees, fugitives, displaced persons, deportees, and expellees jammed the roadways and waterways of Europe and spilled over into Central Asia and the Americas. Hundreds of thousands of people, like the Russian Jew N., were transported eastward, against their will, as prisoners and laborers of the Soviet Union. More of the wave of motion, however, was westward. An estimated 10 million refugees poured into the western zones of occupied Germany alone, those parts controlled by the United States, Britain, and France.

The motivations of those fleeing west varied. Some had experienced Communism in Stalin's Soviet Union and would risk anything to avoid a return to that misery. Some were ethnic Germans whose families had lived in eastern Europe for generations. Nazi authorities had begun evacuating them already before the war ended, aware that they would be targets for revenge. Many ethnic Germans had eagerly served the cause of race and space and benefited from the deprivation and expropriation of their neighbors. In some cases, Soviet and local authorities expelled ethnic Germans, both to remove potential troublemakers and to free up space for resettlement programs of their own. Ethnic Germans were forced out of western Poland, for example, at least partly because the Soviets needed homes for Poles they had pushed out of the eastern parts of the country, territories annexed to the Soviet Union after 1945.

Other east Europeans, who like many ethnic Germans had collaborated with Nazism, also had reasons to flee west, now that their German protectors had retreated. Fearing the wrath of their neighbors, they sought security or at least anonymity. The Red Army's horrific record of rape and plunder as its troops penetrated deeper into central Europe added another urgent reason for many people to try to escape westward.

Throughout 1945 masses of weary travelers crisscrossed Europe— Hungarian Jews trying to go home; ethnic Germans from the Sudetenland making their way north and west; demobilized soldiers, prisoners of war, former slave laborers from Ukraine and Poland. Amid the chaos it is no surprise that war criminals and other fugitives often found it easy to blend in and evade detection. Under such conditions, whose documentation was in order anyway? Who would know if a former SS man or high-ranking Nazi Party boss, or even Heinrich Himmler himself, had simply buried or burned his papers, put on old clothing, and assumed a new identity? Paradoxically, the Nazis, with their obsession with race, blood, and homeland, had created a situation where all of those identities were in flux.

With the creation of the U.N. Relief and Rehabilitation Administration, the newly minted United Nations tried to address some of the most pressing humanitarian concerns stemming from the refugee crisis. U.S. occupation authorities set up camps for displaced persons (DPs) in their zone, which became the first destination of many Jewish survivors. Initially DPs were organized by country of origin, so that Jews, ethnic Germans, and non-German collaborators might find themselves grouped together as Ukrainians, Poles, or Yugoslavians. Subsequently the Americans set up separate facilities for Jews, who had different needs and options from most gentiles.

By late 1946 more than 150,000 Jews lived in DP camps in the U.S. zone, bringing a Jewish presence to parts of Germany that previously had been home to relatively few Jews. Jewish DP camps were sites of Zionist activity, as survivors, especially young people, were urged to leave Europe for Palestine and, after 1948, Israel. Many Jews preferred to wait for visas to the United States, Canada, or Australia, and some accepted options that were often quicker, such as relocation to South Africa, South America, or the Caribbean. An estimated twenty thousand Jews remained in Germany even after the last Jewish DP camp finally closed in 1957. Some of them were too old or sick to travel or be granted visas; some had ties to Germany.

Jewish DP camps were more than just holding places for people waiting to exit. They developed an internal leadership and communal spirit, with cultural and religious activities, educational opportunities, and social and family life. The immediate postwar years saw a baby boom as the birthrate among Jewish DPs rose to remarkable heights, especially in contrast to the unusually low rates for other people in Germany. Those Jewish children must have represented faith in new beginnings and hope for life after so much death.

Despite the urgent demands of daily existence, many people in postwar Europe concerned themselves with questions of justice. Perpetrators and organizers of Nazi crimes went to immense lengths to avoid being brought to account for their deeds. They set up self-help networks and used connections in Turkey, the Middle East, South America, Canada, and the Vatican to get themselves to safety. For example, Franz Stangl, former T-4 operative and subsequently commandant of Sobibor and Treblinka, fled via Turkey and the Middle East to Argentina, where Hitler's expert on Jews and transportation/deportation, Adolf Eichmann, also found refuge. Josef Mengele, the doctor and medical scholar whose vicious experiments at Auschwitz killed thousands of people, made his way to Brazil, where he died in the 1980s.

Of course those victimized by Nazism had very different interests in justice. No acts of revenge or restitution could make up for the deaths of millions, the annihilation of Jewish life in much of Europe, the destruction of property, and the shattering of trust and coexistence. Nevertheless survivors had to begin new lives, and for that they required at least minimal material resources, some acknowledgment of their suffering, and a measure of confidence in the world around them. Seeing some key criminals brought to justice could begin to address those needs as well as combat the sense of meaninglessness that must have threatened to overwhelm many survivors.

Already during the war Allied leaders had agreed that the defeated Germany must be denazified and top perpetrators brought to justice. Doing so was necessary for postwar stability, at least some of them believed, because it would make it possible to effect some kind of separation between "Nazis," who needed to be punished, and "Germans," who could and should be integrated into a peaceable world. The International Military Tribunal with the Nuremberg Trials of 1945–1946, a joint effort of all the Allies, served this purpose.

Contrary to what detractors claimed, the trial of twenty-one major war criminals and a handful of central Nazi German organizations at Nuremberg was not sham "victors' justice" or a reflection of some Allied notion of German "collective guilt." Although the trials were not perfect, and Allied cooperation was severely strained at times, they were real legal proceedings, with witnesses, massive amounts of documentation, and counsels for the defense—

Jewish displaced women pose with Red Army officers in the Zittau camp for German POWs in July 1945. During the war Zittau was one of the subcamps of the Nazis' Gross-Rosen concentration camp system.

and without torture. Some individuals and organizations were acquitted, and those convicted received varying sentences, including death sentences in about half of the cases. The most famous defendant, Hitler's favorite, Hermann Göring, committed suicide in his cell before the order for his execution could be carried out.

The Nuremberg Trials were just one step. The occupying powers, and subsequently local authorities, including Germans and foreign governments—like Israel with the Eichmann trial in 1961—conducted their own hearings, trials, and deportation proceedings of camp guards, doctors, bureaucrats, members of the Einsatzgruppen, and former SS men accused of lying on their immigration applications to the United States, Canada, and elsewhere. Property of all kinds—art, gold, land, buildings, factories—has been grounds for other kinds of legal cases, commissions, and occasionally settlements. These processes are all important, although they can never bring closure to a past that remains an open wound despite remarkable—perhaps unprecedented—efforts by Germans to come to grips with their nation's cruel past.

This history has no happy ending, no uplifting message of redemption. It leaves us only with human beings, with their startling capacities for good and evil, and with an awareness of the complex ties that connect the fates of people and nations all over the world.

One final account may best express these points. This time the story begins in the Netherlands with the birth of a baby girl in 1943. When she was two weeks old, her Jewish parents and older brother were rounded up by German and Dutch police, sent to the transit camp of Westerbork, and from there to Sobibor, where they were murdered.

Somehow the baby escaped that fate. Perhaps her parents hid her or a sympathetic policeman took pity on her. Either way, someone brought her to a beauty parlor run by two young women with connections to the Dutch underground. They helped find hiding places for Jewish children, but this particular organization imposed an unusual requirement: potential rescuers had to promise to return the children to their families after the war.

The women found a family to take the baby, but the arrangement fell through, because the couple would not agree to surrender the girl when the war was over. So one of the beauticians took the child herself and cared for her until 1947, when an uncle from New York managed to locate his niece. In keeping with her promise, the Dutch woman gave the girl up. She never saw her again. Growing up in the United States, the girl remembered little from her early years. Meanwhile her Dutch foster mother suffered severe emotional problems and died quite young.

One could present this account as an inspirational example of heroism and miraculous luck, and those are indeed important messages to take away from a study of the Holocaust. At least as significant, however, are the crushing themes of loss and violence, and the unavoidable, heartbreaking decisions that no one should have to make, decisions the scholar Lawrence Langer has dubbed "choiceless choices." These are the realities of the Holocaust and its bitter legacy, a history specific and unique but at the same time firmly embedded in the all-too-familiar global experiences of war and genocide.

SOURCES AND SUGGESTIONS
FOR FURTHER READING

Note: Books are listed in the chapter(s) to which they most directly relate. Many of the titles given in one place are relevant to material elsewhere in the book too. To the extent possible, I have limited this list to materials available in English.

1. PRECONDITIONS: ANTISEMITISM, RACISM, AND COMMON PREJUDICES IN EARLY-TWENTIETH-CENTURY EUROPE

Bartlett, Roger, and Karen Schönwälder, eds. *The German Lands and Eastern Europe: Essays on the History of Their Social, Cultural and Political Relations.* New York: St. Martin's, 1999.

Bartov, Omer. *Mirrors of Destruction: War, Genocide, and Modern Identity.* New York: Oxford University Press, 2000.

Berenbaum, Michael. *A Mosaic of Victims.* New York: New York University Press, 1990.

Berenbaum, Michael, and Abraham J. Peck, eds. *The Holocaust and History: The Known, the Unknown, the Disputed, and the Reexamined.* Bloomington: Indiana University Press, 1998.

Botwinick, Rita Steinhardt. *A History of the Holocaust: From Ideology to Annihilation.* Upper Saddle River, N.J.: Prentice Hall, 1996.

Breitman, Richard. *The Architect of Genocide: Himmler and the Final Solution.* New York: Knopf, 1991.

Burleigh, Michael. *Death and Deliverance: "Euthanasia" in Germany c. 1900–1945.* New York: Cambridge University Press, 1997.

———. *The Third Reich: A New History.* New York: Hill and Wang, 2000.

Burleigh, Michael, and Wolfgang Wippermann. *The Racial State: Germany 1933–1945.* New York: Cambridge University Press, 1991.

Crowe, David, and John Kolsti, eds. *The Gypsies of Eastern Europe*. Armonk, N.Y.: Sharpe, 1991.

Evans, Richard J. *Rituals of Retribution: Capital Punishment in Germany 1600–1987*. Oxford: Oxford University Press, 1996.

Fout, John C. *Forbidden History: The State, Society, and the Regulation of Sexuality in Modern Europe*. Chicago: University of Chicago Press, 1992.

Friedlander, Henry. *The Origins of Nazi Genocide: From Euthanasia to the Final Solution*. Chapel Hill: University of North Carolina Press, 1995.

Gay, Peter. *My German Question: Growing Up in Nazi Berlin*. New Haven, Conn.: Yale University Press, 1998.

Gellately, Robert, and Nathan Stoltzfus, eds. *Social Outsiders in Nazi Germany*. Princeton, N.J.: Princeton University Press, 2001.

Gutman, Israel. *Encyclopedia of the Holocaust*. 3 vols. New York: Macmillan, 1990.

Hancock, Ian. "The Roots of Antigypsyism: To the Holocaust and After." In *Confronting the Holocaust: A Mandate for the 21st Century*, edited by C. Jan Colijn and Marcia Sachs Littell, 19–49. Studies in the Shoah 19. Lanham, Md.: University Press of America, 1997.

Hilberg, Raul. *The Destruction of the European Jews*. Rev. ed. 3 vols. New York: Holmes and Meier, 1985.

Hull, Isabel. "Military Culture and the Production of 'Final Solutions' in the Colonies: The Example of Wilhelminian Germany." In *Genocide in Historical Perspective*, edited by Robert Gellately. New York: Cambridge University Press, forthcoming.

Kenrick, Donald, and Grattan Puxon. *Gypsies under the Swastika*. Hatfield: University of Hertfordshire Press, 1995.

King, Christine Elizabeth. *The Nazi State and the New Religions: Five Cases in Non-Conformity*. New York: Edwin Mellen, 1982.

Langmuir, Gavin I. *History, Religion, and Antisemitism*. Berkeley: University of California Press, 1990.

Levy, Richard S., ed. *Antisemitism in the Modern World: An Anthology of Texts*. Lexington, Mass.: Heath, 1991.

Marks, Sally. "Black Watch on the Rhine: A Study in Propaganda, Prejudice, and Prurience." *European Studies Review* 13, no. 3 (1983): 297–334.

———. *The Illusion of Peace*. New York: St. Martin's, 1976.

Milton, Sybil. "The Context of the Holocaust." *German Studies Review* 13, no. 2 (1990): 269–83.

Mosse, George. *Fallen Soldiers: Reshaping the Memory of the World Wars*. New York: Oxford University Press, 1990.

———. *The Nationalization of the Masses*. New York: Howard Fertig, 1975.

Müller-Hill, Benno. *Murderous Science: Elimination by Scientific Selection of Jews, Gypsies and Others in Germany, 1933–1945*. Translated by George R. Fraser. Plainview, N.Y.: Cold Spring Harbor Laboratory Press, 1998.

Naimark, Norman. *Fires of Hatred: Ethnic Cleansing in Twentieth-Century Europe*. Cambridge, Mass.: Harvard University Press, 2001.

Poliakov, Léon. *Harvest of Hate: The Nazi Program for the Destruction of the Jews of Europe.* New York: Holocaust Library, 1979.

Pomerantz, Jack, and Lyric Wallwork Winik. *Run East: Flight from the Holocaust.* Urbana: University of Illinois Press, 1997.

Siegal, Aranka. *Upon the Head of the Goat: A Childhood in Hungary, 1939–1944.* New York: Puffin, 1981.

Stern, Fritz. *The Politics of Cultural Despair.* Berkeley: University of California Press, 1961.

Stopes, Marie Carmichael, and Ruth E. Hall, eds. *Dear Dr. Stopes: Sex in the 1920s.* London: Deutsch, 1978.

Weinberg, Gerhard L. *Germany, Hitler, and World War II: Essays in Modern German and World History.* New York: Cambridge University Press, 1995.

Weiss, John. *Ideology of Death: Why the Holocaust Happened in Germany.* Chicago: Ivan R. Dee, 1996.

2. LEADERSHIP AND WILL: ADOLF HITLER, THE NATIONAL SOCIALIST GERMAN WORKERS' PARTY, AND NAZI IDEOLOGY

Allen, William Sheridan. *The Nazi Seizure of Power.* Rev. ed. New York: Watts, 1984.

Bessel, Richard. *Germany after the First World War.* Oxford: Clarendon, 1993.

Bukey, Evan Burr. *Hitler's Hometown.* Bloomington: Indiana University Press, 1986.

Bullock, Alan. *Hitler: A Study in Tyranny.* Rev. ed. New York: Bantam, 1962.

Burrin, Philippe. *Hitler and the Jews: The Genesis of the Holocaust.* Translated by Patsy Southgate. London: Arnold; New York: Routledge, Chapman and Hall, 1994.

Childers, Thomas. *The Nazi Voter: The Social Foundations of Fascism in Germany, 1919–1933.* Chapel Hill: University of North Carolina Press, 1983.

Eubank, Keith, ed. *World War II: Roots and Causes.* 2nd ed. Lexington, Mass.: Heath, 1992.

Fischer, Conan. *Stormtroopers: A Social, Economic and Ideological Analysis 1925–35.* London: Allen and Unwin, 1983.

Fischer, Klaus P. *Nazi Germany: A New History.* London: Continuum, 1995.

Friedländer, Saul. *Nazi Germany and the Jews.* Vol. 1, *The Years of Persecution.* New York: HarperCollins, 1997.

Haffner, Sebastian. *The Meaning of Hitler.* Translated by Ewald Osers. Cambridge: Harvard University Press, 1983.

Hamann, Brigitte. *Hitler's Vienna.* Translated by Thomas Thornton. New York: Oxford University Press, 1999.

Hamilton, Richard F. *Who Voted for Hitler?* Princeton, N.J.: Princeton University Press, 1982.

Hitler's Table Talk, 1941–1944: His Private Conversations. 1953. 3rd ed. Translated by Norman Cameron and R. H. Stevens. Introduction by Hugh R. Trevor-Roper. New York: Enigma, 2000.

Jäckel, Eberhard. *Hitler's World View: A Blueprint for Power.* Cambridge: Harvard University Press, 1981.

Kater, Michael. *The Nazi Party: A Social Profile of Members and Leaders, 1919–1945.* Cambridge: Harvard University Press, 1983.

Kershaw, Ian. *Hitler.* Vol. 1, *1889–1936: Hubris.* New York: Norton, 1998.

———. Vol. 2, *1936–1945: Nemesis.* New York: Norton, 2000.

Lochner, Louis P., ed. *The Goebbels Diaries 1942–43.* Garden City, N.Y.: Doubleday, 1948. (More complete editions of the diaries are available in German. See, for example, *Die Tagebücher von Joseph Goebbels. Sämtliche Fragmente, Teil I, Aufzeichnungen 1924–1941,* edited by Elke Fröhlich. 4 vols. Munich, 1987.)

Marks, Sally. "The Myths of Reparations." *Central European History* 11, no. 3 (1978): 231–35.

Marrus, Michael. *The Holocaust in History.* New York: Meridian, 1989.

Orlow, Dietrich. *The History of the Nazi Party.* 2 vols. Pittsburgh: University of Pittsburgh Press, 1969–73.

Patch, William L., Jr. *Heinrich Brüning and the Dissolution of the Weimar Republic.* Cambridge: Cambridge University Press, 1998.

Pauley, Bruce F. *Hitler and the Forgotten Nazis: A History of Austrian National Socialism.* Chapel Hill: University of North Carolina Press, 1981.

Reck-Malleczewen, Fritz Percy. *Diary of a Man in Despair.* Translated by Paul Ruebens. New York: Macmillan, 1971.

Sax, Benjamin, and Dieter Koontz. *Inside Hitler's Germany.* Lexington, Mass.: Heath, 1992.

Turner, Henry Ashby, Jr. *Hitler's Thirty Days to Power: January 1933.* Reading, Mass.: Addison Wesley, 1996.

Weinberg, Gerhard L. *Germany, Hitler, and World War II: Essays in Modern German and World History.* New York: Cambridge University Press, 1995.

Wistrich, Robert S. *Hitler and the Holocaust.* New York: Modern Library, 2001.

3. FROM REVOLUTION TO ROUTINE: NAZI GERMANY, 1933–1938

Abel, Theodore. *Why Hitler Came into Power.* 1938. Reprint, Cambridge, Mass.: Harvard University Press, 1986.

Abrams, Alan. *Mischlinge: Special Treatment, the Untold Story of Hitler's Third Race.* Secaucus, N.J.: Lyle-Stuart, 1985.

Bankier, David. *The Germans and the Final Solution: Public Opinion under Nazism.* Cambridge, Mass.: Basil Blackwell, 1992.

Bergen, Doris L. *Twisted Cross: The German Christian Movement in the Third Reich.* Chapel Hill: University of North Carolina Press, 1996.

Engelmann, Bernd. *Inside Hitler's Germany.* Translated by Krishna Wilson. New York: Pantheon, 1985.

Friedländer, Saul. *Pius XII and the Third Reich: A Documentation.* New York: Knopf, 1960.

Fromm, Bella. *Blood and Banquets: A Social Diary.* New York: Harper and Brothers, 1942.

Giles, Geoffrey. "'The Most Unkindest Cut of All': Castration, Homosexuality, and Nazi Justice." *Journal of Contemporary History* 27, no. 1 (1992): 41–61.

Grossmann, Atina. *Reforming Sex: The German Movement for Birth Control and Abortion Reform 1920–1950.* New York: Oxford University Press, 1995.

Heck, Alfons. *A Child of Hitler.* Frederick, Colo.: Renaissance House, 1985.

Jaskot, Paul. *The Architecture of Oppression.* London: Routledge, 2000.

Johnson, Eric A. *Nazi Terror: The Gestapo, Jews, and Ordinary Germans.* New York: Basic, 2000.

Kaplan, Marion. *Between Dignity and Despair: Jewish Life in Nazi Germany.* New York: Oxford University Press, 1998.

Kershaw, Ian. *The "Hitler Myth": Image and Reality in the Third Reich.* Oxford: Clarendon, 1987.

———. *The Nazi Dictatorship: Problems and Perspectives of Interpretation.* London: Arnold, 1993.

Klemperer, Victor. *I Will Bear Witness: A Diary of the Nazi Years, 1933–1941.* Vol. 1. Translated by Martin Chalmers. New York: Random House, 1998.

Koehn, Ilse. *Mischling, Second Degree: My Childhood in Nazi Germany.* New York: Bantam, 1977.

Koonz, Claudia. *Mothers in the Fatherland: Women, the Family, and Nazi Politics.* New York: St. Martin's, 1987.

Koshar, Rudy. *Social Life, Local Politics, and Nazism: Marburg, 1880–1935.* Chapel Hill: University of North Carolina Press, 1986.

Lewy, Guenter. *The Nazi Persecution of the Gypsies.* New York: Oxford University Press, 2000.

Maschmann, Melitta. *Account Rendered.* Translated by Geoffrey Strachan. London: Abelard-Schuman, 1964.

Merkl, Peter. *Political Violence under the Swastika.* Princeton, N.J.: Princeton University Press, 1975.

Mommsen, Hans. *From Weimar to Auschwitz: Essays in German History.* Translated by Philip O'Connor. Cambridge, Mass.: Polity Press; Oxford: Basil Blackwell, 1991.

Opitz, May, Katharina Oguntoye, and Dagmar Schultz, eds. *Showing Our Colors: Afro-German Women Speak Out.* Translated by Anne V. Adams. Amherst: University of Massachusetts Press, 1992.

Owings, Alison. *Frauen: German Women Recall the Third Reich.* New Brunswick, N.J.: Rutgers University Press, 1993.

Petropolous, Jonathan. *Art as Politics in the Third Reich.* Chapel Hill: University of North Carolina Press, 1996.

Peukert, Detlev. *Inside Nazi Germany: Conformity, Opposition, and Racism in Everyday Life.* New Haven, Conn.: Yale University Press, 1987.

Plant, Richard. *The Pink Triangle.* New York: Henry Holt, 1986.

Steinweis, Alan. *Art, Ideology, and Economics in the Third Reich*. Chapel Hill: University of North Carolina Press, 1993.

Thimme, Annelise. "Geprägt von der Geschichte. Eine Aussenseiterin." In *Erinnerungsstücke: Wege in die Vergangenheit*. Edited by Hartmut Lehmann and Gerhard Oexle, 153–223. Vienna: Boehlau, 1997.

Welch, David A. *The Third Reich: Politics and Propaganda*. London: Routledge, 1993.

4. OPEN AGGRESSION:
IN SEARCH OF WAR, 1938–1939

Bridenthal, Renate, Atina Grossmann, and Marion Kaplan, eds. *When Biology Became Destiny: Women in Weimar and Nazi Germany*. New York: Monthly Review Press, 1984.

Bukey, Evan Burr. *Hitler's Austria*. Chapel Hill: University of North Carolina Press, 2000.

Conway, John S. *The Nazi Persecution of the Churches 1933–45*. London: Westfield and Nicolson, 1968.

Ericksen, Robert P., and Susannah Heschel, eds. *Betrayal: German Churches and the Holocaust*. Minneapolis, Minn.: Fortress, 1999.

Friedlander, Henry. *The Origins of Nazi Genocide: From Euthanasia to the Final Solution*. Chapel Hill: University of North Carolina Press, 1995.

Friedländer, Saul. *When Memory Comes*. New York: Farrar, Straus, and Giroux, 1979.

Gellately, Robert. *The Gestapo and German Society: Enforcing Racial Policy, 1933–1945*. New York: Oxford University Press, 1990.

Grau, Günter, ed. *Hidden Holocaust? Gay and Lesbian Persecution in Germany, 1933–1945*. Translated by Patrick Camiller. London: Cassell, 1995.

Hayes, Peter. *Industry and Ideology: IG Farben in the Nazi Era*. New York: Cambridge University Press, 2000.

Heilbronner, Oded. *Catholicism, Political Culture, and the Countryside: A Social History of the Nazi Party in South Germany*. Ann Arbor: University of Michigan Press, 1998.

Hesse, Hans, ed. *Persecution and Resistance of Jehovah's Witnesses during the Nazi-Regime, 1933–1945*. Bremen: Edition Temmen, 2001.

Jehovah's Witnesses Stand Firm against Nazi Assault. 1 hr. 45 min. Watchtower Society, 1995. Videocassette.

Klüger, Ruth. *Still Alive: A Holocaust Girlhood Remembered*. New York: Feminist Press, 2001.

Opfermann, Charlotte. *The Ides of November*. Unpublished manuscript, 1999.

Phayer, Michael. *The Catholic Church and the Holocaust*. Bloomington: Indiana University Press, 2000.

Quack, Sibylle, ed. *Between Sorrow and Strength: Women Refugees of the Nazi Period*. Washington, D.C.: German Historical Institute; New York: Cambridge University Press, 1995.

Rigg, Bryan Mark. *Hitler's Jewish Soldiers*. Lawrence: University Press of Kansas, 2002.

Sofsky, Wolfgang. *The Order of Terror: The Concentration Camp*. Translated by William Templer. Princeton, N.J.: Princeton University Press, 1997.

Steinhoff, Johannes, Peter Pechel, and Dennis Showalter, eds. *Voices from the Third Reich.* Washington, D.C.: Regnery Gateway, 1989.

Weinberg, Gerhard L. *Germany, Hitler, and World War II: Essays in Modern German and World History.* New York: Cambridge University Press, 1995.

5. EXPERIMENTS IN BRUTALITY, 1939–1940: WAR AGAINST POLAND AND THE SO-CALLED EUTHANASIA PROGRAM

Adelson, Alan, and Robert Lapides, eds. *Lodz Ghetto: Inside a Community under Siege.* New York: Viking, 1989.

Aly, Götz. *"Final Solution": Nazi Population Policy and the Murder of the European Jews.* Translated by Belinda Cooper and Allison Brown. London: Arnold, 1999.

Arad, Yitzhak. *Ghetto in Flames.* New York: Holocaust Library, 1982.

Arendt, Hannah. *Eichmann in Jerusalem.* New York: Viking, 1963.

Bartov, Omer. *Hitler's Army: Soldiers, Nazis, and War in the Third Reich.* New York: Oxford University Press, 1991.

Cornwell, John. *Hitler's Pope: The Secret History of Pius XII.* New York: Viking, 1999.

Dobroszycki, Lucien. *The Chronicle of the Lodz Ghetto, 1941–1944.* New Haven, Conn.: Yale University Press, 1984.

Gerlach, Christian. "Failure of Plans for an SS Extermination Camp in Mogilev, Belorussia." Translated by Deborah Cohen and Helmut Gerlach. *Holocaust and Genocide Studies* 11, no. 1 (1997): 60–78.

Gotfryd, Bernard. *Anton the Dove Fancier and Other Tales of the Holocaust.* New York: Washington Square Press, 1990.

Gross, Jan. *Neighbors: The Destruction of the Jewish Community in Jedwabne, Poland.* Princeton, N.J.: Princeton University Press, 2001.

Hilberg, Raul. *The Destruction of the European Jews.* Rev ed. 3 vols. New York: Holmes and Meier, 1985.

Hilberg, Raul, Stanislaw Staron, and Josef Kermisz, eds. *The Warsaw Diary of Adam Czerniaków: Prelude to Doom.* Translated by Stanislaw Staron and the staff of Yad Vashem. New York: Stein and Day, 1979.

Klein, Gerda Weissmann. *All But My Life.* New York: Hill and Wang, 1995.

Knappe, Siegfried, and Ted Brusaw. *Soldat: Reflections of a German Soldier, 1936–1949.* New York: Orion Books, 1992.

Kogon, Eugen, Hermann Langbein, and Adalbert Rückerl, eds. *Nazi Mass Murder: A Documentary History of the Use of Poison Gas.* Translated by Mary Scott and Caroline Lloyd-Morris. New Haven, Conn.: Yale University Press, 1993.

Lukas, Richard C. *Did the Children Cry? Hitler's War against Jewish and Polish Children.* New York: Hippocrene, 1995.

————. *Out of the Inferno: Poles Remember the Holocaust.* Lexington: University Press of Kentucky, 1989.

————. *The Forgotten Holocaust: The Poles under German Occupation, 1939–1944.* Rev. ed. New York: Hippocrene, 1997.

Noakes, Jeremy, and Geoffrey Pridham, eds. *Nazism 1919–1945: A Documentary Reader.* 4 vols. Exeter: University of Exeter Department of History and Archeology, 1983–1998.

Polonsky, Antony, ed. *"My Brother's Keeper?": Recent Polish Debates on the Holocaust.* London: Routledge, 1990.

Rossino, Alexander. "Destructive Impulses: German Soldiers and the Conquest of Poland." *Holocaust and Genocide Studies* 11, no. 3 (1997): 351–65.

Tec, Nechama. *Defiance: The Bielski Partisans.* New York: Oxford University Press, 1993.

Yahil, Leni. *The Holocaust: The Fate of European Jewry.* Translated by Ina Friedman and Haya Galai. New York: Oxford University Press, 1990.

6. EXPANSION AND SYSTEMATIZATION: EXPORTING WAR AND TERROR, 1940–1941

Bartoszewski, Wladyslaw. *The Warsaw Ghetto: A Christian's Testimony.* Translated by Stephen G. Cappellari. Boston: Beacon, 1987.

Bartov, Omer. *The Eastern Front, 1941–1945: German Troops and the Barbarisation of Warfare.* London: St. Martin's, 1985.

Borowski, Tadeusz. *This Way for the Gas Ladies and Gentlemen.* Translated by Barbara Vedder. New York: Penguin, 1976.

Breitman, Richard. *The Architect of Genocide: Himmler and the Final Solution.* New York: Knopf, 1991.

————. *Official Secrets: What the Nazis Planned and What the British and Americans Knew.* New York: Hill and Wang, 1998.

Browning, Christopher. *Fateful Months: Essays on the Emergence of the Final Solution.* New York: Holmes and Meier, 1985.

Dallin, Alexander. *German Rule in Russia 1941–1945: A Study of Occupation Policies.* 2nd ed. London: Macmillan, 1981.

Dobroszycki, Lucjan, and Jeffrey S. Gurock, eds. *The Holocaust in the Soviet Union.* Armonk, N.Y.: Sharpe, 1993.

Dwork, Debórah. *Children with a Star: Jewish Youth in Nazi Europe.* New Haven, Conn.: Yale University Press, 1991.

Eliach, Yaffa. *Hasidic Tales of the Holocaust.* New York: Vintage, 1988.

Fonseca, Isabel. *Bury Me Standing: The Gypsies and Their Journey.* New York: Knopf, 1995.

Frank, Anne. *The Diary of a Young Girl.* New York: Doubleday, 1995.

Friedländer, Saul. *When Memory Comes.* New York: Farrar, Straus and Giroux, 1979.

Gellately, Robert. *Backing Hitler: Consent and Coercion in Nazi Germany.* New York: Oxford University Press, 2001.

Goda, Norman J. W. *Tomorrow the World: Hitler, Northwest Africa, and the Path toward America.* College Station: Texas A&M University Press, 1998.

Hirschfeld, Gerhard, ed. *The Policies of Genocide: Jews and Soviet Prisoners of War in Nazi Germany.* London: Allen and Unwin, 1986.

Mazower, Mark. *Inside Hitler's Greece: The Experience of Occupation, 1941–1944.* New Haven, Conn.: Yale University Press, 1993.

Megargee, Geoffrey. *Inside Hitler's High Command.* Lawrence: University Press of Kansas, 2000.

My Knees Were Jumping: Remembering the Kindertransports. Directed and produced by Melissa Hacker. 1 hr. 16 min. National Center for Jewish Film, 1996. Videocassette.

Ramras-Rauch, Gila. *Aharon Appelfeld: The Holocaust and Beyond.* Bloomington: Indiana University Press, 1994.

Sachse, William L. *English History in the Making: Readings from the Sources.* Vol. 2 *Since 1689.* New York: Wiley, 1970.

Schulte, Theo J. *The German Army and Nazi Policies in Occupied Russia.* Oxford: St. Martin's, 1989.

Steinberg, Jonathan. *All or Nothing: The Axis and the Holocaust: 1941–1943.* London: Routledge, 1990.

Steinert, Marlis. *Hitler's War and the Germans: Public Mood and Attitude during the Second World War.* Athens: Ohio University Press, 1977.

Tec, Nechama. *Dry Tears.* New York: Oxford University Press, 1982.

Toll, Nelly S. *Behind the Secret Window: A Memoir of a Hidden Childhood during World War Two.* New York: Dial, 1993.

Tolstoy, Nikolai. *Stalin's Secret War.* New York: Holt, Rinehart and Winston, 1982.

Weinberg, Gerhard L. *A World at Arms: A Global History of World War II.* New York: Cambridge University Press, 1994.

7. THE PEAK YEARS OF KILLING: 1942 AND 1943

Améry, Jean. *At the Mind's Limits: Contemplations by a Survivor on Auschwitz and Its Realities.* New York: Schocken, 1986.

Bauer, Yehuda. *A History of the Holocaust.* New York: F. Watts, 1982.

Browning, Christopher R. *Nazi Policy, Jewish Labor, German Killers.* Cambridge: Cambridge University Press, 2000.

———. *Ordinary Men: Reserve Police Battalion 101 and the Final Solution in Poland.* New York: HarperCollins, 1992.

Cesarani, David, ed. *The Final Solution: Origins and Implementation.* London: Routledge, 1994.

Delbo, Charlotte. *None of Us Will Return.* Translated by John Githens. Boston: Beacon, 1967.

Donat, Alexander, ed. *The Death Camp Treblinka: A Documentary*. New York: Holocaust Library, 1979.

Felstiner, Mary Lowenthal. *To Paint Her Life: Charlotte Salomon in the Nazi Era*. New York: HarperCollins, 1995.

Fenelon, Fania. *Playing for Time*. Edited by Marcelle Routier. Translated by Judith Landry. Syracuse, N.Y.: Syracuse University Press, 1976.

Friedländer, Saul. *Kurt Gerstein: The Ambiguity of Good*. Translated by Charles Fullman. New York: Knopf, 1969.

Goda, Norman J. W. "Black Marks: Hitler's Bribery of His Senior Officers during World War II." *Journal of Modern History* 72, no. 2 (2000): 413–52.

Goldenberg, Myrna. "Different Horrors, Same Hell: Women Remembering the Holocaust." In *Thinking the Unthinkable: Meanings of the Holocaust*, edited by Roger Gottlieb. New York: Paulist Press, 1990.

Hackett, David A. *The Buchenwald Report*. Boulder, Colo.: Westview, 1995.

Heger, Heinz. *The Men with the Pink Triangle*. Translated by David Fernbach. Boston: Alyson Publications, 1980.

Herbermann, Nanda. *The Blessed Abyss: Inmate #6582 in Ravensbrück Concentration Camp for Women*. Edited by Hester Baer and Elizabeth R. Baer. Translated by Hester Baer. Detroit: Wayne State University Press, 2000.

Herbert, Ulrich, ed. *National Socialist Extermination Policies: Contemporary German Perspectives and Controversies*. New York: Berghahn Books, 2000.

Hilberg, Raul, Stanislaw Staron, and Josef Kermisz, eds. *The Warsaw Diary of Adam Czerniaków: Prelude to Doom*. Translated by Stanislaw Staron and the staff of Yad Vashem. New York: Stein and Day, 1979.

Hillesum, Etty. *An Interrupted Life: The Diary of Etty Hillesum*. New York: Pocket Books, 1981.

———. *Letters from Westerbork*. New York: Pantheon, 1986.

Hoess, Rudolf. *Commandant of Auschwitz*. Translated by Andrew Pollinger. Buffalo, N.Y.: Prometheus, 1992.

Hoffmann, Peter. *The History of the German Resistance, 1933–1945*. 3rd ed. Montreal: McGill-Queen's University Publishing, 1996.

Horwitz, Gordon J. *In the Shadow of Death: Living outside the Gates of Mauthausen*. New York: Free Press, 1990.

Klemperer, Victor. *I Will Bear Witness: A Diary of the Nazi Years, 1941–1945*. Vol. 2. Translated by Martin Chalmers. New York: Random House, 1999.

Korczak, Janusz. *Ghetto Diary*. Edited and translated by H. Goldsmitz. New York: Holocaust Library, 1978.

Laks, Szymon. *Music of Another World*. Translated by Chester A. Kisiel. Evanston, Ill.: Northwestern University Press, 1989.

Lanzmann, Claude. *Shoah: An Oral History of the Holocaust, The Complete Text of the Film*. New York: Pantheon, 1985.

Laska, Vera. *Women in the Resistance and the Holocaust*. Westport, Conn.: Greenwood, 1983.

Levi, Primo. *Survival in Auschwitz*. New York: Collier, 1958.

Muller, Filip. *Eyewitness Auschwitz*. Edited and translated by Susanne Flatauer. Chicago: Ivan R. Dee, in association with the U.S. Holocaust Memorial Museum, 1999.

Noakes, Jeremy, and Geoffrey Pridham, eds. *Nazism 1919–1945: A Documentary Reader*. 4 vols. Exeter: University of Exeter Department of History and Archeology, 1983–1998.

Nomberg-Przytyk, Sara. *Auschwitz: True Tales from a Grotesque Land*. Translated by Roslyn Hirsch. Chapel Hill: University of North Carolina Press, 1985.

Przyrembel, Alexandra. "Transfixed by an Image: Ilse Koch, the 'Kommandeuse of Buchenwald.'" Translated by Pamela Selwyn. *German History* 19, no. 3 (2001): 369–99.

Ringelheim, Joan. "Women and the Holocaust: A Reconsideration of Research." *Signs* 10 (1985): 741–61.

Rittner, Carol, and John Roth, eds. *Different Voices: Women and the Holocaust*. New York: Paragon, 1993.

Scholl, Inge. *The White Rose*. 2nd ed. Translated by Arthur R. Schultz. Hanover, N.H.: Wesleyan University Press, 1983.

Scrase, David, and Wolfgang Mieder, eds. *The Holocaust: Introductory Essays*. Burlington: Center for Holocaust Studies at the University of Vermont, 1996.

Sereny, Gitta. *Into That Darkness: An Examination of Conscience*. New York: Vintage, 1983.

Shoah. Produced by Les Films Aleph and Historia Films. Directed by Claude Lanzmann. 9 hrs. 30 min. Paramount Home Video, 1986. Videocassette.

Spiegelman, Art. *Maus: A Survivor's Tale*. 2 vols. New York: Pantheon, 1986.

Stabholz, Thaddeus. *Seven Hells*. Translated by Jacques Grunblatt and Hilda R. Grunblatt. New York: Holocaust Library, 1990.

Stoltzfus, Nathan. *Resistance of the Heart: Intermarriage and the Rosenstrasse Protest in Nazi Germany*. New York: Norton, 1996.

Szwajger, Adina Blady. *I Remember Nothing More*. Translated by Tasja Darowska. New York: Pantheon, 1990.

Tec, Nechama. *When Light Pierced the Darkness*. New York: Oxford University Press, 1985.

Troller, Norbert. *Theresienstadt: Hitler's Gift to the Jews*. Chapel Hill: University of North Carolina Press, 1991.

Tydor, Judith Baumel. *Double Jeopardy: Gender and the Holocaust*. London: Vallentine-Mitchell, 1998.

Weinberg, Gerhard L. *A World at Arms: A Global History of World War II*. New York: Cambridge University Press, 1994.

Wood, E. Thomas, and Stanislaw M. Jankowski. *Karski: How One Man Tried to Stop the Holocaust*. New York: Wiley, 1994.

8. DEATH THROES AND KILLING FRENZIES, 1944–1945

Braham, Randolph L. *The Politics of Genocide: The Holocaust in Hungary*. Condensed ed. Detroit: Wayne State University Press, 2000.

Braham, Randolph L., and Scott Miller, eds. *The Nazis' Last Victims: The Holocaust in Hungary.* Detroit: Wayne State University Press, 1998.

Dean, Martin. *Collaboration in the Holocaust: Crimes of the Local Police in Belorussia and Ukraine, 1941–1944.* New York: St. Martin's, 2000.

Elias, Ruth. *Triumph of Hope: From Theresienstadt and Auschwitz to Israel.* Translated by Margot Bettauer Dembo. New York: Wiley, 1998.

Fein, Helen. *Accounting for Genocide: National Responses and Jewish Victimization during the Holocaust.* Chicago: University of Chicago Press, 1984.

Goldhagen, Daniel Jonah. *Hitler's Willing Executioners.* New York: Knopf, 1996.

Gutman, Israel, and Michael Berenbaum, eds. *Anatomy of the Auschwitz Death Camp.* Bloomington: Indiana University Press, 1994.

Hellman, Peter, Lili Meier, and Serge Klarsfeld. *The Auschwitz Album: A Book Based upon an Album Discovered by a Concentration Camp Survivor.* New York: Random House, 1981.

Hoffmann, Peter. *Stauffenberg: A Family History, 1904–1944.* Cambridge: Cambridge University Press, 1995.

Ioanid, Radu. *The Holocaust in Romania: The Destruction of Jews and Gypsies under the Antonescu Regime, 1940–1944.* Chicago: Ivan R. Dee, 2000.

Isaacson, Judith Magyar. *Seed of Sarah: Memoirs of a Survivor.* Urbana: University of Illinois Press, 1990.

Klein, Gerda Weissmann. *All But My Life.* New York: Hill and Wang, 1957.

Moltke, Helmuth James von. *Letters to Freya 1939–1945.* Edited and translated by Beate Ruhm von Oppen. New York: Knopf, 1990.

Perel, Solomon. *Europa, Europa.* Translated by Margot Bettauer Dembo. New York: Wiley, in association with the U.S. Holocaust Memorial Museum, 1997.

Rotem, Simha. "Kazik." In *Memoirs of a Warsaw Ghetto Fighter,* translated by Barbara Harshav. New Haven, Conn.: Yale University Press, 1994.

Sereny, Gitta. *Albert Speer: His Battle with Truth.* New York: Knopf, 1995.

Siegal, Aranka. *Grace in the Wilderness.* New York: Puffin, 1985.

Speer, Albert. *Inside the Third Reich: Memoirs.* Translated by Richard Winston and Clara Winston. New York: Macmillan, 1970.

Volavkova, Hana, ed. *I Never Saw Another Butterfly: Children's Drawings and Poems from Terezin Concentration Camp, 1942–1944.* 2nd ed. New York: Pantheon, 1994.

Wallenberg, Raoul. *Letters and Dispatches: 1924–1944.* Translated by Kjersti Board. New York: Arcade, 1995.

Wells, Leon Welickzer. *The Janowska Road.* New York: Macmillan, 1999.

Wiesel, Elie. *Night.* Translated by Stella Rodway. New York: Bantam, 1960.

CONCLUSION: THE LEGACIES OF ATROCITY

Abzug, Robert H. *Inside the Vicious Heart: Americans and the Liberation of Nazi Concentration Camps.* New York: Oxford University Press, 1985.

Baldwin, Peter, ed. *Reworking the Past: Hitler, the Holocaust and the Historians' Debate*. Boston: Beacon, 1990.

Brenner, Michael. *After the Holocaust: Rebuilding Jewish Lives in Postwar Germany*. Princeton, N.J.: Princeton University Press, 1997.

Dinnerstein, Leonard. *America and the Survivors of the Holocaust*. New York: Columbia University Press, 1982.

Friedländer, Saul. *Reflections on Nazism: An Essay on Kitsch and Death*. New York: Harper and Row, 1982.

Langer, Lawrence. *Holocaust Testimonies: Ruins of Memory*. New Haven, Conn.: Yale University Press, 1991.

———. *Preempting the Holocaust*. New Haven, Conn.: Yale University Press, 1998.

Levi, Primo. *The Drowned and the Saved*. Translated by Raymond Rosenthal. New York: Summit, 1988.

Mankowitz, Zeev W. *The Survivors of the Holocaust in Occupied Germany*. New York: Cambridge University Press, 2002.

Marrus, Michael. *The Nuremberg War Crimes Trial 1945–46: A Documentary History*. Boston: Bedford Books, 1997.

Miller, Judith. *One, by One, by One: Facing the Holocaust*. New York: Simon and Schuster, 1990.

Myers, Margarete. "The Jewish Displaced Persons: Reconstructing Individual and Community in the U.S. Zone of Occupied Germany." *Leo Baeck Institute Yearbook* 42 (1997): 302–24.

Naimark, Norman. *The Russians in Germany: A History of the Soviet Zone of Occupation, 1945–1949*. Cambridge, Mass.: Belknap, 1995.

Niewyk, Donald. *Fresh Wounds: Early Narratives of Holocaust Survival*. Chapel Hill: University of North Carolina Press, 1998.

Novick, Peter. *The Holocaust in American Life*. Boston: Houghton Mifflin, 1999.

Rubenstein, Richard. *After Auschwitz*. Baltimore: Johns Hopkins University Press, 1992.

Trials of War Criminals before the Nuremberg Military Tribunals under Control Council Law No. 10, October 1946–April 1949. 42 vols. Nuremberg: U.S. Government Printing Office, 1947–1949.

PHOTO CREDITS

CHAPTER 1

Page 9: Betty Speier April, courtesy of USHMM Photo Archives
Page 15: Nederlands Instituut voor Oorlogsdocumentatie, courtesy of USHMM Photo Archives
Page 21: Paul Flacks, courtesy of USHMM Photo Archives
Page 23: Schwules Museum, courtesy of USHMM Photo Archives
Page 25: Hans Pauli, courtesy of USHMM Photo Archives

CHAPTER 2

Page 31: Estelle Bechoefer, courtesy of USHMM Photo Archives
Page 41: James Sanders, courtesy of USHMM Photo Archives
Page 43: Alfred Eisenstaedt/Pix Inc./TimePix
Page 44: Richard Freimark, courtesy of USHMM Photo Archives

CHAPTER 3

Page 56: John Heartfield, 1933
Page 59: Bezirkskrankenhaus Kaufbeuren, courtesy of USHMM Photo Archives
Page 61: Der Stuermer Archive, Stadtarchiv Nuremberg, courtesy of USHMM Photo Archives

Page 64: Roland Klemig, courtesy of USHMM Photo Archives

Page 65: Foto–Willinger Collection, Hoover Institution Archives, courtesy USHMM Photo Archives

Page 68: M. Hershenson, courtesy of USHMM Photo Archives

CHAPTER 4

Page 84: Bundesarchiv Koblenz (146/87/111/21)

Page 87: Michael Irving Ashe, courtesy of USHMM Photo Archives

Page 89: Stadtarchiv Neustadt, courtesy of USHMM Photo Archives

Page 91: Stadtarchiv Singen am Hohentwiel, courtesy of USHMM Photo Archives

Page 94: Hans Hesse, ed. *Persecution and Resistance of Jehovah's Witnesses during the Nazi-Regime 1933–1945*. Bremen, Germany: Edition Temmen, 2000. Used by permission.

Page 95: Hans Hesse, ed. *Persecution and Resistance of Jehovah's Witnesses during the Nazi-Regime 1933–1945*. Bremen, Germany: Edition Temmen, 2000. Used by permission.

CHAPTER 5

Page 105: Main Commission for the Prosecution of the Crimes against the Polish Nation, courtesy of USHMM Photo Archives

Page 106: Main Commission for the Prosecution of the Crimes against the Polish Nation, courtesy of USHMM Photo Archives

Page 112: Courtesy of USHMM Photo Archives

Page 120: Zydowski Instytut Historyczny Instytut Naukowo-Badawczy, courtesy of USHMM Photo Archives

Page 124: Brenda Szyr Senders courtesy of USHMM Photo Archives

CHAPTER 6

Page 136: Jacqueline Levy, courtesy of USHMM Photo Archives

Page 144: Jewish Historical Museum of Yugoslavia, courtesy of USHMM Photo Archives

Page 145: Mrs. John Titak III, courtesy of USHMM Photo Archives

Page 151: Dokumentationsarchiv des Oesterreichischen Widerstandes, courtesy of USHMM Photo Archives

Page 154: Dokumentationsarchiv des Oesterreichischen Widerstandes, courtesy of USHMM Photo Archives

CHAPTER 7

Page 175: YIVO Institute, courtesy of USHMM Photo Archives

Page 177: Leopold Page Photographic Collection, courtesy of USHMM Photo Archives

Page 190: Archiwum Dokumentocji Mechanizney, courtesy of USHMM Photo Archives

Page 194: Muzej Revolucije Narodnosti Jugoslavije, courtesy of USHMM Photo Archives

Page 195: Toni Boumans, courtesy of USHMM Photo Archives

Page 197: Sara Ginaite, courtesy of USHMM Photo Archives

Page 202: Jewish Historical Museum of Yugoslavia, courtesy of USHMM Photo Archives

CHAPTER 8

Page 209: Marion I. Cassirer, courtesy of USHMM Photo Archives

CONCLUSION

Page 226: Lilly Rosenzweig Wolnerman, courtesy of USHMM Photo Archives

INDEX

ABOUT THE AUTHOR

Doris L. Bergen is an associate professor of history at the University of Notre Dame where, in addition to courses on the Holocaust and related subjects, she teaches German history, modern Europe, and European women's history. Bergen received her Ph.D. from the University of North Carolina, Chapel Hill, in 1991 and taught from 1991 to 1996 at the University of Vermont. In 1996 she taught history in the summer program at the University of Tuzla in Bosnia; in the summer of 2001 she taught English at the University of Pristina in Kosovo. Major awards from both the University of Vermont and the University of Notre Dame attest to Bergen's commitment to teaching.

Bergen's research focuses on issues of religion, ethnicity, gender, and violence in Europe in the Nazi era. Her book *Twisted Cross: The German Christian Movement in the Third Reich* was published by the University of North Carolina Press in 1996. She has published many articles and essays on aspects of the Holocaust, Christian antisemitism, and the Volksdeutschen (ethnic Germans) of eastern Europe during World War II. She is the editor of a forthcoming collection of essays on military chaplains in Europe and North America titled *The Sword of the Lord: Military Chaplains from the First to the Twenty-First Century* (University of Notre Dame Press). Her monograph *Between God and Hitler: German Military Chaplains in the Third Reich* is nearing completion. Bergen has received grants from the Alexander von Humboldt Foundation, the German Marshall Fund of the United States, the German Academic Exchange Service, the Max Planck Institute for History, and the Center for Advanced Holocaust Studies at the U.S. Holocaust Memorial Museum.

Critical Issues in History

Series Editor: Donald T. Critchlow